Corrosion Control in Petroleum Production

TPC Publication 5
Second Edition

Harry G. Byars

INTERNATIONAL
THE CORROSION SOCIETY

1999 Houston, Texas

NACE International
1440 South Creek Drive, Houston, TX 77084
(281) 228–6200, http://www.nace.org

The photographs on the cover illustrate various facets of the petroleum production industry where corrosion presents problems and corrosion control methods are used. Clockwise from the upper left are:

1. Oil Well Pumping Unit.
2. Drilling Rig.
3. Gas Condensate Well.
4. Lease Storage Tanks.
5. Offshore Platforms.
6. Gas Processing Facility.
7. Separation Facility Offshore.
8. Emulsion Treaters.
Center. Corroded Tubing.

Copyright © 1999 NACE International. All rights reserved.
Published by Forbes Custom Publishing, a Division of Forbes Inc.

CIP Data is available.
Printed in Canada.
10 9 8 7 6 5 4 3 2

ISBN 0–8281–1274–6

TABLE OF CONTENTS

Chapter 9: Control of the Corrosive Environment. 227

Appendix 9A: Check List for Troubleshooting

FOREWORD

The objective of this revision of "Corrosion Control in Petroleum Production" is to provide an expanded, updated introduction, overview, and reference on the subject. It is written for people who are not corrosion specialists, but who have an interest in and/or responsibility for corrosion control in oil and gas production operations. A goal is to provide the information and terminology necessary for the reader to be able to communicate with corrosion specialists, consultants, suppliers, and vendors. It is hoped that the addition of such items as sample coating specifications, check lists, guidelines, and field examples will enhance its value as a reference. The book covers the basic causes and types of oilfield corrosion, methods of control and related material. While some theory is presented, the practical aspects are emphasized. Examples, charts, and guidelines are given where appropriate. Reference and bibliographies are cited for each chapter.

Although this edition is listed as the "Second Edition," in reality it is the third writing. The original book, published in 1958 under the title of "Corrosion of Oil- and Gas-Well Equipment," was a joint effort of the American Petroleum Institute (API) and NACE International, The Corrosion Society. NACE published an expanded version in 1979 as TPC 5 with the present title. API kept the original book as Book 2 of their Vocational Training Series for field operating personnel. A second edition (1990) is still available from API (1220 L Street, N.W., Washington, D.C. 20005). Those of you who are familiar with both books will recognize that some of the text and many of the illustrations, particular photographs of corrosion failures, are the same in both editions. Once again proving that, when it comes to corrosion, some things never change.

The previous edition was dedicated to the memory of Dorsey R. Fincher, who was chairman of its Editorial Committee. I would like to rededicate this edition to Dorsey, and to add the names of two gentlemen who greatly influenced my career as a corrosion engineer and my activity in NACE. Thus, I would like to dedicate this volume to the memory of J. H. (Sully) Sullivan, a long-time supervisor who was responsible for getting me involved in NACE activities, and to the memory of W .C. (Cliff) Koger, a mentor in my NACE and API activities and former NACE President.

I must recognize and publicly thank several people for their help and contributions on this book. First, I'd like to thank the TPC Group Committee T-1 reviewers, Erwin Buck, Donald Drake, and R. N. (Bob) Tuttle. Not only did they provide a technical review that contributed greatly to the accuracy of the technical content, they provided editorial comments and suggestions that immensely added to the book's clarity and readability.

Second, I'd like to express my appreciation to other folks and companies for their contributions: Lee Bone and ARCO Exploration and Production Technology, Plano, TX, for allowing the use of their protective coatings specifications; T. F. (Ted) Bruno and Metallurgical Consultants, Inc., Houston, TX, for supplying the photomicrographs of metallurgical structure, and K. B. (Ken) Tator, Sr. and KTA-Tator, Inc., Pittsburgh, PA, for furnishing the photographs of coating inspection equipment. I would also like to acknowledge ARCO Exploration and Production Technology's generosity upon my retirement for presenting me with the slides and photographs I have collected during my career; thus, they were available for illustrations in this book.

Third, I want to thank the NACE book editor, Lori R. Tourangeau, for turning a manuscript into a book. In addition, a special thanks to Warren I. Pollock who provided extremely valuable help in the final editing.

Last, but in no way least, I must express my appreciation and love for my wife, Shirley; who, not only has put up with being married to a corrosion engineer for more than 40 years, but read, at least once, every word in the manuscript and offered many suggestions that helped clear up ambiguous statements and improve the readability for the "noncorrosion" reader.

In closing, I would like to thank T-1 for the opportunity for preparing this edition.

Most appreciatively,

—Harry G. Byars

CHAPTER 1

INTRODUCTION

Corrosion is defined as "the deterioration of a material, usually a metal, by a chemical or electro-chemical reaction with its environment." The most common metal in oil production operations is steel. The outside pipe and facility environments are air, water, and soils, and the inside environments are produced fluids (oil, gas, and water) and other substances (such as chemicals, glycols, coolants, etc.).

The basic corrosion cell **(Figure 1.1)** has four components: an anode and a cathode connected by a metallic path in contact with an electrolyte. The anode and cathode may be different areas of the same metal surface. The electrolyte is water in some form. It does not take much—a thin film will do. If any one of the four items is missing, corrosion will not occur. By the same token, if the circuit is interrupted in any way, then corrosion may be controlled.

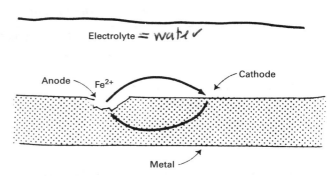

Figure 1.1 Schematic of a basic corrosion cell (electrochemical cell). Illustrating an anodic area (the anode) and the cathodic area (the cathode) on the surface of steel immersed in an electrolyte.

Many methods of breaking up the corrosion cell are available for use in the oil-patch. The most common methods of corrosion control are listed in **Table 1.1.**
(Note: the causes of corrosion, corrosion mechanisms, and types of corrosion attack in oil and gas production are discussed in greater detail in Chapters 2 and 3.) Anyone unfamiliar with oil and gas production equipment and terminology may want to refer to the American Petroleum Institute (API) book, "Introduction to Oil and Gas Production," cited in this chapter's bibliography.

TABLE 1.1 Corrosion Control Methods Used In Oil & Gas Production

1.	*Cathodic Protection*	—Externally to protect buried or submerged piping and equipment.
		—Internally in water portions of tanks and vessels.
2.	*Coating*	—Externally as atmospheric coatings and pipeline coatings.
		—Internally in tubing, piping, and vessels.
3.	*Corrosion Inhibitors*	—Internally in wells, facility piping, and water systems.
4.	*Corrosion-Resistant Materials*	—Both metals (such as stainless steels) and nonmetals (such as plastic and fiberglass piping and vessels.
5.	*Control of the Corrosive Environment*	—Internally: dehydration, deaeration, solids/scale control, oxygen-free operation, microbiological control, design to avoid building in corrosion problems, etc.

The selection of the corrosion control technique for a specific application is a technical/economic decision. That is, the selection is based on the determination of the techniques that are technically appropriate for the application, plus an economic comparison to select the most profitable solution for the life of the project. Often times two or more techniques in combination often are the most profitable (for example, the use of an external pipe coating supplemented with cathodic protection).

CORROSIVE ENVIRONMENTS

Table 1.1 mentions both internal and external environments. When discussing corrosive environments, it is very important to remember that these are separate environments. What is inside a pipe does not affect the corrosion on the outside of the pipe and vice versa.

EXTERNAL ENVIRONMENTS

Atmospheric Corrosion. As far as atmospheric corrosion is concerned, the severity of corrosion depends upon the moisture, pollutants, salts, and temperature of the air. Consequently, the severity of atmospheric corrosion is quite dependent on geographical location and the degree of industrial activity. **Table 1.2** presents a ranking of the severity of different atmospheric conditions. Thus, atmospheric corrosion severity varies from its worst at an industrial area on the coast to the least at a rural location in the high desert.

TABLE 1.2 The Severity of the Atmosphere

THE ATMOSPHERE'S SEVERITY CAN BE RATED (MOST SEVERE TO LEAST SEVERE):
1. Industrial and marine or seacoast.
2. Industrial and high humidity.
3. Marine or seacoast.
4. High humidity only.
5. Inland, industrial, low humidity.
6. Rural, nonindustrial, low humidity.

Soil Corrosion. The severity of corrosion for facilities buried in the ground or sitting on soil is largely dependent on the composition and condition of the soil around and/or under the structure **(Table 1.3).**

TABLE 1.3 Factors Effecting the Corrosivity of Soils

THE FACTORS MOST EFFECTING THE SEVERITY OF CORROSION IN SOILS ARE:
- Moisture—How wet is the soil, swamp or dry sand dunes.
- Salts That May be Present—Some happen naturally, such as in coastal areas, others happen due to brine leaks from previous corrosion or other failures.
- Temperature of the Soil at the Pipe Surface—A hot line can have a surface temperature greater than the average soil temperature.
- Oxygen Availability—The amount of oxygen in the soil is a function of depth. Soil on the surface may have a relatively high-oxygen content. The oxygen level will decrease with depth from the surface and with the difference in concentration. Oxygen concentration cells can occur, particularly with large diameter lines. The top of the pipe is nearer to the surface; therefore, the oxygen content is higher than under the bottom of the pipe, and thus a corrosion cell is set up.

Submerged Corrosion. Like soils, the severity of corrosion for facilities in water is largely dependent on the composition and conditions of the water **(Table 1.4).**

TABLE 1.4 Factors Effecting the Corrosivity of Waters

FACTORS MOST EFFECTING THE SEVERITY OF CORROSION IN WATER ARE:
• **Dissolved Salts**—The amount and composition are important; is it seawater, brackish wetlands water, or freshwater from a river or lake?
• **Dissolved Oxygen**—The dissolved oxygen content will vary with the salt content of the water and the temperature, as well as the water's depth. The saltier the water, the less oxygen it will hold, and the lower the temperature, the more oxygen will be dissolved. The oxygen content at the surface will approach saturation. The content decreases with depth and in deep water the content will approach zero.
• **Velocity Plays an** Important Role—Particularly if the water contains suspended solids and has a high velocity, such as the tidal currents in the Cook Inlet, Alaska.
• **Marine Growth**—Can set up differential concentration cells which will accelerate corrosion.

INTERNAL ENVIRONMENTS

Corrosion inside pipes and equipment involves the numerous factors that make up the internal environments. These environments not only involve chemical and physical properties of metals and fluids, they include the physical characteristics of the system (*i.e.*, temperature, pressure, flow rates, gas/oil and water/oil ratios, sizes, times, and schedules).

TABLE 1.5 Factors Effecting Corrosion Rates

CORROSION RATES IN A SPECIFIC SYSTEM ARE EFFECTED BY MANY FACTORS, INCLUDING:
1. Properties of the fluid (compositions, ratios, wet-ability, etc.).
2. Physical conditions in the system (such as temperatures, pressures, and flow rates).
3. Temperature differentials.
4. Potential differences (bi-metallic couples).
5. Heat treatment of the metal.
6. Surface conditions (cleanliness).
7. Velocity (erosion effects of high velocities).
8. Stagnant conditions ("dead" areas).
9. Impurities.
10. Deposits (scales, corrosion products, precipitates, dirt or debris).
11. Time (exposure or contact).
12. Stresses (imposed stresses and built in stresses from fabrication).
13. Differential aeration.
14. Differential concentration.
15. Biological and microbiological.

The single most important factor in most oil and gas system corrosion is the presence of water. It doesn't take much water; a thin film on the metal surface is sufficient to create a problem. This water may contain dissolved salts, acids, acid gases (carbon dioxide [CO_2] and/or hydrogen sulfide [H_2S]), and oxygen that may affect corrosion rates. Internal corrosion can be expected to occur anywhere water can condense, flow or collect in wells, lines, vessels, or equipment. The severity of the corrosion (how soon it will create problems and cause failures) is influenced by many factors and will vary from system to system. **Table 1.5** lists some of these factors.

The corrosive environments can be changed by something as simple as changes in times and schedules. (See the sidebar on Changing Times.)

CHANGING TIMES—Are Environments Really What They Seem?

Sometimes apparently unrelated events can change the corrosive environment, as cited in the following two cases.

The **first case** involves sucker rod pumping oil wells in the East Texas Field. The Woodbine crude produced in the East Texas Field has unusual oil wetting properties. Downhole failure studies in the late 1950s revealed that the first corrosion failures (rod or tubing) occurred after a well's water cut reached about 85%. Above that water percentage the corrosion was very aggressive, but the wells responded unusually well to corrosion inhibitors. Routine inhibitor treatments virtually eliminated downhole corrosion failures. Wishing to avoid the first failure, the operator initiated the practice of adding the well to the inhibition program when a well test indicated 75% water. This practice essentially eliminated downhole failures for quite some time. Then failures started on wells that were not on the Inhibition schedule—wells making considerably less than 75% water. Furthermore, these failures were occurring within a few joints of the pump. What had happened?

This was at a time of more severe proration. Full allowable wells could be produced only a few days each month. This was also during one of the oil patch's "downsizing" cycles. In order to operate with fewer field personnel, pumper assignments were adjusted so that each person had two assignments (two leases or two sets of wells). He would alternate the wells producing; that is, operate one set of wells during the last half of a month and the first half of the next month. Then he would shut those wells in and move to the other assignment and produce those wells during the last half of that month, the first half of the second month. He would shut the second wells in and return to his previous assignment, and the cycle would be repeated.

With this approach, a given well would be shut-in for at least 30 days each cycle. Thirty days was long enough for the crude and water to separate in the tubing and for the water to settle. Thus, the rods and tubing above the pump were exposed to essentially 100% water. The shut-in time also was long enough for the oil to desorb off the rods and tubing, leaving them water-wet and corroding.

Something as seemingly unrelated to corrosion as the pumper's work schedule was able to change a well's status from "noncorrosive" to "corrosive." The problem was handled by adding all water-producing oil wells to the inhibition schedule.

The **second case** involves a small water flood. The source water for the flood was freshwater from a shallow aquifer. The purchased water was untreated and contained dissolved oxygen (DO). Sulfur dioxide and a catalyst were injected into the water stream entering the source water tank. DO measurement indicated the scavenger was doing its job and reducing the oxygen to less than 50 parts/billion (ppb). Corrosion monitoring showed that corrosion was not under control. Indications were that oxygen and higher-than-design velocities were both involved.

A review of the operation revealed that the injection plant was being operated only during the operator's daily 8-hour shift. The required daily injection volumes were injected—but in less than 8 hours—not over the 24 hours that the reported 8,000 barrels per day would imply. The water velocities were more than three times the velocities that would be assumed. Furthermore, during the day, at the 24,000 plus rate, the water channeled through the water tank so fast the oxygen scavenger did not have time to react. Thus, near the plant, oxygenated water was corroding the pipe, and the higher velocities kept a ready oxygen supply available. During the off hours, when the pumps were not running, the oxygen scavenger and oxygen had time to fully react. When DO tests were run in the morning the oxygen was gone, and specification water was injected. This is another case where the operating schedule had a big impact on the corrosion control effort.

These internal and external environments will affect all types of production equipment, systems, and facilities, both onshore and offshore:

- Drilling wells.
- Producing oil wells.
- Gas wells.
- Water supply wells.
- Injection wells (*i.e.*, water flood, water disposal or gas injection and storage).
- Piping, flow lines, gathering lines, and injection lines.

- Vessels.
- Tankage.
- Exchangers (shell and tube or fin fan).
- Auxiliary equipment (*i.e.*, furnaces, heaters, pumps, dehydration, sweetening, and other plant type equipment).

Each field project is not only unique, but each type of equipment and system has multiple corrosion environments. For example, the environment in the casing/tubing annulus of a well is different from the environment inside the tubing; these vary from bottom to top in the well. Downhole conditions are different from surface conditions due to differences in pressures, temperatures, and compositions. The conditions before a choke are different from those after a choke. The conditions before heaters are different from those after heaters, etc.

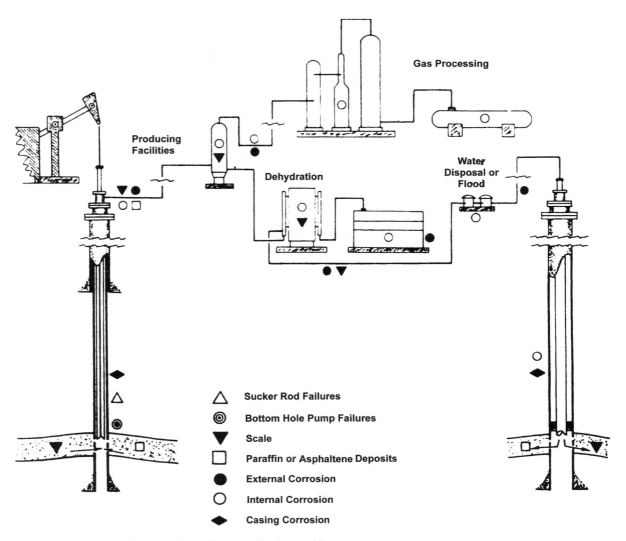

△	Sucker Rod Failures
◎	Bottom Hole Pump Failures
▼	Scale
□	Paraffin or Asphaltene Deposits
●	External Corrosion
○	Internal Corrosion
◆	Casing Corrosion

Figure 1.2 Locations and types of petroleum production problems.

EQUIPMENT, SYSTEMS, AND FACILITIES

Figure 1.2 is a schematic of an oil field that shows locations and types of corrosion and other production problems. As noted, corrosion can occur anywhere in a production system, from the bottom of the well to the equipment used to process the oil and gas for sale and the water for injection.

Appendix 1A lists internal corrosion and corrosion control for various types of wells, facilities, and equipment. The usual problem areas, evaluation methods (detection and monitoring), and the most common corrosion control method are listed for each item.

WELLS

All wells have five basic environment areas for potential corrosion problems (**Figures 1.3** and **1.4**).

- External casing.
- Casing/tubing annuli (internal casing/external tubing).
- Internal casing below the bottom of the packer in packered wells, or below the bottom of the tubing in wells without packers.
- Internal tubing.
- Internal wellhead and Christmas tree.

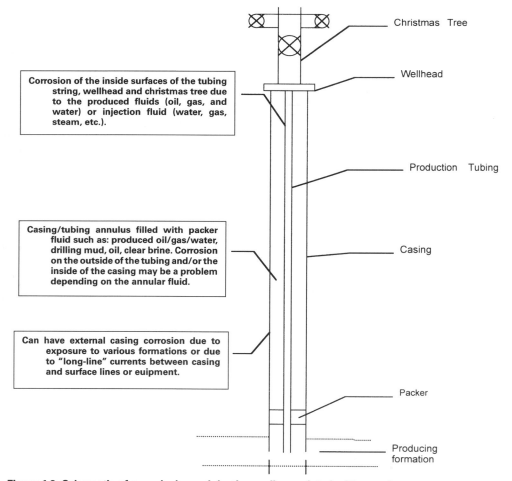

Corrosion of the inside surfaces of the tubing string, wellhead and christmas tree due to the produced fluids (oil, gas, and water) or injection fluid (water, gas, steam, etc.).

Casing/tubing annulus filled with packer fluid such as: produced oil/gas/water, drilling mud, oil, clear brine. Corrosion on the outside of the tubing and/or the inside of the casing may be a problem depending on the annular fluid.

Can have external casing corrosion due to exposure to various formations or due to "long-line" currents between casing and surface lines or euipment.

Christmas Tree

Wellhead

Production Tubing

Casing

Packer

Producing formation

Figure 1.3 Schematic of a producing or injection well completed with a packer. Note the comments on areas of possible corrosion problems.

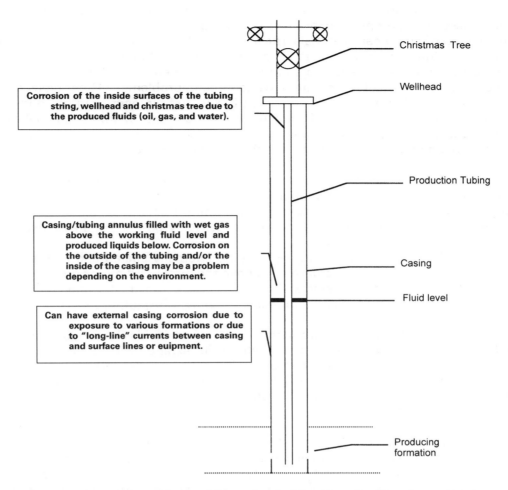

Corrosion of the inside surfaces of the tubing string, wellhead and christmas tree due to the produced fluids (oil, gas, and water).

Casing/tubing annulus filled with wet gas above the working fluid level and produced liquids below. Corrosion on the outside of the tubing and/or the inside of the casing may be a problem depending on the environment.

Can have external casing corrosion due to exposure to various formations or due to "long-line" currents between casing and surface lines or euipment.

Christmas Tree

Wellhead

Production Tubing

Casing

Fluid level

Producing formation

Figure 1.4 Schematic of a producing well completed without a packer. Note the comments on areas of possible corrosion problems.

Artificial Lift Wells. The vast majority of oil wells throughout the world are produced with some form of artificial lift. Although sucker rod pumping is the most common, when offshore wells are considered, the use of electric submersible pumps (ESP) continues to expand. Other forms of pumping include hydraulic pumps and progressive cavity pumps. The other type of artificial lift is "gas lift," in which gas injected down the annulus or a second tubing string is used to lighten the hydraulic load (oil or oil/water column) to lift the fluids to the surface. In general, gas lift wells are completed with a packer, while pumping wells are not (the annuli are open).

Most of today's operators attempt to keep their wells "pumped off," *e.g.*, maintain a minimum fluid level over the pump intake. Thus, when pumping, there is very little liquid in the casing/tubing annulus, and what there is usually will be oil. The gases in the annular space are saturated with water at bottom hole conditions. The water will condense when the temperature decreases. Any CO_2 or H_2S will dissolve in the water, lower the pH, and increase the potential for corrosion. Corrosion often occurs on the internal walls of the casing where water has condensed because of cooler zones outside the casing.

Sucker rod pumping wells corrosion-related problems involve rods, tubing, and pumps. The most common problems have been rod parts (breaks) caused by corrosion fatigue and tubing leaks caused by corrosion/wear. Both of these failure mechanisms can be profitably controlled by proper design of the rod string and corrosion inhibition programs.[1] The third category, corrosion and failure of the sucker rod pumps, is controlled by selection of the proper pump design and the proper combination of pump part materials. The selection of materials for bottom hole pumps is of utmost importance. Pumps must be able to resist the corrosive nature of the produced fluids and at the same time pump abrasives such as sand without experiencing failures. Many times pump alloys can be selected to virtually eliminate downhole pump problems.[2,3] Other types of failures in rod pumped wells (including failures of sucker rod boxes, rod pin ends, and rod body problems) have been drastically reduced or eliminated by the correct use of improved makeup, correct handling techniques, and improved pumping practices. These are spelled out in detail in API RP 11BR, "Recommended Practice for Care and Handling of Sucker Rods." [4]

ESP pumped wells corrosion problems may occur in the casing/tubing annulus, to the ESP components themselves, and inside the tubing. Since the ESP basically is a high-speed multistage centrifugal pump, the usual method of corrosion control is selection of materials to match well conditions (materials selected for oil wells will not necessarily be the same as those selected for water flood water supply wells).

In severely corrosive situations the tubing may be internally coated and corrosion inhibitors may be used. Since the ESP's intake is normally above the motor and motor protector, those parts often are protected with coating systems. The power cable run in the annulus is quite often armored cable. The cable sheath is a corrosion-resistant alloy (CRA) (often a high nickel alloy).

Hydraulic pumped wells corrosion problems usually occur inside the production tubing. If the power fluid tubing is installed as a concentric string, its exterior will be exposed to the same produced fluids as the tubing interior. The power fluid side usually does not present corrosion problems unless the power fluid is recycled produced water and the operation allows oxygen (air) entry. Historically, corrosion inhibitors introduced with the power fluid have been used to control corrosion of the produced fluids.

Progressive cavity pumped wells, from the corrosion and corrosion control standpoints, are similar to sucker rod pumps. Other than the design of the pump itself, the main operating difference is the rotating drive shaft of the progressive cavity pump rather than the reciprocating sucker rod string. Rod on tubing corrosion/wear can be a significant problem. Inhibition and materials selection should be the choices for corrosion control.

Gas-lifted oil wells usually contain packers and the lift gas is dry; thus, annular corrosion is not a severe problem. When the lift gas is wet or there is no packer, annular corrosion can be a problem if the lift gas is high in acid gas (or if the gas is gasoline plant residue gas that contains oxygen). Oxygen is not unusual if the gasoline plant has a vacuum gathering system. In most gas lift wells, internal tubing corrosion may be costly to control. Internal plastic coatings, CRA tubing strings, and specialized corrosion inhibition programs have all been used.

Flowing Wells. The term "flowing wells" is used to describe both oil wells and gas wells.

Oil wells will usually flow when initially completed and continue to produce in this manner until the bottom hole pressure declines to a level too low to lift the fluids to the surface. Deep high pressure oil wells (and those offshore) routinely are completed with packers **(Figure 1.3)**. Low-pressure or shallow oil wells have been completed with an open annulus (*e.g.*, without a packer [Figure 1.4]). From the corrosion and corrosion control standpoints, the main difference is the corrosive environment in the casing/tubing annulus—produced fluids in the packer-less completion—packer fluids in wells with packers.

Most flowing oil wells do not have internal corrosion problems. The oil tends to oil-wet the steel surfaces. Later in the well's life, as water percentages and water volumes increase, the tendency is to water-wet the steel. Water-wet steel will corrode, and corrosion control will be required.

Gas wells, on the other hand, almost always are completed with a packer. Gas wells usually are the most corrosive during their early life when the pressures are the highest. Many gas wells are referred to as "gas condensate wells." In the classic gas condensate well the fluids are all in the vapor state in the reservoir; as the gas travels up the well, the liquifiable hydrocarbons and water condense. In most cases, corrosion occurs where water condenses and wets the steel. Since the gas and liquid phases are a function of pressure, temperature, and gas composition, the water-wet area may "move." In such cases, corrosion will occur in a particular "zone" that can move during the life of the well. In many cases corrosion will be a problem in the upper portion of a well during its early life and will move downhole as the well is depleted. Inhibitors, coatings, and CRA are used alone or together, depending on the problems in a particular well.

Of special interest to some operators have been the deep (>10,000 ft [3,000 m]), high pressure (>10,000 [60 MPa] psi bottomhole), hot (>250°F [121°C]) gas wells with high mole percentages and resulting high partial pressures of CO_2 and/or H_2S. These deep hot acid gas wells represent special cases. The technology and economics for control of corrosion is an evolving and changing situation; therefore, each well should be approached with the latest developments.

Auxiliary equipment that may be used downhole includes such items as packers, tail pipe, safety valves, etc. These are especially critical in high-pressure gas wells and often are made from selected corrosion-resistant materials. Obviously, it is possible to eliminate many high-pressure well failures by proper design and materials of construction.

Casing Corrosion. The casing in producing wells may vary from a limited amount of surface pipe and a single production string in shallow low-pressure wells, to several strings of concentric casing in deep, high-pressure wells.

External casing corrosion can occur when corrosion cells are created between different geological zones, when the casing is exposed to a particularly aggressive water zone, or when the casing is anodic to surface lines, tank bottoms, or other wells. External casing corrosion has not been a problem in all fields; however, it is severe enough in some fields to cause casing failures. In many cases, cathodic protection has been found to be an adequate remedy for external casing corrosion. In the drilling and completion of a well, drilling fluid left between the hole wall and the external surface of the casing should be considered. Such fluids can contribute to external corrosion of the casing. Some operators attempt to cement the entire production casing (at least from the casing shoe up to the inside of the intermediate string of surface pipe). A good cement sheath will reduce the amount of bare casing exposed to corrosion, as well as reduce the amount of cathodic protection required.

Internal casing/tubing annulus corrosion is largely dependent upon the composition of the annular fluids or packer fluids. Low-pressure and artificial lift wells usually are completed without a packer **(Figure 1.4)**. Thus, the annular space is exposed to wet gas above the annular fluid level and the produced liquids below the fluid level. The water vapor in the gas space may condense where the inner casing wall is cooled and acid gases may dissolve in the water to cause internal casing corrosion. The liquid below the fluid level will usually be oil even in high water cut wells, and corrosion in that area may not be a problem. Packered annuli are fairly standard in gas wells, high-pressure oil wells and water injection wells. The fluid in the annulus may be produced, drilling, or completion fluids that were in the well bore when the packer was set **(Figure 1.3)**. More and more "packer fluids" specifically designed to meet requirements of a particular well are being used.

These fluids are generally three types: (1) oil-based (weighted or unweighted), (2) water-based weighted with solids, (3) water-based with no undissolved solids (the "clear brines").

From the corrosion and corrosion control standpoints, the clean oil or oil-based fluids are most desirable. Water-based fluids weighted with solids (including drilling mud) are least desirable. Water-based muds are corrosive and can become more corrosive with time due to breakdown of certain components. Inhibition is not practical due to the high undissolved solids content of such muds. On the other hand, corrosion can be controlled in clear brine packer fluids. However, the very heavy zinc salt brines present special problems due to their native corrosiveness.

SURFACE EQUIPMENT

Wellheads and Christmas Trees. Wellhead and Christmas tree equipment can be severely corroded, especially on high-pressure gas wells. High velocities and turbulence prevent self healing processes, and the wellhead and tree components and valving are quite vulnerable to erosion/corrosion as protective corrosion products are removed and fresh steel surfaces are exposed to further corrosion. In addition, wells that produce a high-mole percentage of acid gases usually subject the wellhead to attack. The use of corrosion-resistant metals is the usual solution. API Specification 6A, "Specification for Wellhead and Christmas Tree Equipment,"[5] discusses material requirements for various types of service and various pressure levels. (Note API definitions: "A wellhead is all permanent equipment between the uppermost portion of the surface casing and the tubing head adapter connection." "Christmas Tree—An assembly of valves and fittings attached to the uppermost connection of the tubing head, used to control well production."[5])

Flow Lines. Flow lines (sometimes called lead lines) can range from new pipe to downgraded used tubing, depending on the specific situation. Accumulation of deposits and other debris in the lines can promote corrosion and pitting, resulting in leaks. Water will tend to settle out and flow along the bottom of the line. In those cases, the bottom of the line will see (be exposed to) water only, the metal will be water-wet and corrosion can occur. Optimum sizing of equipment, depending on anticipated velocities, is important. Internal corrosion of flow lines can be prevented by inhibitors and/or coatings.

In many older producing areas, flow lines were laid on top of the ground. In such cases external corrosion was due to atmospheric conditions on the top side and soil conditions on the bottom. Thus, the severity of corrosion was largely dependent upon the location and moisture available (both in the atmosphere and soil). When lines laid on the ground experienced corrosion failures, the usual approach was to repair the leak with a pipe clamp or to rotate the pipe to move the thicker steel to the soil side. As fields were unitized and/or higher pressures were carried into central locations, the lines were buried, and cathodic protection and external pipe coatings came into widespread use to control external corrosion.

Processing Equipment. Gas-oil separators usually do not present a serious corrosion problem. However, mineral scales can be detrimental to sustained production. Corrosion is sometimes associated with the scale, especially downstream of regulators and dehydration equipment.

Equipment used for crude oil dehydration (such as free-water knockouts, gun-barrels and emulsion treaters [heater-treaters]) is subject to scale and corrosion problems. Elevated temperatures increase the corrosion and scaling tendency in heater-treaters and similar vessels used to heat incoming liquids to break emulsions. Inhibitors that might perform well in a hydrocarbon-water mixture in the flow line may not protect the water section of a heater. Therefore, heater-treaters and similar vessels often are internally coated and/or have cathodic protection in the free-water sections.

Gas plant processing equipment is subject to corrosion, especially if oxygen enters with the incoming gas, or with steam used to aid fractionation or with water used to remove salt from liquid hydrocarbon streams. Corrosion probably will occur where acid gases are present and water is condensed from the hydrocarbon stream in a fractionation process.

Amine sweetening equipment corrosion is caused by improper gas loading, oxygen entry, or amine degradation. Corrosion is controlled by operating the system at the proper loading and maintaining amine quality.

Storage Tanks. Lease storage tanks are subject to both internal and external corrosion. Internal corrosion is a problem on the underside of the roof when water droplets condense and acid gas and/or oxygen are present and where water and/or solids settle on the bottom. Oxygen should not be a problem today because most air quality regulations do not allow tank vents open to the atmosphere. However, some vapor recovery systems may draw sufficient vacuum on the tank to cause the vacuum relief to open and allow air entry.

The internal attack on the bottoms of storage tanks is a result of the water layer that is generally found on the bottom of all tanks. Under deposit (concentration cell) corrosion will occur on the bottom under sludge deposits and under corrosion product that drops from the underside of the tank deck. Corrosion of the oil tank's shell (walls) normally is negligible. However, severe attack has been noted on the portion below the oil-water interface. Sometimes, severe hydrogen blistering is a major storage tank problem. (A picture of tank wall blistering is in Chapter 3 on forms of corrosion). **Figure 1.5** shows the corrosion zones inside a sour crude tank.

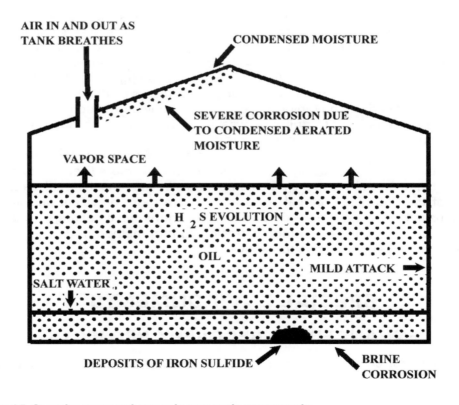

Figure 1.5 Corrosive zones and causes in sour crude storage tanks.

External surfaces of tank bottoms are subject to corrosion where water or water wet-soil is present. Foundation design, cathodic protection and coatings are used to control those problems. Regulations concerning leak prevention and corrosion control are continually changing for above-ground storage tanks (ASTs), and the current local regulations must be considered in the planning and execution of a corrosion control program.

Water Systems. Water flood or salt water disposal (SWD) systems are subject to corrosion, primarily as a result of the entry of air into the system,[6] poor water quality, microbiological activity, or acid gases in the water. Small amounts of corrosion products can cause plugging of equipment and plugging of injection wells. Oxygen can also cause injection well plugging if the injected water contains dissolved iron or manganese compounds that react with the oxygen to form insoluble products. Well plugging can become a very serious problem in systems handling produced water because the insoluble products will become oil coated. The oil coated solids tend to agglomerate and can plug even relatively porous formations. Water source wells, gathering lines and storage tanks, injection pumps and lines, and injection wells all have potential corrosion problems. Oxygen exclusion, dissolved gas removal, inhibitors, equipment design, microbiological control, and internal coatings and linings are used in various portions of oilfield water systems. Nonmetallic pipe (such as fiber reinforced plastic [FRP] piping) is used for both surface and downhole applications, particularly in SWD applications.

DRILLING OPERATIONS

Oxygen and fluctuating stresses (fatigue) are considered the principal cause of failure in drill pipe. Pits caused by oxygen corrosion, slip marks and mechanical scratches serve as stress raisers, concentrating and increasing local stresses in drill pipe. These stress raisers enable cracks to start under fluctuating or reversing loads. During the drilling operation, the presence of oxygen in the drilling mud aggravates the fatigue action. As a corrosion pit deepens, the corrosion fatigue cracking proceeds at an accelerated rate. Each of these actions aggravates the other, and a vicious cycle is created. The failure occurs when a crack or pit progresses all the way through the pipe wall and fluid is forced out. Fluid cutting rapidly enlarges even a tiny perforation into a sizable hole. This action is sometimes referred to as "drill pipe wash-out." The pipe, thus weakened, can be easily twisted off. (A picture of a drill pipe fatigue crack is in Chapter 3).

External corrosion of drill pipe does not usually form pits. Because of continual rubbing on the sides of the hole or intermediate casing strings, external wear is more likely. Also, oxygen content often is reduced due to reaction with the mud components by the time the mud starts its return trip up the outside of the drill pipe. Internal corrosion pits are more prevalent and, for this reason, fatigue failures usually start on the inside of the pipe. Internal pipe coatings have been used to minimize this corrosion. The most common corrosion control method in drilling is to control the mud pH and maintain a basic condition (pH above 7).

SPECIAL ENVIRONMENTS

ENHANCED OIL RECOVERY PROJECTS

Injection systems for enhanced oil recovery (EOR) projects can present unique corrosion and control problems.

WAG Injection. Projects that alternately inject water and gas (often referred to as water alternate gas systems [WAG]) have injection wells that must be designed to handle the alternate environments. Often the water and gas are brought to the well through separate distribution lines, which are designed to handle corrosion due to the gas being injected or designed to meet the needs of the injection water. In cases when the gas is very dry, bare carbon steel lines are quite satisfactory. Bare carbon steel also may be used successfully with many waters as long as air-free (oxygen-free) conditions are maintained. However, the tree, wellhead, tubing, and downhole equipment must be designed to withstand both environments. The period during the switch from one injection media to the other is the most challenging, particularly when the injection gas contains acid gases (CO_2 or H_2S).

In-Situ Combustion. In-situ combustion projects (also called fire floods) involve injecting air or oxygen gas into a reservoir to sustain a fire that has been ignited in the reservoir. The objective is to heat the oil, and thus increase its ability to flow through the formation. Corrosion on the injection side may be controlled by injecting only dry air or dry oxygen. Corrosion at the producing well will tend to increase as combustion products break through (CO, CO_2, and NO_x), particularly if there is excess oxygen, and as the temperature increases as the fire front nears the well. Until oxygen breaks through or extreme temperatures occur, conventional corrosion inhibitor programs may be successful, although the treating frequencies and inhibitor dosages may need to be increased periodically. When the fire front reaches the producing well bore, wells may be shut-in unless special high temperature metals have been used.

COAL SEAM GAS

Another type of project that has offered unique challenges is one that recovers coal seam gas. These relatively low-pressure systems often contain acid gases (CO_2 and H_2S), and many have reported microorganism (bacteria) problems, particularly sulfate-reducing bacteria (SRB). If part of the gathering system is operated at a vacuum, oxygen can cause greatly accelerated corrosion in parts of the system downstream of the point of oxygen entry.

OFFSHORE OPERATIONS

From the corrosion and corrosion control standpoint, offshore oil and gas production has many similarities to onshore operations. Internal corrosion environments are essentially the same as onshore—the oil, gas, and water do not know whether they are onshore or offshore. When it comes to corrosion control, the basic differences have to do with space, logistics, and economics—not necessarily in that order.

- Space for equipment, such as tanks and pumps for chemical injection, or space for a deaeration tower to remove dissolved oxygen from seawater to be used as water flood source water.
- Logistics of getting supplies and equipment to the platform when it is needed.
- Economics (including risks) of the increased costs of operation at a remote location and of repairs or remedial work if corrosion failures occur.

The technical aspects of internal corrosion control are not much different offshore or onshore.

On the other hand, external corrosion can be quite a challenge offshore where the facilities will see a variety of external environments. External corrosion on offshore structures may be divided into three zones of attack. These zones overlap somewhat, and some differences in corrosion rate may be expected within the same zone as illustrated in **Figure 1.6**.

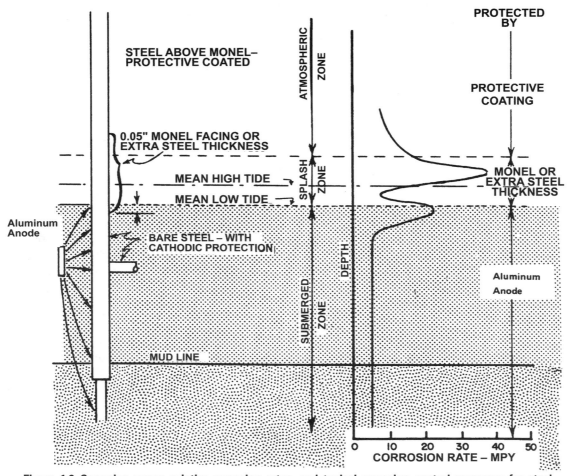

Figure 1.6 Corrosion zones, relative corrosion rates, and typical corrosion control measures for steel offshore structures.

The three zones as defined by NACE RP0176–94, "Corrosion Control of Steel Fixed Offshore Platforms Associated with Petroleum Production"[7] are as follows:

- **The Submerged Zone**—The zone that extends downward from the splash zone and includes that portion of the platform below the mud line.

- **The Splash Zone** (or tidal zone)—The portion of the structure that is alternately in and out of water because of tides, winds, and seas. Excluded from this zone are surfaces that are wetted only during major storms.

- **The Atmospheric Zone**—The portion of the platform that extends upward from the splash zone and is exposed to sun, wind, spray, and rain. It is where the metal appears to be dry most of the time.

Submerged Zone. In the submerged zone, the corrosion tends to be rather uniform. Shallow, general pitting is common. Corrosion rates will vary around the world in different seawater environments. This is discussed further in the section on offshore structures in Chapter 7, and in the appendix of NACE RP0176.[7] Cathodic protection is the usual method of corrosion control in the submerged zone throughout the world's offshore industry.

Splash Zone. Damage to offshore structures is most severe in the splash zone. Here the washing action of well aerated salt water removes corrosion products before a protective coating can be formed, resulting in deep pits. The vertical extent of the splash zone depends on the tidal range and the normal height of waves. A greater metal area will be exposed in this zone in the Pacific Coast area than in the Gulf Coast where the waves are not so high and the tidal range not as great. Cook Inlet, Alaska has an extremely large tidal zone where the difference between high and low tides can be greater than 33 ft (10 m) with tidal currents up to eight knots (9.2 mph or 15 km/h). Cook Inlet water also carries a large amount of suspended solids, mostly abrasive volcanic ash. The splash zone problem in the inlet is further aggravated by the rubbing and scouring of the legs by large ice floes in the winter. **Figure 1.6** shows additional steel thickness (also referred to as "wear plates") as a method of minimizing corrosion failures in the splash zone. An alternative is the use of a highly corrosion-resistant metal wrap over the steel in this zone. Other alternatives listed in NACE RP0176 include: vulcanized chloroprene, high-build organic coating, high-performance platform coatings 250 to 500 mm (10–20 mils), heat-shrink sleeves, thermal-sprayed aluminum, and petroleum/wax-based tape systems.

The design of the structure and the method used to join the members can reduce corrosion damage in this zone. Because this zone is the most difficult to protect, it is desirable to limit the number of cross members to a minimum. Ideally the cross members are located in the submerged zone. In winter ice areas, cross members need to be well below the depth of submerged ice.

Atmospheric Zone. The atmospheric zone usually appears dry, but it has a thin layer of salt on its surface. As the structure cools at night and the humidity increases, the salt absorbs water from the air forming a salty film of moisture on the surface. The sun dries the film of moisture and reduces the rate of corrosion. The corrosion products tend to flake off and this irregular spalling of rust promotes pitting. High-performance coatings systems are the usual corrosion control technique for the atmospheric zone. Conventional paints, surface preparation, and application methods should not be used in extremely corrosive offshore environments. Some of the details are discussed further in Chapter 6. NACE RP0176 provides detailed coverage of offshore coatings systems, surface preparation, coating application, and inspection.

CORROSION UNDER INSULATION

An environment often overlooked until a problem occurs is the environment under thermal insulation. This should be a dry area without water. In fact, most pipe and vessel insulation is jacketed to prevent water entry—wet insulation loses its insulating properties. However, experience has shown that, with time, jackets leak, and insulation exposed to atmospheric conditions gets wet. In some cases, materials such as chlorides are leached out of the insulation (which can lead to chloride pitting of stainless steel). The insulation can trap and hold water against the metal structure. Oxygen that enters through the same openings in the jacket as the water will cause severe oxygen corrosion **(Figures 1.7 through 1.9)**. Coating the pipe prior to insulation is a preferred method of controlling corrosion.

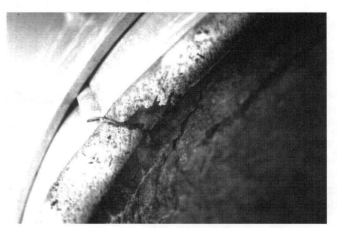

Figure 1.7 Corrosion Under Insulation—Moisture and oxygen, entering through an opened jacket seam, led to the corrosion in this photograph.

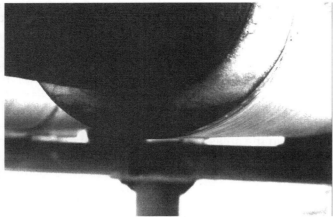

Figure 1.8 Corrosion Under Insulation—Staining of the insulation indicates that at least two different water levels had been present since the damaged weather jacket allowed water to enter, and corrosion to take place.

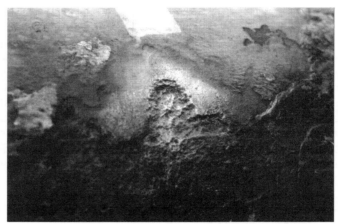

Figure 1.9 Corrosion Under Insulation—Severe corrosion attack was revealed when the insulation and rust deposits were removed from this pipe.

SUMMARY

Corrosion can present problems in all parts of oil and gas production operations, wherever water is produced, condensed, or collected; and inside and outside wells, piping, and equipment. Corrosion control is a continuous job in production operations. The selection of control approaches is a technical/economic decision dependent upon many considerations. The remainder of this book is devoted to a more detailed examination of these considerations along with the methods used to detect, monitor, and control corrosion in oil and gas production.

REFERENCES

1. NACE Standard RP0195-95, "Recommended Practice for Corrosion Control of Sucker Rods by Chemical Treatment" (Houston, TX: NACE, 1995).
2. NACE Standard MR0176 (latest edition), "Metallic Materials for Sucker Rod Pumps for Corrosive Oilfield Environments" (Houston, TX: NACE).
3. NACE Standard MR0175 (latest edition), "Sulfide Stress Cracking Resistant Metallic Materials for Oilfield Equipment" (Houston, TX: NACE).
4. API RP 11BR (latest edition), "Recommended Practice for Care and Handling of Sucker Rods" (Washington, D.C.: American Petroleum Institute).
5. API Specification 6A, "Specification for Wellhead and Christmas Tree Equipment" 16th ed. (Washington, D.C.: American Petroleum Institute, Oct. 1, 1989).
6. H.G. Byars, B.R. Gallop, "Injection Water + Oxygen = Corrosion and/or Well Plugging Solids," MP 13, 12 (1974): p. 34.
7. NACE Standard RP0176-94, "Corrosion Control of Steel Fixed Offshore Platforms Associated with Petroleum Production" (Houston, TX: NACE, 1994).

BIBLIOGRAPHY

American Petroleum Institute. *Introduction to Oil and Gas Production—Book One of the Vocational Training Series.* 5th ed. Washington, D.C.: API Publishing Services, 1996.

Pollock, W.I., and C.N. Steely, eds. *Corrosion Under Thermal Insulation.* Houston, TX: NACE, 1990.

APPENDIX 1A

INTERNAL CORROSION AND CORROSION CONTROL IN OIL AND GAS PRODUCTION

System or Equipment (Environment)	Usual Problem Areas	Evaluation Methods (Detection and Monitoring)	Most Common Corrosion Control Methods
OIL WELLS			
Natural Flow	-Usually no problem downhole at low water cuts (percentages) -Unusual circumstances: pits under hygroscopic scales; highly deviated holes -Casing-tubing annuli: due to packer fluids or high acid gas	-Failure history -Inspection -Calipers -Coupons	-Downhole equip: inhibition and/or coatings, metal selection -Packered annuli: fluid selection plus inhibitor and/or biocide -Unpackered annuli: inhibition and neutralization
Artificial Lift			
Sucker Rod Pump	-Rods, tubing, pumps, annulus -Rods usually fail due to corrosion fatigue	-Failure history -Inspection -Sometimes: coupons, iron count	-Inhibition -Metallurgy of pumps -Closed annuli
Hydraulic Pump	-Tubing, downhole pump	-Failure history -Inspection	-Inhibition -Pump metallurgy -Clean power fluid
Submersible Pump	-Tubing, annulus, pumps, cable	-Failure history -Inspection	-Inhibition -Coatings on pumps case -Pump metallurgy
Gas Lift	-Tubing, annulus, gas lift valves	-Failure history -Calipers -Inspection -Occasionally: coupons, iron content	-Tubing: coating, CRA -Inhibition (inhibitor must get to bottom of hole) -Annuli: lift gas dehydration NOTE: lift gas should be O_2-free
OIL FLOWLINES AND GATHERING SYSTEMS	-Along bottom of pipe where free water flows and in low places where water collects	-Failures -Inspection -Coupons, probes	-Coatings -Thermoplastic pipe (for low pressure), FRP (high pressure) -Inhibitor—downhole may be sufficient—or inject at wellhead

System or Equipment (Environment)	Usual Problem Areas	Evaluation Methods (Detection and Monitoring)	Most Common Corrosion Control Methods
OIL WELL PRODUCED FLUIDS HANDLING			
Oil and Gas Separators (Traps)	-Wet gas area (where water condenses) -Free water section (bottom) -Water dump valves	-Failure history -Inspection: visual, sometimes ultrasonic thickness	-Coatings -Cathodic protection in free water -Metallurgy of internals and water dump valves
Free Water Knockout (FWKO)	-Free water section, shell, baffles, piping -Along bottom under deposits -Water dump valves and piping	-Failure history -Inspection	-Coatings -Cathodic protection in free water -Periodic flushing and/or clean out of bottom
Heater Treaters	-Gas section when water condenses -Free water and treating sections: shell and baffles, bottom under deposits -Fire tube—particularly under scale deposits -Water dump valves and water lines	-Failure history -Inspection	-Gas section: coatings -Fire tube: cathodic protection and/or scale control chemical -Free water and treating sections; coating and cathodic protection -Routine flushing and clean out of deposits -Siphons and water lines: coatings and plastics -Water dump valves: metallurgy
Gun Barrels (Wash Tanks, Settling Tanks)	-Free water section -Under side decks -Gas boot and piping in high H_2S areas -Water dump valves	-Failure history -Inspection	-Coatings -Cathodic protection in free water -Aluminum decks -Plastics and nonmetallics for gas boots and piping -Water dump valves: metallurgy -Oxygen exclusion -Routine flushing and clean out
Lease Tanks	-Under side of deck -Bottom and lower portion of bottom ring	-Failure history -Inspections	-Coatings -Aluminum deck -Cathodic Protection for bottom area if maintain water lever -Oxygen exclusion -Routine clean out of bottom

System or Equipment (Environment)	Usual Problem Areas	Evaluation Methods (Detection and Monitoring)	Most Common Corrosion Control Methods
Hydraulic Pumping Equipment			
Power Fluid Tanks Power Fluid Pumps Power Fluid Lines	-Power oil tanks—similar to lease tanks -Power water tanks—similar to SWD and WI tanks	-Failure history -Inspection	Tanks: coating -CP where appropriate -Pumps: metallurgy -Lines: inhibition -All: oxygen exclusion -Routine flushing and clean out NOTE: power fluid must be clean
Gas Lift Systems	-Along bottom of line where free water flows or collects -On vessel walls where water condenses	-Failure history -Inspection -Occasionally: coupons, iron content	-Dehydration -Oxygen exclusion -Occasionally inhibition
GAS WELLS	-Tubing interior, downhole equipment (such as subsurface safety valves), fittings, etc. -Wellhead & Christmas tree -Annulus above packer (depends on packer fluid)	-Tubing: calipers, coupons, iron content, inspection -Wellhead & Christmas tree inspection (visual, radiographic) -Casing internal: failures, calipers, inspection	-Tubing: metal selection, coating and/or inhibition -Downhole valve, etc., metallurgy -Wellhead & Christmas tree: metallurgy and coating Annulus: packer fluid selection and/or inhibitor
GAS WELLS FLOWLINES	-Along bottom of line where free water flows or collects -Along top of line where water condenses -Bends and ells	-Failure history -Inspection: visual, ultrasonic, and/or Radiographic when critical -Coupons, iron content	-Inhibition (downhole and well site injection) -Routine pigging to remove water and deposits -Well site dehydration in serious situations
GAS GATHERING SYSTEMS AND GAS PIPELINES	-Along bottom of line where free water flows or collects -Along top of line where water condenses	-Failure history -Inspection: visual, ultrasonic, radiographic, smart pigs -Coupons	-Dehydration -Sometimes inhibition and pigging -Oxygen exclusion (particularly important on vacuum systems)
GAS HANDLING EQUIPMENT			
Coolers	-Where water condenses	-Failure history -Visual inspection, exchanger tube calipers	-Metallurgy -Neutralization
Accumulators	-Where water collects	-Failure history -Inspection: visual, ultrasonic	-Coating -Metallurgy -Neutralization -CP in free water

System or Equipment (Environment)	Usual Problem Areas	Evaluation Methods (Detection and Monitoring)	Most Common Corrosion Control Methods
Vessels	-Where water condenses and in free water portions	-Failure history -Inspection: visual, ultrasonic	-Coatings -Neutralization -Metallurgy -Inhibition -CP in free water
Compressors	-Valves, cylinders, bottles	-Failure history -Inspection: visual	-Metallurgy
Glycol Dehydrator	-Wet glycol lines, contactors: trays and shell -Regeneration equipment	-Failure history -Inspection -Coupons -Glycol analysis	-Metallurgy -pH control -Oxygen exclusion -Glycol quality
Dry Bed Dehydrator	-Wet gas handling areas, regeneration condensers, etc.	-Failure History -Inspection	-Metallurgy -Coatings (where temp allow)
WATER HANDLING AND INJECTION (DISPOSAL & FLOOD)			
Vessels and Tanks	-Shell when water very corrosive -Bottom under deposits -Vapor space when sour	-Inspections -Failure history -Coupons, probes -Occasionally iron content and/or bacterial activity -Galvanic probes (oxygen detection)	-Oxygen-free operation (exclusion and/or removal) -CP -Coatings -Periodic clean out -Occasionally: biocides or inhibitors -Nonmetals
Filters	-Connections when bi-metallic -At filter media (sand) level	-Same as Vessels	-Same as vessels
Gathering & Injection Lines and Plant Piping	-Along bottom under deposits	-Same as vessels	-Oxygen-free operation -Coatings & linings (including Cement) -Periodic pigging lines -Occasionally: biocides or inhibitors
Injection & Transfer Pumps	-All wetted parts -Seals leaking air	-Failure history -Inspection -Galvanic probe (oxygen detector)	-Oxygen-free operation -Metallurgy
Injection Wells	-Tubing interior, inhole valves, fittings, etc. -Wellhead & Christmas tree -Annulus above packer (depends on packer fluid)	-Failure history -Coupons, probes -Occasionally iron content and/or bacterial activity -Galvanic probes (oxygen detection)	-Oxygen-free operation -Coatings & linings (including cement) -Occasionally: biocides or inhibitors

System or Equipment (Environment)	Usual Problem Areas	Evaluation Methods (Detection and Monitoring)	Most Common Corrosion Control Methods
MISCELLANEOUS FACILITIES			
Glycol-Water Heat Transfer Systems (Heating and Cooling)	-Anywhere in system (particularly where deposits could occur)	-Failure history -Inspection -Coupons -Fluid analysis	-Inhibition -Oxygen exclusion -Fluid quality
Boilers and Steam Systems	-Boiler tubes -Condensers and condensate return lines	-Failure history -Inspections -Coupons -Iron content	-Water quality control -Deaeration -Inhibition
Gas Sweetening (MEA & Similar Amine Systems)	-Contact tower -Reconcentration system	-Failure history -Inspections -Coupons -Iron content	-CO_2 loading -Inhibition (usually inorganic) -Oxygen exclusion -Fluid quality

CHAPTER 2

CORROSION BASICS

The majority of oilfield equipment and facilities are constructed of a metal—usually steel. The most common steel used, both downhole and surface, is called carbon steel. By definition carbon steel is: "An alloy of carbon and iron containing up to 2% carbon and up to 1.65% manganese and residual quantities of other elements, except those intentionally added in specific quantities for deoxidization (usually silicon and/or aluminum). Carbon steels used in the petroleum industry usually contain less than 0.8% carbon" (NACE MR0175-98).[1] Thus, oilfield steels often are referred to as "low carbon steels." Metals other than low carbon steel are used for special applications in oil and gas facilities—usually for their resistance to specific corrosive environments. These metals will be discussed in the section on corrosion-resistant materials. Unless otherwise noted, the following discussion of the fundamentals of corrosion and its reactions apply to oilfield steels.

WHY IRON AND STEELS CORRODE

Corrosion is a natural act of metals trying to return to their lowest level of energy. In the case of iron, it is iron ore. Iron ore consists of iron oxides, iron sulfides, iron carbonate, and similar iron compounds. This iron ore is mined, and its energy level is increased as it is processed and converted to steel. From that time on, it is trying to return to the lowest level of energy. Thus, the tendency is for iron to corrode—to become corrosion product. Corrosion products are iron oxides, iron sulfides, iron carbonates, and similar iron compounds. The energy released when the iron converts to corrosion product is, in fact, the energy stored in the metal during the refining and steel-making process. This energy supplies the driving force for corrosion. Because corrosion is a natural act, it cannot be prevented—only slowed down. Therefore, corrosion control programs are efforts to postpone the inevitable for the life of the project.

CORROSION REACTIONS

By definition corrosion is an electrochemical reaction. As noted in **Figure 1.1**, this reaction requires an anode, cathode, electrolyte, and metal path. In oil and gas production facilities, the electrolyte is water, (or water-based fluids or water-wet solids), and the metallic path is the steel pipe or equipment. Electrical current flows during the corrosion process. In order for current to flow, there must be a driving force, or a voltage source, and a complete electrical circuit.

The source of voltage in the corrosion process is the energy stored in the metal by the refining process. Different metals require varying amounts of energy for refining and, therefore, have different tendencies to corrode. See **Table 2.1**. Note that the standard hydrogen electrode [SHE] by definition is an electrode whose potential is arbitrarily zero. The difference in potential between the SHE and a metal's potential is the value listed in the table.

TABLE 2.1 Electromotive Force Series of Metals

	Metal	Volts[1]	
Most energy required for refining	Magnesium	-2.37	Greatest tendency to corrode
	Aluminum	-1.66	
	Zinc	-0.76	
	Iron	-0.44	
	Tin	-0.14	
	Lead	-0.13	
	Hydrogen	0.00	
	Copper	+0.34 to +0.52	
Least energy required for refining	Silver	+0.80	
	Platinum	+1.20	Least tendency to corrode
	Gold	+1.50 to +1.68	

[1] vs standard hydrogen electrode.

The size of the driving voltage generated by a metal in a water solution is called the potential of the metal. It is related to the energy released when the metal corrodes. The absolute value of the potential of a given metal is influenced by the water composition, temperature, velocity, and many other factors. However, their relative values remain about the same in most production waters.

Besides a source of voltage, there must be a complete electrical circuit. As noted earlier, in addition to the metallic path, the electrical circuit of the corrosion cell consists of three parts—an anode, a cathode, and an electrolyte.

The **anode** is the area of the metal surface that corrodes—where the metal dissolves (goes into solution). When a metal dissolves, the metal atom loses electrons, and it goes into solution as a metal ion. The chemical reaction for the corrosion of iron is:

$$Fe \longrightarrow Fe^{2+} + 2e^-$$

Iron atom $\longrightarrow$ iron ion (ferrous) + electrons

$$(1)$$

The iron ion goes into solution, and two electrons are left behind in the metal. The iron in solution can react with other ions to form corrosion products (such as iron oxide, iron sulfide, iron carbonate, or iron chloride).

The **cathode** is the area of the metal surface that does not dissolve. The electrons from the anode travel through the metal to the cathodic area. At the cathodic area, the electrons, which carry a negative charge, react with ions in the water that carry a positive charge. A typical reaction at the cathode is:

$$2H^+ + 2e^- \longrightarrow H_2 \uparrow$$

Hydrogen ions + electrons $\longrightarrow$ hydrogen gas

$$(2)$$

Or, if oxygen is present, two other reactions may occur:

In acid solutions:

$$O_2 + 4H^+ + 4e^- \longrightarrow 2H_2O \qquad (3)$$

In neutral and alkaline solutions:

$$O_2 + 2H_2O + 4e^- \longrightarrow 4OH^- \qquad (4)$$

Thus, the reaction at the anode areas produces electrons, and the reaction(s) at the cathode areas consume the electrons. By definition, electrical current is the passage of electrons from one point to another. Convention says the electrical current flows in the opposite direction of electron travel. Thus, as electrons flow from the anode area to the cathode area, electrical current flows in the opposite direction, from the cathode to the anode. This current flow is within the metal. Therefore, the metallic path between the anode and the cathode is always a conductor of electricity.

To complete the electrical circuit, the metal surface (both the anode and the cathode) must be covered with electrically conductive solution. Such a solution is called an **electrolyte**. Pure water is a poor electrolyte, but electrical conductivity increases rapidly with addition of dissolved salts.

This combination of anode, cathode, and electrolyte is referred to as a corrosion cell. The schematic of the corrosion process in **Figure 1.1** is shown merely as an illustration. Metal atoms do not necessarily dissolve at a single point on a metal surface, nor are cathode areas restricted to one area on the surface.

CORROSION VARIABLES

The corrosion reactions and the corrosion reaction rates (corrosion rates) are affected by the many variables that make up the corrosion environment. For example, the electrolyte's conductivity and pH, dissolved gases (particularly oxygen, carbon dioxide [CO_2], and hydrogen sulfide [H_2S]), microbiological conditions, and physical variables (such as temperature, pressure, and velocity) all play an important role in the corrosion of a specific situation.

CONDUCTIVITY

As previously stated, the metal surface must be wetted by an electrically conductive solution (the electrolyte) to conduct electrical current from the anode to the cathode of the corrosion cell. Thus, the more conductive the electrolyte, the easier current can flow. If nothing else slows down the corrosion reaction, the faster the corrosion rate becomes. The less conductive the electrolyte, the greater the resistance to current flow and the slower the reaction. It is important to realize that the amount of metal that dissolves is directly proportional to the amount of current that flows between the anode and the cathode. [Note: One ampere of current flowing for one year represents a loss of 20 pounds (9.1 kilograms [kg]) of iron.]

Distilled water is not very conductive and is not very corrosive. In contrast, salt water is quite conductive and can be very corrosive depending on what else is dissolved in the water. A very salty water may be virtually noncorrosive if it contains no dissolved gases or other corrosive agents. The importance of conductivity is its effect on the ease of current flow from the anode to the cathode.

pH

The pH of a water is a measure of the acidity or alkalinity of the water; pH is expressed as a number between 0 and 14. The midpoint of the pH scale is 7; a solution with this pH is neutral. Numbers below 7 denote acid solutions; those above 7 denote alkaline (often called "basic") solutions.

Neutral														
<<<<<<< Increasingly Acid <<<<<<<							>>>>>> Increasingly Alkaline >>>>>>							
0	1	2	3	4	5	6	7	8	9	10	11	12	13	14

By definition pH is the negative logarithm of the hydrogen ion concentration. In other words:

$$pH = -\log [H^+] \qquad (6)$$

The greater the concentration of hydrogen ions, the more acid the solution and the lower the pH value. Since pH is a logarithmic function, solutions having a pH of 6.0, 5.0, and 4.0 are 10, 100, and 1,000 times more acidic than one with a pH of 7.0. Hydrogen ions make a solution acid and, therefore, force the pH toward zero. Hydroxyl ions (OH^-) make a solution basic or alkaline and push the pH upward.

The corrosion rate of steel usually increases as the pH of the water decreases (becomes more acidic), although extremely high pH solutions can also be corrosive. The general variation of the corrosion rate of steel with pH is shown in **Figure 2.1**. The actual variation of corrosion rate with pH is obviously dependent on the composition of the water or electrolyte. In many oilfield waters, protective scales, such as iron hydroxides or carbonate scales, may form on the steel surface and slow down the corrosion rate.

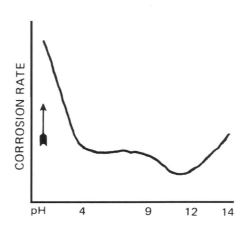

Figure 2.1 Steel corrosion rate curve typical of variations related to hydrogen ion concentration (ph) in the electrolyte.

DISSOLVED GASES

Oxygen, CO_2, or H_2S dissolved in water, drastically increases its corrosivity. In fact, dissolved gases are the primary cause of most oil and gas corrosion problems. If they could be excluded and the water maintained at a neutral pH or higher, most oilfield waters would cause very few corrosion problems.

Dissolved oxygen (DO) serves as a strong oxidizer to promote the corrosion reaction. CO_2 and H_2S ionize in water to form acids that lower the pH. The presence of buffers, such as bicarbonates, moderate the pH and make the system less corrosive. **Figure 2.2** illustrates the effect of bicarbonate (HCO_3^-) on pH at three temperatures and at various partial pressures of CO_2. The lines labeled "water" are the pH of unbuffered water saturated with CO_2 at different partial pressures. The lines labeled "305 ppm HCO_3^-" reflect the buffering effect of the bicarbonate on the water's pH at the same conditions.[2]

kPa

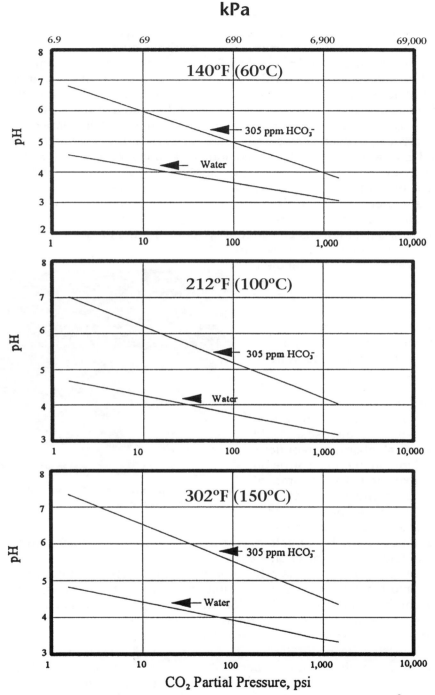

Figure 2.2 CO_2 partial pressure vs pH. Note the affect of bicarbonate (HCO_3^-) buffer.[2]

Dissolved Oxygen (DO). Of the three dissolved gases mentioned, oxygen is by far the worst of the group. It can cause severe corrosion at very low concentrations. Less than 0.05 parts per million (ppm) (50 parts per billion [ppb]) can cause accelerated corrosion. If either or both of the other two gases (CO_2 and H_2S) are present, it drastically increases their corrosivity. Oxygen usually causes pitting type attack.

It should be noted that oxygen is not naturally present in subsurface formations. Most formations contain a number of compounds that react readily with oxygen. Presumably, in geologic time any oxygen originally present in the reservoir has been consumed by those compounds. Thus, oxygen should not contribute to corrosion downhole or in surface equipment. Oxygen should be rigorously excluded from producing oil and gas wells, surface facilities, and water supply and injection systems. When it is present, the fluids are allowed to contact air through an inadvertent leak or by exposure to the atmosphere. Of course, water flood source waters from lakes, oceans, or streams will contain oxygen, and water from shallow wells may contain some oxygen.

Sometimes, however, oxygen corrosion is found in downhole equipment. When this occurs, it usually is caused by careless operating techniques or faulty equipment. A common cause of oxygen entry into pumping wells has been operating with the annulus vented to the atmosphere, thus reducing back pressure on the producing formation. Air quality regulations have eliminated this practice in many areas. The most likely cause of oxygen entry today in rod pumping and ESP wells is leaking wellhead seals and packing glands. Oxygen can cause problems in gas lifted wells if the lift gas compressor suction drops below atmospheric, or if the lift gas is plant return gas from a gasoline plant with a vacuum gathering system.

Often, aerated waters must be handled. Surface waters will contain some oxygen whether it is a water flood source water or fire water, cooling water, or water for the fresh water "water maker" on an offshore platform. Corrosion control should be considered when handling surface waters. The limited supply of oxygen may cause the formation of distinct lumps called tubercles **(Figure 2.3)**. The corrosion product is a soft jelly-like material, and deep sharp-bottom pits may occur under the deposits. Rapid perforation of the metal, obstruction of flow, and equipment plugging by the corrosion products can be expected. The volume of corrosion products compared with the amount of oxygen can be surprisingly large and may cause more damage than the level

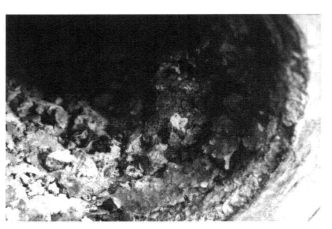

Figure 2.3 Oxygen Corrosion Tubercles—Seawater supply line on offshore platform.

of oxygen would indicate. Small amounts of corrosion products can cause plugging of equipment and plugging of the formation at injection wells.

The solubility of oxygen in water is a function of pressure, temperature, and dissolved solids content (primarily chlorides). Oxygen is less soluble in salt water than in fresh water. **Appendix 2A** presents oxygen solubility data and calculation methods for fresh water and for seawaters of various chloride contents at various temperatures.[3] Similar data for very heavy brines indicates ambient temperature oxygen saturation as low as 2 to 3 ppm.

Oxygen accelerates corrosion under most circumstances. It is a strong and rapid oxidizing agent in cathodic reactions (that is, it provides a high electrochemical potential). Thus, oxygen will easily combine with electrons at the cathode and allow the corrosion reaction to continue at a rate limited primarily by the rate at which oxygen can reach the cathode.

Oxygen can change protective scales to nonprotective ones. As will be noted in Chapter 3 on forms of corrosion attack, oxygen concentration cells, or differential aeration cells, can cause preferential attack or pitting. Any time there is a difference in the oxygen content of water, attack will take place preferentially in the area exposed to the lowest oxygen concentration. Typical examples are corrosion at water-air interfaces, crevices, under deposits or scales, and "oxygen tubercles" in water systems.

Dissolved Carbon Dioxide (CO_2). When CO_2 dissolves in water, it forms carbonic acid, decreases the pH of the water, and increases its corrosiveness **(Figure 2.2)**. CO_2 is not as corrosive as oxygen, but usually results in pitting **(Figures 2.4** and **2.5)**.[4] Corrosion primarily caused by dissolved CO_2 often is referred to as "sweet" corrosion, as opposed to corrosion caused by H_2S, commonly called "sour" corrosion.

Figure 2.4 CO_2 corrosion along bottom of gas well flow line.[4] Note the sharp edges and more or less flat bottom of pits and grooves.

Figure 2.5 CO_2 corrosion in gas piping.[4]

Because CO_2 plays such a prominent role in oilfield corrosion, some of the factors governing its behavior should be considered. The important factors governing the solubility of CO_2 are pressure, temperature, and composition of the water. Pressure increases the solubility to lower pH; temperature decreases the solubility to raise pH **(Figure 2.2)**. Many dissolved minerals prevent pH reduction (that is, buffer the water).

In a gas condensate well with few dissolved minerals and at relatively high temperatures, pressure is the controlling factor influencing CO_2 solubility. In fact, the partial pressure of CO_2 can be used as a yardstick to predict corrosion problems in gas condensate wells. The partial pressure of CO_2 can be determined by the formula:

Partial pressure = total pressure x mole fraction of CO_2 in the gas

For example, in a well with a bottom-hole pressure of 3,500 psi (24.1 MPa) and a gas containing 2% CO_2:

$$CO_2 \text{ partial pressure } = 3,500 \times 0.02 = 70 \text{ psi (0.5 MPa) at the bottom of the well} \qquad (7)$$

Using the partial pressure of CO_2 as a yardstick to predict CO_2 corrosion, the following "rule of thumb" relationships have been found:

- A partial pressure above 30 psi (0.2 MPa) statistically indicates CO_2 corrosion will cause sufficient problems to justify corrosion control. (Some operators consider 15 psi (0.1 MPa) as the break over partial pressure.)

- At a partial pressure between 3 and 30 psi (0.02 and 0.2 MPa), CO_2 corrosion may cause problems, but other factors seem to control.

- A partial pressure below 3 psi (0.02 MPa) statistically indicates CO_2 corrosion will not be a problem, and the gas may be considered non-corrosive—corrosion may cause problems, but CO_2 will not be the primary cause.

The CO_2 partial pressure rule of thumb does not predict corrosion rate, rather it indicates the need for corrosion control. Much work has been done (and continues) to develop computer models that will predict corrosion rates.[5-7] Several currently are being used by various companies in the industry. Since this is a developing technology, if more detailed estimates than the rule of thumb are required, the latest literature should be consulted.

Although originally developed for gas condensate wells, the CO_2 partial pressure rule of thumb has proven to work well in gas gathering systems, gas handling facilities, and gas pipelines.

On the other hand, oil wells with CO_2 usually produce a salt water that contains dissolved minerals, and the foregoing relationship may not always apply. However, corrosion most often is encountered when the CO_2 content is high. As a first approximation, the partial pressure of CO_2 is useful in predicting corrosion of oil wells. The calculated solubility of CO_2 in a typical well is shown in **Figure 2.6**.

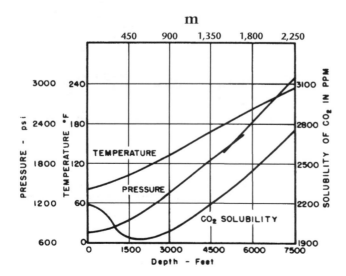

Figure 2.6 Solubility of CO_2 at various depths of a typical oil well.

Dissolved Hydrogen Sulfide (H_2S). H_2S, when present in oil or gas, will dissolve in any accompanying water and lower the pH in much the same manner as CO_2. "A sour system" is the most common term used to identify an environment when H_2S is present. Corrosion possibilities do exist in sour systems, but they may be considerably different than other corrosive environments. The presence of H_2S, even in very low concentrations, can cause a rapid metal failure problem from sulfide stress cracking (SSC). An example of a tubing failure due to SSC is shown in **Figure 2.7** On the other hand, pitting and weight loss corrosion may or may not be a significant problem, depending upon many factors. Pitting on tubing exterior due to H_2S in the annulus is shown in **Figure 2.8**.

Figure 2.7 SSC of tubing—hard tubing that failed while being run into well (circa 1950s).

Figure 2.8 Pitting on external surface of tubing in sour service—annulus was open (*i.e.*, no packer).

The SSC of metallic materials in the presence of H_2S (partial pressure of H_2S is greater than 0.0003 MPa [0.05 psia] has been recognized by NACE MR0175 (latest edition) since 1975.[8] The carbon and low-alloy steels are satisfactory for use when H_2S is present as long as they meet NACE MR0175 (latest edition). In general, the steel requirements are:

- Heat treatment is either hot-rolled, or normalized, or normalized and tempered, or quenched and tempered, or hot finished.
- Hardness is 22 Rockwell C (22 HRC) maximum.
- Nickel is less than 1%.
- Free machining steels are not permitted.
- Cold working is less than 5% of outer fiber stress.

A hardness exception has been made for the quenched and tempered modified grade 4130 (UNS G41300) steels where the maximum hardness limit has been increased to 26 HRC. The presence of NACE MR0175 has made it possible for the industry to operate very successfully with a minimum of SSC problems. The failures that have occurred have been a result of inadequate metal selection, inadequate inspection, or damage during operation (examples are cold working, slip marks from tubing tongs, etc.). Selection of corrosion-resistant alloys also can be affected by the presence of H_2S. This topic is discussed later under CRAs.

It is very important to remember that resistance to SSC does not mean resistance to other forms of corrosion. Most oilfield steels that are resistant to SSC require corrosion protection such as inhibition or coating. Weight loss and pitting corrosion because of the H_2S is a very complicated situation. Under ideal conditions, the H_2S will form an iron sulfide (FeS) film on the steel surface and protect the steel from further corrosion. The presence of oxygen, sulfur, temperature (above 200 to 250°F [93 to 121°C]), chlorides, high levels of CO_2, etc., can damage or change the film characteristics and lead to severe corrosion. Many uninhibited sour gas condensate wells have operated for many years without any significant corrosion provided the H_2S/CO_2 ratio is at least two. On the other hand, pitting occurred when the environmental conditions caused a disruption, or change in crystalline structure, of the iron sulfide film. Sour gas wells with high H_2S contents (10 to 35 mol%) may produce sulfur along with the gas and greatly increase the corrosion potential. Sour gas wells that do not produce associated hydrocarbon liquids should be considered corrosive, and protective measures taken. Deep hot sour gas wells without hydrocarbon liquids have been very corrosive and hard to protect. The choice for these situations has been either continuous inhibition or use of corrosion-resistant alloys.

The presence of H_2S in oil wells may or may not be a significant factor in weight loss/pitting corrosion depending upon the water phase pH and the presence or absence of oxygen. Water produced along with the oil and associated gas normally has a relatively neutral pH because of the buffers (bicarbonates) available. When reservoir pressure is less than the bubble point pressure, fresh water may condense from the associated gas while being produced and cause corrosion if buffers are not present (low levels of produced formation water). In low-pressure oil wells being artificially lifted, the presence or absence of oxygen may be critical to minimize corrosion.

The presence of H_2S in injection water or produced formation water may present a difficult situation. The contamination of the water by oxygen in surface equipment will greatly accelerate corrosion and make corrosion control very difficult. Without oxygen the corrosiveness of the system depends on the water pH and, if a problem, inhibition should be effective. The iron sulfide corrosion products also may cause a significant injection well plugging problem.

OTHER INFLUENCES

DISSOLVED ORGANIC ACIDS

In addition to acidity produced by CO_2, low molecular-weight organic acids (such as acetic acid) contribute to corrosion. Sometimes these acids play a major role in determining the corrosion rate in a specific system, although they are seldom the primary cause of corrosion.

MICROBIOLOGICAL

It should be pointed out that H_2S also can be generated by microorganisms. In oil and gas production, the primary source of problems is *Desulfovibrio desulfuricans*, commonly known as SRB.

SRB are anaerobes—for the most part they require a complete absence of oxygen and a highly reduced environment to function efficiently. Investigators have noted that SRB circulate (probably in a resting state) in aerated waters until they find a site to their liking. There also is a growing body of evidence that some SRB strains can tolerate low levels of oxygen.[9]

These bacteria contribute to a form of corrosion called microbiologically influenced corrosion (MIC). A number of theories have been proposed to explain the mechanism of SRB corrosion. One theory considers that the anaerobic conditions under a group of colonies may constitute a differential aeration cell with the bulk of the electrolyte, resulting in rapid corrosion under the colonies. Another credits the difference between the H_2S content under the colonies and the H_2S content in the bulk of the water for causing differential concentration cell corrosion. Still another proposes that corrosion is simply due to the low pH produced by the H_2S. Another approach credits the SRB's contribution to corrosion to their ability to change sulfate ions to H_2S. Then the H_2S reacts with any iron in solution to form FeS precipitate and scale. The FeS scale is cathodic to steel, resulting in corrosion of scale-free areas, which, in turn, adds more iron to the solution. Regardless of the mechanism, SRB may contribute to corrosion in oil and gas operations—usually in water flood or disposal systems and, at times, external corrosion on buried pipelines.

It has been stated that: "The reasons the petroleum industry suffers from MIC fall into three related categories: industry operational practices, industry failure to recognize the impact of MIC, and the lack of standardized methods to diagnose, control, and monitor MIC."[10] Probably the most critical of these are the operational practices. The industry has tended to ignore methods to avoid microbiological concerns until a system has become contaminated. (MIC control and monitoring are further discussed in Chapters 9 and 10.)

PHYSICAL VARIABLES

TEMPERATURE

Like most chemical reactions, corrosion rates generally increase with temperature. A rough "rule of thumb" suggests that the reaction rate doubles for every 18°F (10°C) rise in temperature. Corrosion rates do increase with temperature in closed systems. However, in a system open to the atmosphere, corrosion rates may increase at first as the temperature is increased and then decrease with a further temperature increase. As the solution gets hotter, the dissolved gases come out of solution, decreasing the corrosivity of the water. In a closed system, corrosion rates do not exhibit this behavior, since system pressure prevents the gases from escaping.

PRESSURE

Pressure affects the rates of chemical reactions, and corrosion reactions are no exception. In oilfield systems, the primary importance of pressure is its effect on dissolved gases. More gas goes into solution as the pressure is increased. This may, in turn, increase the corrosivity of the solution.

VELOCITY

Velocity, or lack thereof, affects corrosion in several ways. Stagnant or low velocity fluids usually give low corrosion rates. However, dead (no flow) areas in piping and vessels can serve as incubation sites for bacteria and collection areas for solids. In such instances corrosion may be accelerated, and pitting is more likely.

Corrosion rates usually increase with velocity. High velocities and/or the presence of suspended solids or gas bubbles can lead to erosion-corrosion, impingement, or cavitation.

REFERENCES

1. NACE Standard MR0175-98, "Sulfide Stress Cracking Resistant Metallic Materials for Oilfield Equipment" Section 2, Definitions (Houston, TX: NACE).
2. R. M. Tuttle, private communication, October 1997.
3. Standard Methods for the Examination of Water and Waste Water, 18th ed. (Washington, D.C.: American Public Health Association, American Water Works Association, Water Environment Federation, 1992): p. 4–101.
4. R. M. Tuttle, private communication, October 1997.
5. J. L. Crolet, M. R. Bonis, "An Optimized Procedure for Corrosion Testing Under CO_2 and H_2S Gas Pressure" MP 29, 7 (1990).
6. C. de Waard, U. Lotz, "Prediction of CO_2 Corrosion of Carbon Steel," CORROSION/93, paper no. 69 (Houston, TX: NACE, 1993).
7. C. D. Adams, J. D. Garber, R. K. Singh, "Computer Modeling to Predict Corrosion Rates in Gas Condensate Wells Containing CO_2," CORROSION/96, paper no. 31 (Houston, TX: NACE, 1996).
8. NACE Standard MR0175 (latest edition), "Sulfide Stress Cracking Resistant Metallic Materials of Oilfield Equipment" (Houston, TX: NACE).
9. R. E. Tatnall, "Introduction," in A Practical Manual on Microbiologically Influenced Corrosion, ed. G. Korbin (Houston, TX: NACE, 1993): p. 6.
10. G. L. Horacek, E. S. Littmann, R. E. Tatnall, "MIC in the Oilfield," in A Practical Manual on Microbiologically Influenced Corrosion, ed. G. Kobrin (Houston, TX: NACE, 1993): p. 45.

BIBLIOGRAPHY

Atkinson, J. T. N., and H. Van Droffelaar. Corrosion and its Control—An Introduction to the Subject, 2nd ed. Houston, TX: NACE, 1995.

Landrum, R. J. Fundamentals of Designing for Corrosion—A Corrosion Aid for the Designer. Houston, TX: NACE, 1989.

APPENDIX 2A

SOLUBILITY OF OXYGEN IN WATER

Solubility of Oxygen in Water Exposed to Water-Saturated Air at Atmospheric Pressure (101.3kPa)[A]

Temperature °C	Oxygen Solubility mg/L					
	Chlorinity: 0	5.0	10.0	15.0	20.0	25.0
0.0	14.621	13.728	12.888	12.097	11.355	10.657
1.0	14.216	13.356	12.545	11.783	11.066	10.392
2.0	13.829	13.000	12.218	11.483	10.790	10.139
3.0	13.460	12.660	11.906	11.195	10.526	9.897
4.0	13.107	12.335	11.607	10.920	10.273	9.664
5.0	12.770	12.024	11.320	10.656	10.031	9.441
6.0	12.447	11.727	11.046	10.404	9.799	9.228
7.0	12.139	11.442	10.783	10.162	9.576	9.023
8.0	11.843	11.169	10.531	9.930	9.362	8.826
9.0	11.559	10.907	10.290	9.707	9.156	8.636
10.0	11.288	10.656	10.058	9.493	8.959	8.454
11.0	11.027	10.415	9.835	9.287	8.769	8.279
12.0	10.777	10.183	9.621	9.089	8.586	8.111
13.0	10.537	9.961	9.416	8.899	8.411	7.949
14.0	10.306	9.747	9.218	8.716	8.242	7.792
15.0	10.084	9.541	9.027	8.540	8.079	7.642
16.0	9.870	9.344	8.844	8.370	7.922	7.496
17.0	9.665	9.153	8.667	8.207	7.770	7.356
18.0	9.467	8.969	8.497	8.049	7.624	7.221
19.0	9.276	8.792	8.333	7.896	7.483	7.090
20.0	9.092	8.621	8.174	7.749	7.346	6.964
21.0	8.915	8.456	8.021	7.607	7.214	6.842
22.0	8.743	8.297	7.873	7.470	7.087	6.723
23.0	8.578	8.143	7.730	7.337	6.963	6.609
24.0	8.418	7.994	7.591	7.208	6.844	6.498
25.0	8.263	7.850	7.457	7.083	6.728	6.390
26.0	8.113	7.711	7.327	6.962	6.615	6.285
27.0	7.968	7.575	7.201	6.845	6.506	6.184
28.0	7.827	7.444	7.079	6.731	6.400	6.085
29.0	7.691	7.317	6.961	6.621	6.297	5.990
30.0	7.559	7.194	6.845	6.513	6.197	5.896
31.0	7.430	7.073	6.733	6.409	6.100	5.806
32.0	7.305	6.957	6.624	6.307	6.005	5.717
33.0	7.183	6.843	6.518	6.208	5.912	5.631
34.0	7.065	6.732	6.415	6.111	5.822	5.546
35.0	6.950	6.624	6.314	6.017	5.734	5.464
36.0	6.837	6.519	6.215	5.925	5.648	5.384
37.0	6.727	6.416	6.119	5.835	5.564	5.305
38.0	6.620	6.316	6.025	5.747	5.481	5.228
39.0	6.515	6.217	5.932	5.660	5.400	5.152
40.0	6.412	6.121	5.842	5.576	5.321	5.078
41.0	6.312	6.026	5.753	5.493	5.243	5.005
42.0	6.213	5.934	5.667	5.411	5.167	4.933
43.0	6.116	5.843	5.581	5.331	5.091	4.862
44.0	6.021	5.753	5.497	5.252	5.017	4.793
45.0	5.927	5.665	5.414	5.174	4.944	4.724
46.0	5.835	5.578	5.333	5.097	4.872	4.656
47.0	5.744	5.493	5.252	5.021	4.801	4.589
48.0	5.654	5.408	5.172	4.947	4.730	4.523
49.0	5.565	5.324	5.094	4.872	4.660	4.457
50.0	5.477	5.242	5.016	4.799	4.591	4.392

Note:

1. The table provides three decimal places to aid interpolation. When computing saturation values to be used with measured values, such as in computing DO deficit in a receiving water, precision of measured values will control choice of decimal places to be used.

2. Equations are available to compute DO concentration in fresh water and in seawater at equilibrium with water-saturated air. Figures and tables are also available.

   Calculate the equilibrium oxygen concentration (C^*) from equation:

   $$\ln C^* = -139.344\,11 + (1.575\,701 \times 10^5/T) - (6.642\,308 \times 10^7/T^2)$$
   $$+ (1.243\,800 \times 10^{10}/T^3) - (8.621\,949 \times 10^{11}/T^4)$$
   $$- \text{Chl}\,[(3.1929) \times 10^{-2}) - (1.9428 \times 10^1/T)]$$
   $$+ (3.8673 \times 10^3/T^2)]$$

   where:

   C^* = equilibrium oxygen concentration at 101.325 kPa mg/L

   T = temperature (°K) = °C + 273.150, (°C is between 0.0 and 40.0 in the equation; the table is accurate up to 50.0)

   Chl = Chlorinity (see definiton in Note 4)

   Example 1: At 20°C and 0.000 Chl. $\ln C^*$ = 2.207 442 and C^* = 9.092 mg/L

   Example 2: At 20°C and 15.000 Chl
   $$\ln C^* = (2.207\,442) - 15.000(0.010\,657)$$
   $$= 2.0476 \text{ and } C^* = 7.749 \text{ mg/L}$$

   When salinity is used, replace the chlorinity term (−Chl[. . .]) by:

   $$- S(1.7674 \times 10^{-2}) - (1.0754 \times 10^1/T) + (2.1407\ 10^3/T^2)$$

   where:

   S = salinity (see definition in Note 4)

3. For nonstandard conditions of pressure:

   $$C_p = C^*P \left[\frac{(1 - P_{wv}/P)(1 - \theta P)}{(1 - P_{wv})(1 - \theta)} \right]$$

   where:

   C_p = equilibrium oxygen concentration at nonstandard pressure, mg/L

   C^* = equilibrium oxygen concentration at standard pressure of 1 atm, mg/L

   P = nonstandard pressure, atm.

   P_{wv} = partial pressure of water vapor, atm, computed from: $\ln P_{wv} = 11.8571 - (3840.70/T) - (216\,961/T^2)$

   T = temperature, °K

   θ = $0.000\,975 - (1.426 \times 10^{-5}t) + (6.436 \times 10^{-8}t^2)$

   t = temperature, °C

   Note: Although not explicit in the above, the quantity in brackets in the equation for C_p had dimensions of atm^{-1}, so that P multiplied by this quantity is dimensionless.

   Also, the equation for $\ln P_{wv}$ is strictly valid for fresh water only, but for practical purposes no error is made by neglecting the effect of salinity.

   Example 3: At 20°C, 0.000 Chl, and 0.700 atm:
   $$C_p = C^*P(0.990\,092) = 6.30 \text{ mg/L}$$

4. Definitions:

Salinity: Although salinity has been defined traditionally as the total solids in water after all carbonates have been converted to oxides, all bromide and iodide have been replaced by chloride, and all organic matter has been oxidized, the new scale used to define salinity is based on the electrical conductivity of seawater relative to a specified solution of potassium chloride (KCl) in water. The scale is dimensionless and the traditonal dimension of parts per thousand (*i.e.*, g/kg of solution) no longer applies.

Chlorinity: Chlorinity is defined in relation to salinity as follows:

$$\text{Salinity} = 1.806\,55 \times \text{chlorinity}$$

Although chlorinity is not equivalent to chloride concentration, the factor for converting a chloride concentration in seawater to include bromide, for example, is only 1.0045 (based on the relative molecular weights and amounts of the ions). Therefore, for practical purposes, chloride concentration (in g/kg of solution) is nearly equal to chlorinity in seawater. For waste water, it is necessary to know the two ions responsible for the solution's electrical conductivity to correct for their effect on oxygen solubility and use of the tabular value. If this is not done, the equation is inappropriate unless the relative composition of the waste water is similar to that of seawater.

(A) Adopted From Table 4500–0:1. Standard Methods for the Examination of Water and Waste Water, 18th ed. (Washington, D.C.: American Public Health Association, American Water Works Association, Water Environment Federation, 1992): p. 4–101. Permission Granted by APHA, copyright 1992).

CHAPTER 3

FORMS OF CORROSION (TYPES OF CORROSION)

Failures due to corrosion take many forms. The various causes and mechanisms of corrosion can result in metal loss that appears in several forms. **Table 3.1** lists the most common forms found in oilfield operations and their respective mechanisms.

General corrosion is the uniform loss of metal over a large area of the corroded vessel, pipe, or tank. The overall impression is "thinning of the metal." General corrosion is not the usual form occurring in oilfield operations. It is more prevalent in the process industries and refining operations. In oilfield operations, metal loss is usually localized in the form of discrete pits, grooves, gouges, crevices, or larger localized areas. In addition, metals may crack due to corrosion without perceptible loss of material.

TABLE 3.1 Types or Forms of Corrosion

General—(overall metal loss, general thinning)

Localized Corrosion—(pits, gouges, grooves, etc.)

Localized attack may be caused by or show up in a number of forms:

Concentration Cells
—(under deposits, in crevices, in cracks)

Galvanic
—(dissimilar metals are connected)

Preferential at Welds
—(related to galvanic)

Erosion/Corrosion and/or Wear/Corrosion

Microscopic
—(intergranular attack—stress corrosion cracking)

Corrosion Fatigue

Microbiological Corrosion
—(corrosion associated with bacteria such as sulfate reducers)

Other types of localized attack not normally found in oil and gas production:

Leaching (Dezincification)
Differential Thermal Cell Attack

In some cases, metallurgical factors become predominant. Discussion of forms of corrosion which fall in this category necessarily involve the use of basic metallurgical terms. A discussion of metallurgy is presented in Chapter 4, and familiarity with that material will help in the understanding of some of the following discussion. In addition, as noted in **Table 3.1**, certain forms of corrosion are not commonly encountered in oilfield operations. However, they are included for the sake of thoroughness.

GENERAL CORROSION

While localized attack is the most common form of corrosion in oilfield environments, general corrosion occasionally may be noted, particularly on metals exposed to uninhibited acid. It also may be observed in some types of process equipment, such as the trays from contact towers in amine sweetening service **(Figure 3.1)**. In the extreme case of general corrosion **(Figures 3.2A** and **3.2B)**, the corrosion is so uniform it appears as if the tower trays had been chemically etched. In the edge view **(3.2B)**, the thick part of the plate is the original plate thickness. That area was protected from the corroding fluid by a mounting clip. Note that all the corrosion is on the top (immersed) side of the plate. The bottom side, which only contacted vapors, was essentially corrosion-free. The piece

Figure 3.1 General Corrosion—Tray sections from an amine sweetening tower.

of gas well flow line **(Figure 3.3)** shows general corrosion along the bottom of the line where water had flowed. Although the surface of general corrosion may appear as uniform attack, in many cases it will be the result of pitting so closely packed that the result is overall metal loss.

A

B

Figure 3.2 A & B General Corrosion—Tray from a distillation column in a crude oil topping plant producing diesel fuel for field operations.
A. Top View—The washer covered the "plateau" area.
B. Edge View—The thicker section had been covered by a clip, and is the original tray thickness. The top side of the tray was in contact with the corrosive liquid, while the bottom side was exposed to vapors.

Figure 3.3 General Corrosion—Section of gas well flowline thinned along the bottom by corrosion where water flowed. Note that it appears, during the life of this line, there were two different water levels.

LOCALIZED CORROSION

A review of **Table 3.1** shows that localized corrosion's pits, groves, gouges, and crevices are the results of several different corrosion mechanisms or phenomena. Most of these occur frequently in oilfield environments. The most prevalent form of attack shows up as pitting, sometimes as isolated pits, other times as groups, clusters, or in lines. The configuration depends on the specific details of the environment. **Figures 3.4** through **3.7** show examples of pitting attack. **Figures 3.8A** and **3.8B** are photographs of the exterior and interior of a joint of tubing from the highly deviated portion of an oil well, and the groove of corrosion along the bottom side.

Figure 3.4 Pitting Corrosion—Isolated pits inside oil well tubing. Note the sharp edges and flat bottom of the pits, indicative of CO_2 attack.

Figure 3.5 Pitting Corrosion—Isolated pit from gas well gathering line.

TOP   BOTTOM

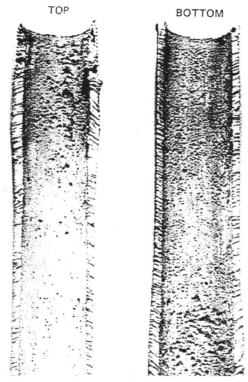

Figure 3.7 Pitting Corrosion—Pits on casing pulled from a West Texas oil well.

Figure 3.6 Pitting Corrosion—Severe pitting of gas condensate well tubing.

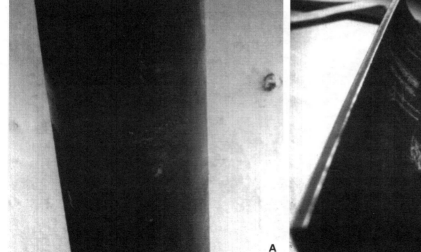

A   B

Figure 3.8 A & B Localized Corrosion—Oil well tubing from a highly deviated well. Water collected and traveled along the lower side of the tubing in the deviated section of the well.
A. External of a joint showing full penetration.
B. Internal view of joint in "A." Note the corroded groove.

PITTING

Pitting occurs when the corroding metal suffers metal loss at localized areas rather than over its entire surface. The entire driving force of the corrosion reaction is concentrated at these localized areas. The corrosion rate at the areas being attacked will be many times greater than the average corrosion rate over the entire surface. The pits that result may be large and shallow or narrow and deep. They may be nearly perfectly round or elliptic or have an irregular shape. A measure of pitting severity is the ratio of the deepest metal penetration at the local areas to the average metal penetration calculated by the overall weight loss. Another method of evaluating pits is to calculate a "pitting rate equivalent" based on the deepest pit and the exposure time converted to an annual penetration rate. Pitting can be much more important than general corrosion because the pitted area can penetrate a pipe or vessel wall in a very short time. Pitting attack is not limited to carbon steels but can occur in the variety of metals used in oil and gas facilities (**Figures 3.9** through **3.11**).

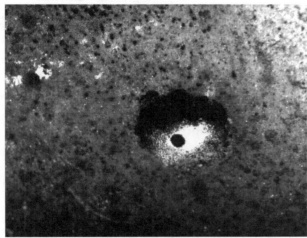

Figure 3.9 Pitting Corrosion—Pit in type 316L stainless steel line. Note that failure occurred in a matter of months. The line had been accidentally hydrotested with brackish water that was left in the line for several months.

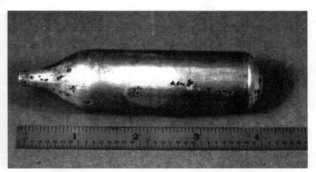

Figure 3.10 Pitting Corrosion—An aluminum instrument float. Note the pitting.

Figure 3.11 Pitting Corrosion—Severely pitted copper hot water line from crew quarters.

CONCENTRATION CELLS

Theoretically, there are many causes of pitting in metals and alloys. All of these causes center around localized differences in the metal and/or in the electrolyte in contact with the metal. Localized differences in electrolyte composition generally are referred to as concentration cells. Depending on the particular situation, concentration cells are referred to as differential aeration cells, metal-ion cells, deposit attack, or crevice corrosion, to name a few. **Figure 3.12** is a schematic cross section of a differential aeration cell. The same type of electrochemical cell can occur with species other than oxygen in the electrolyte.

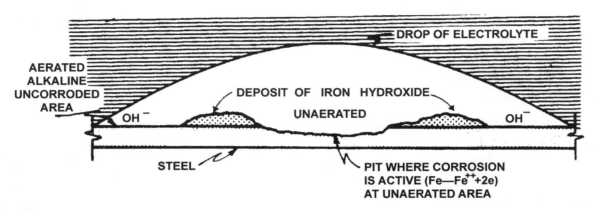

AERATED ALKALINE UNCORRODED AREA

DROP OF ELECTROLYTE

DEPOSIT OF IRON HYDROXIDE

UNAERATED

OH^-

OH^-

STEEL

PIT WHERE CORROSION IS ACTIVE ($Fe \rightarrow Fe^{++} + 2e$) AT UNAERATED AREA

Figure 3.12 Concentration Cell Corrosion—Schematic of reactions in a differential aeration cell. Edges of the drop are high in oxygen, while the center is low in oxygen.

Crevice Corrosion. Corrosion in crevices is a serious form of deterioration that can be minimized by careful design and fabrication. This type of corrosion is actually a particular form of concentration cell corrosion. Because it is very common, crevice corrosion generally is considered a class of corrosion by itself. A crevice may, of course, be formed in many ways, such as by a metal contacting another metal or a nonmetal (such as a gasket) or simply an inadvertent crack in the metal. Most metals and alloys, with the exception of a few noble ones, are susceptible to this type of attack.[1]

Figure 3.13 shows crevice attack on the pin end of a pipe.[2] (Also see **Figures 3.14** and **3.15**) Except for a few special configurations, tubular goods joints will have crevice areas. A crevice can cause localized corrosion by providing a situation where the concentration inside the crevice is different than the concentration outside the crevice. Crevice corrosion can be especially serious in oxygenated systems (*e.g.*, raw water systems) where the oxygen in the crevice may be consumed more rapidly than fresh oxygen can diffuse into the crevice. This causes the pH in the crevice to decrease, resulting in a more acidic environment that accelerates corrosion and increases the oxygen differential.

Figure 3.13 Concentration Cell Corrosion—Example of crevice attack in pipe joint.[2]

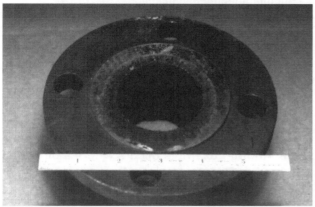

Figure 3.14 Concentration Cell Corrosion—
Example of crevice attack and complete
penetration in connection of integral
joint in tubing.

Figure 3.15 Concentration Cell Corrosion—
Example of crevice attack on raised
face flange.

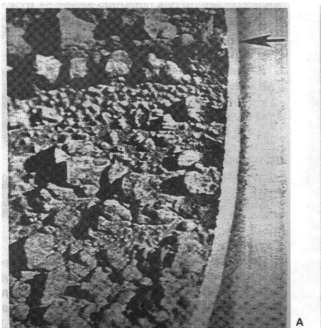

Figure 3.16 A & B Concentration Cell Corrosion—Examples of corrosion from raw river water pumped to a drilling rig
after 6 months of service.[3]
A. Tubercles of rust in pipe.
B. Pitting under rust.

Oxygen Tubercles. This is a form of pitting that results from the same type of mechanism as crevice corrosion. It is encouraged by the formation of a porous layer of iron oxide or hydroxide, which partially shields the steel surface. **Figures 3.16A** and **3.16B** illustrate one form of this attack.[3]

Differential Aeration Cells. An air-water interface is one example of a differential aeration cell. The water at the surface contains more oxygen than the water slightly below the surface. The difference in concentrations can cause preferential attack just below the water line. A similar situation can occur in process vessels and tanks at an interface between an electrolyte (water in most oilfield situations) and a gas or between two liquids when there is a difference in

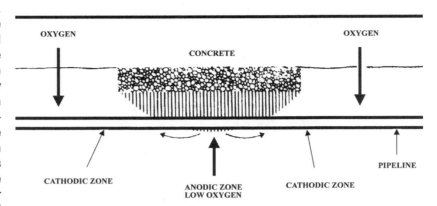

Figure 3.17 Concentration Cell Corrosion—Drawing showing how different oxygen concentration in the soil can affect a pipeline.

concentration of the corroding species at the interface. Another example occurs where a pipeline is buried in a soil containing different amounts of oxygen at certain areas along the line. Under these conditions, the pipe in the well-aerated soil will be cathodic, and the pipe in the poorly aerated soil will be anodic and corroded. In **Figure 3.17**, pipe is shown passing under a paved road where it is in contact with soil having a restricted oxygen supply as compared to pipe on either side of the road in soil not sealed by surface paving. Corrosion of the pipe under the paving can be severe. Another pipeline situation can occur when the soil's oxygen content on the top of the line is quite different from that at the bottom.

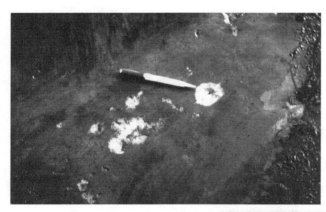

Figure 3.18 Underdeposit Corrosion—Pitting under bottom sediments on lease storage tank. Note that the primer paint is still evident on most of surface.

Figure 3.19 Underdeposit Corrosion— Pitted type 304 stainless steel tray clip from deaeration tower handling silty seawater. Solids deposited in the trays created differential aeration cells in the oxygen rich water. (Corrosion mechanism similar to that illustrated in Figure 3.12.)

Figure 3.20 Underdeposit Corrosion—Pitted admiralty brass (UNS C44000) tube from a shell and tube heat exchanger using silty seawater as the cooling medium.

Figure 3.21 Underdeposit Corrosion—Pitted section of a heater treater fire tube handling a scaling produced water. The fire tube was in service only nine months when complete penetration occurred. Use of a scale inhibitor solved the problem.

Scale and Deposits. The deposition of any solid on a metal surface insufficiently tight and nonporous to completely protect the metal surface can cause increased corrosion under the deposit due to differential concentration. **Figures 3.18** through **3.21** are examples of corrosion under deposits. Even tight, adherent scales can create problems if they form only in spots rather than uniformly over the metal surface. Sulfate-reducing bacteria (SRB) thrive under scales, sludge, sand, formation solids, and other debris, creating hydrogen sulfide (H_2S) and causing localized pitting. **Figures 3.22** through **3.24** show the results of such bacterial activities.

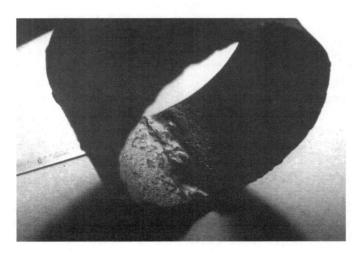

Figure 3.22 Underdeposit Corrosion—Corrosion under sand deposits along the bottom on a water supply line in a water flood project. The line had been laid in a sandy area. Sand that had blown into the pipe during construction was not cleaned from the line before commissioning. The water contained an inactive strain of sulfate reducing bacteria. The bacteria became active when they set up colonies in the sand. Under deposit, microbiologically influenced corrosion (MIC) was the result.

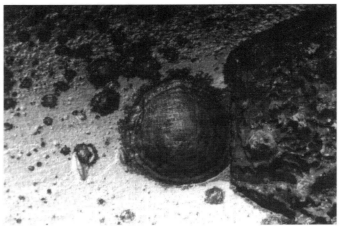

Figure 3.23 Underdeposit Corrosion— Microbiologically influenced corrosion (MIC). The pit in the center of the photograph is a "classic" MIC pit; that is, it has the "stair step" configuration often referred to resembling an open pit mine.

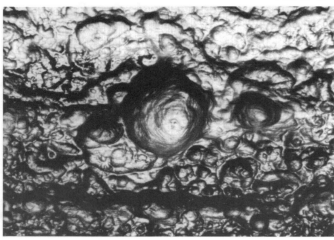

Figure 3.24 Underdeposit Corrosion— Microbiologically influenced corrosion (MIC). Like Figure 3.23, this photograph shows pitting that occurred under colonies of SRB. Note that this photograph is susceptible to an optical illusion and the pits may appear as raised bumps rather than pits.

PITTING AND METALS

Carbon and Low-Alloy Steel. Pitting of carbon steel is of particular importance to oil production because the majority of oil production equipment is made of carbon and low-alloy steels. Pitting is a problem on sucker rods, tubing and casing, and drill pipe, as well as on other downhole and surface equipment.

A common cause of pitting in carbon steel is the formation of local cells due to the partial breakdown or destruction of protective scales. When a corroding metal becomes covered with a corrosion product that is dense and adherent, the product protects the metal from its environment, and corrosion slows down and may ultimately cease. If the protective scale is removed from some areas, those areas become anodic to the areas beneath scale that are still protective. The anodic areas corrode preferentially and result in pitting. H_2S and carbon dioxide (CO_2) are two corrosives that frequently cause pitting of oilfield equipment. Oxygen is also a major cause of pitting even when present in extremely small quantities.

Corrosion-Resistant Alloys (CRAs).[4] The oil and gas industry is currently using a wide selection of CRAs to solve the difficult corrosion problems associated with deep hot wells and CO_2-enhanced recovery projects. These materials range from martensitic stainless steel to very expensive nickel or cobalt alloys. The presence of H_2S and chlorides complicates the selection of alloys for specific service. NACE MR0175 (latest edition)[5] provides guidance on material selection for resistance to stress corrosion cracking (SCC).

The primary concerns for the CRAs are SCC and crevice corrosion attack. The most common CRAs are martensitic stainless steel (UNS S41000 and S42000 [grades 410 and 420]), austenitic stainless steels (UNS S30400, S31600 [types 304 and 316]), and duplex stainless steels (UNS S31803). A number of more resistant, high-cost alloys also are available and are used in some severe environments. These CRAs include both the high-nickel and cobalt alloys.[6]

The corrosion resistance of austenitic stainless steels, such as types 304 and 316, are affected by the presence of chlorides and temperature. Type 304 is less resistant than type 316, since it contains no molybdenum. Crevice corrosion resistance of type 304 is also less than type 316. Both materials are subject to SCC when chlorides are present and the temperature is above 150°F (66°C).[6]

Austenitic stainless steels probably are the most susceptible of all ferrous alloys to pitting chiefly because of the property that makes them "stainless." This property is the ability to form a thin oxide film that protects the metal from further corrosion in many environments. When this film is locally destroyed, that area becomes an anode in a corrosion cell, and pitting is initiated. The pitting process tends to be autocatalytic in that the acidity in the pit does not permit the protective oxide film to reform. Pitting generally initiates in areas of stagnant flow, such as crevices or under deposits, and is promoted by the presence of chloride ions. Resistance to pitting increases with increased molybdenum content. For example, type 316 is more resistant than type 304, and some of the highly alloyed austenitic stainless steels are very resistant to pitting in chloride systems. Pitting can be prevented by cathodic protection.[6]

Duplex stainless is more corrosion resistant than the martensitic stainless steels and is often compared to the lower end of the austenitic alloys. Duplex is susceptible to low pH corrosion in mineral acids, such as hydrochloric acid (HCl), and to SCC/SSC in the presence of H_2S.[6]

Many other CRAs are available and have been used for severely corrosive conditions. These specialty alloys can be made to very high strengths and are used for special items, such as springs.[6]

Other Alloys. All metals commonly used in oilfield applications involving corrosion are subject to pitting under some conditions. As with the ferrous alloys, the most common causes of pitting are concentration cells beneath deposits and at crevices, local breakdown of protective scales, and the presence of aggressive ions that cause loss of passivity.

BIMETALLIC CORROSION

When two different metals are placed in contact in an electrolyte containing an oxidizing agent, the more reactive one will corrode and the other will not. This coupling of dissimilar metals is referred to as a bimetallic couple. It can be extremely destructive, drastically accelerating the corrosion rate of the more reactive of the two metals **(Figure 3.25)**. This principle is utilized in a beneficial way in cathodic protection (Chapter 7). When steel is connected to a more reactive metal, such as magnesium, it is "protected" (does not corrode). The steel becomes a cathode, and the more reactive metal an anode.

One general rule indicating the acceleration of damage in a bimetallic couple is the "area

Figure 3.25: Bimetallic Corrosion (Galvanic Attack)—This steel nipple was screwed into a brass water meter at a waterflood injection well. The failure occurred after about 10 months of service.

principle." This rule states that the total corrosion is proportional to the total cathodic area exposed to the corrosive electrolyte. If there is a marked tendency for one metal to corrode in preference to another, such as iron over copper both exposed in aerated salt water, the less resistant metal suffers the entire corrosion. Thus, steel rivets in copper sheet corrode very rapidly; copper rivets in steel plate cause little damage. The total corrosion in terms of metal weight loss is proportional to the total cathodic area exposed. In more common terms, the rule of thumb states:

"Large cathode and small anode = severe corrosion" (1)

"Small cathode and large anode = minor corrosion" (2)

In many cases the area principle explains how we have "gotten by" with some bimetallic couples in our field operations. For example, it has been common to use 1/4 or 1/2 in. (6 or 12mm) stainless steel needle valves screwed onto carbon steel nipples, even in salt water service, with very few corrosion failures. In most cases, examination shows the area of stainless is small compared to the area of carbon steel. The area principle plus the lack of available oxygen may also explain why bimetallic corrosion has not been a major problem when stainless steel specialty items are used in carbon steel tubing strings.

Although not common in the oil patch, there can be cases where the area relationship changes with time. As an example, a bare copper wire might be coupled with a sheet of aluminum in a tank of stagnant aerated water. After a period of time, copper would plate out on most of the surface of the aluminum, and the area of copper then would be much greater than when originally connected.

When corrosion-resistant alloy steels were first used in condensate wells, it was feared that coupling nickel or chromium steels with N-80 casing would result in severe corrosion of the casing. However, experience in the field demonstrated little corrosion damage to the casing. The important point to be learned from this example is that coupling dissimilar metals together in a neutral nonaerated electrolyte will not necessarily cause corrosion. An oxidant, such as oxygen, is required to continue the reaction. The electrolyte has to be corrosive to at least one member of the dissimilar metal couple if there is to be bimetallic corrosion.

The area principle can be applied to pitting of steel pipe. As it comes from the steel mill, the pipe is usually covered with mill scale. This mill scale is a fair conductor of electricity and, at the same time, it also is insoluble in water and weak acid. This means that the areas covered with mill scale are protected and act to concentrate the corrosion where there is no mill scale. After awhile, the mill scale loosens. Consequently, the acceleration of attack is important only in the early life of the pipe. **Figure 3.26** shows the bimetallic corrosion effects caused by mill scale. The section of tubing is from a well in which acid leaked into the annulus during the acidizing process. Mill scale concentrated the corrosion effect on the patches of bare metal immediately adjacent to the mill scale.

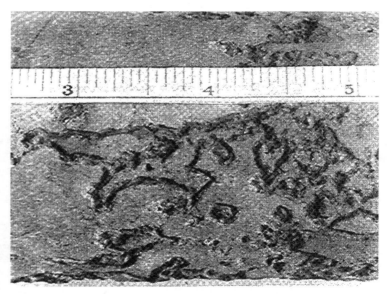

Figure 3.26 Bimetallic Corrosion (Galvanic Attack)—Bimetallic effect of mill scale vs bare steel. Note that this figure is susceptible to an optical illusion. The attack consists of grooves in the metal, not raised irregularities.

New sections of pipe in an old line are sometimes attacked because the old pipe is covered with heavy layers of oxide and rust that are cathodic to the new pipe. This effect is depicted in **Figure 3.27**.

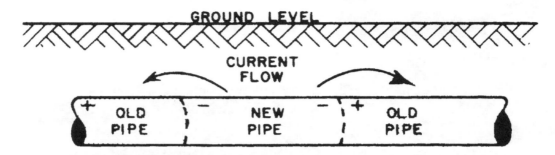

Figure 3.27 Electrochemical Corrosion—New pipe connected to old pipe. New clean pipe will often be anodic to the old corroded pipe covered with corrosion product.

When a metal is welded, the welding process can create microstructures at the weld which differ from the microstructure of the parent steel. The result can be three different microstructures—parent metal, weld metal, and the heat-affected zone (HAZ) between. The areas can act as different metals (bimetallic couples), and "weld line" corrosion can occur **(Figures 3.28** through **3.30)**. The corrosion may show up in the weld metal, at the HAZ, or in the parent metal. Weld line attack is avoided by proper welding practices.

Figure 3.28 Weld Line Corrosion—An example of "weld line" attack caused by microstructure differences between the weld metal, the base metal, and the HAZ.

Figure 3.29 Weld Line Corrosion—An extreme example of "weld line" attack. In this case, a very poor weld created sufficient microstructural differences to cause severe corrosion in an otherwise mildly corrosive system (only minor pitting evident on the rest of the pipe).

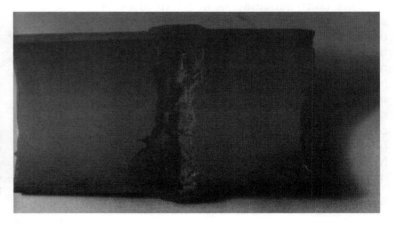

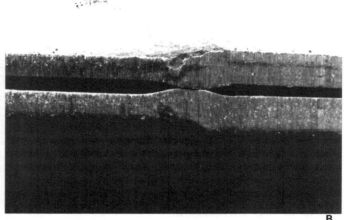

B

Figure 3.30 A & B Weld Line Corrosion—Improperly welded stainless steel is subject to attack at the weld:
  A. An overall view of the split type 316L Stainless Steel pipe. Note the severe attack along the weld.
  B. Close up of pit at the cut edge.

Another type of corrosion sometimes found in tubing installed in oil or gas wells (particularly those of high CO_2 content in the gas phase) is known as ringworm corrosion. As the term implies, the corrosion occurs in a ring a few inches from the upset (**Figure 3.31**).

This corrosion may take the form of very smooth corrosion or severe pitting near the upset. The cause of ringworm corrosion has been traced to the upsetting process. The heat required in upsetting causes the heated end to have a different grain structure from the rest of the pipe. A transition zone in grain structure near the upset runout usually is susceptible to corrosion. This condition can be overcome by fully normalizing the tubing after upsetting. Normalizing is a heat treatment that gives uniformity to grain structure.

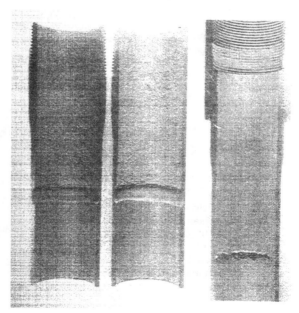

Figure 3.31 Ringworm Corrosion—Examples of "ringworm" attack inside tubing where microstructure differences caused by the upsetting operation accelerated corrosion in tubing that had not been fully normalized.

EROSION-CORROSION OR IMPINGEMENT AND WEAR-CORROSION

Since most metals owe their corrosion resistance to the formation and maintenance of a protective scale, removal of this scale at local areas can lead to accelerated attack. High-velocity flow or turbulence frequently will erode away the protective scale to expose fresh metal, which can be corroded. This combination of erosion of the scale and corrosion of the underlying metal is termed erosion-corrosion and is a common cause of failure of oilfield equipment. Carbon and low-alloy steels are particularly susceptible in environments which form scales that are easily removed, such as iron carbonate. The attack normally occurs only at certain areas, such as changes of sections or connections where there is turbulence from flow or at bends and elbows. **Figure 3.32** shows examples of this type of attack in bends and fittings. **Figure 3.33** shows a ball and seat cage from a sucker rod pump where the flow lines are clearly visible.

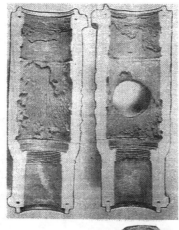

Figure 3.32 Erosion-Corrosion—These fittings are examples of instances where changes of direction and turbulence create conditions that allow erosion to remove corrosion products from the metal surface. The clean surfaces are anodic to the surfaces covered with corrosion product.

Figure 3.33 Erosion-Corrosion—Sucker rod pump valve cage. Note the "flow lines."

A form of corrosion closely related to erosion-corrosion is wear-corrosion. Rather than high-velocity or turbulence-removing corrosion products and protective scales to expose the base metal, mechanical wear does the damage. **Figures 3.34** through **3.36** present examples of wear-corrosion. **Figure 3.34** presents a section of failed tubing from a sucker rod pumping well showing what is usually referred to in the field as "rod wear." The usual comment was, "the rods wore a hole in the tubing." **Figure 3.34A** is a slice of the tubing showing the severe thinning of the damaged area. **Figure 3.34B** provides a look at the section of tubing with the hole. **Figure 3.35** shows a severely damaged tubing collar from a rod pumping well. The well was not equipped with a tubing hold down; thus, the tubing with the collar moved up and down with each pump stroke. The collar rubbed on the casing, the annulus contained corrosive well fluids, and wear-corrosion took place. Gas wells can also have wear-corrosion **(Figure 3.36)**. The clue that these damages are a combination of wear and corrosion is the appearance of the thinned and damaged surfaces. Note that the surfaces in these figures are not smooth "wear" surfaces; they are basically rough, pitted, corroded-looking surfaces with a few smooth spots. Pure wear surfaces are smooth. **Figure 3.37** shows the results of a laboratory wear test. Note the smooth surfaces on the pin and box—no pitting, and no signs of corrosion.

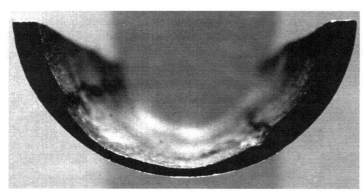

Figure 3.34 A & B Wear-Corrosion—A sucker rod coupling rubbing corrosion product from this pumping well tubing resulted in this so-called "rod wear" form of wear-corrosion.
A. End view showing thinning.
B. Section with hole. Note that this is not a smooth wear surface.

A

B

Figure 3.35 Wear-Corrosion—Pumping well tubing collar. Note that the well did not have a tubing anchor, thus the collar could rub on the casing with each pump stroke.

Figure 3.36 Wear-Corrosion—Wire-lines rubbing corrosion product from this gas well tubing resulted in the so-called "wire-line cut" form of wear-corrosion. ⟶

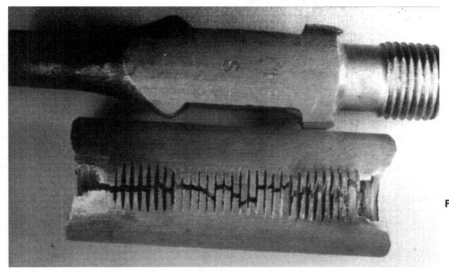

Figure 3.37 Pure Wear Surface—Note smooth surface—no roughness, no pitting, no corrosion. This specimen was prepared in a laboratory test.

Another manifestation of erosion-corrosion, and often a more localized attack, is known as impingement or velocity-related corrosion. This occurs when a stream impinges upon a metal surface and breaks down protective films at very small areas. The resulting attack is in the form of pits that are characteristically elongated and undercut on the downstream end. Impingement also results from turbulence surrounding small particles adhering to a metal surface. It is a problem particularly in copper and copper-based alloys. **Figure 3.38** shows a copper alloy condenser with this type of attack, and **Figure 3.39** illustrates velocity attack on a high-velocity-produced fluids line. The austenitic stainless steels have high resistance to both erosion-corrosion and impingement type attack.

FLOW DIRECTION

Figure 3.38 Erosion-Corrosion—Impingement attack in copper alloy condenser tube.

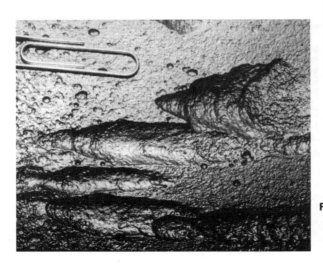

Figure 3.39 Erosion-Corrosion—Velocity attack in produced fluids line. Note that this photograph is susceptible to an optical illusion and the grooves and pits may appear as raised bumps and ridges.

CHAPTER 3: FORMS OF CORROSION (TYPES OF CORROSION)   **55**

CAVITATION

Cavitation is the formation and collapse of vapor bubbles in fluids (*e.g.*, water) because of rapid changes in pressure. It can occur whenever the absolute pressure at a point in the liquid stream is reduced to the vapor pressure of the fluid so that bubbles form, and this is followed by a rapid rise in pressure, resulting in bubble collapse. Cavitation damage is the wearing away of a metal from repeated impact blows from collapse of bubbles within a fluid. Corrosion usually plays a minor role in the rate of cavitation damage. Pump impellers **(Figure 3.40)** often show cavitation damage effects.

INTERGRANULAR CORROSION

As the name implies, intergranular corrosion is preferential attack of a metal's grain boundaries. (Intergranular corrosion often is confused with stress corrosion cracking. However, intergranular corrosion can occur in the absence of stress; stress corrosion cracking occurs only while the metal is under stress.) Intergranular corrosion has occurred in many alloys including austenitic stainless steels, copper alloys, aluminum alloys, and nickel alloys. **Figure 3.41** is a photograph of intergranular attack. In most cases, intergranular corrosion results from a metallurgical structure that causes the grain boundaries to be more susceptible to attack than the grains themselves. Proper heat treatment or control of chemistry of the steel generally can eliminate the susceptible grain boundary constituent and render the alloy resistant to intergranular attack. The most serious occurrence of intergranular corrosion involves austenitic stainless steels.

When these steels are held in, or cooled slowly through, a temperature range of 800°F to 1,600°F (427°C to 871°C), chromium carbides precipitate in the grain boundary, and the steel is said to be sensitized. Exposure of the sensitized steel to nonaggressive solutions such as weak acids results in intergranular attack. **Table 3.2** shows corrosives that cause intergranular corrosion of sensitized austenitic stainless steels.

Figure 3.40 Cavitation Attack—A pump impeller with severe cavitation attack due to the collapse of bubbles in the liquid at the metal-liquid interface. (Figure 17-9, NACE Basic Corrosion Course.)

Figure 3.41 Inter-granular Corrosion—Photomicrograph of intergranular attack.

TABLE 3.2 Corrosives that Cause Intergranular Attack on Austenitic Stainless Steels[1]

Caustic soda	Hydrogen sulfide
Cerium oxide	Lithium
Copper sulfate-Al sulfate	Nitric acid
Fe sulfate-Al sulfate	Oxalic acid
High temperature, high purity water	Polythionic acid
Hydrochloric acid	Sea water
Hydrofluoric acid	Sodium
	Sulfuric acid

[1] See NACE 3, page 262.

There are several theories to account for sensitization of austenitic stainless steels. The most popular is that precipitation of chromium carbides depletes areas immediately adjacent to grain boundaries of chromium. The depleted zones become anodic to the grains and corrode preferentially.

Sensitization becomes a problem whenever stainless steels are welded or when they are exposed to temperatures from 800°F to 1,600°F (427°C to 871°C). To prevent intergranular corrosion, two methods are used: heat treatment and control of chemical composition. Sensitized stainless steel can be solution annealed by heating to 1,950°F to 2,050°F (1,066°C to 1,121°C) and cooling rapidly, which does not allow time for precipitation. Another treatment is to hold them at 1,600°F to 1,650°F (871°C to 899°C) for several hours, thus allowing chromium to diffuse from the grain boundaries back to the depleted zones.

Precipitation of carbides can be controlled in two ways. First: Use a stainless steel with very low carbon (below 0.03%) so that there is not enough carbon available to tie up the chromium. The second approach is to add either titanium or columbium (niobium), both of which have a greater affinity for carbon than chromium. This results in precipitation of columbium or titanium carbides, rather than chromium carbides. The best method depends upon the particular application. The "L" grades of austenitic stainless steels restrict carbon content to 0.03% maximum. These are the grades specified if the stainless steels are to be welded. For example types 304L (UNS S30403) and 316L (UNS S31603).

HYDROGEN-INDUCED FAILURES

Hydrogen atoms may be produced on a metal surface in an aqueous environment by a corrosion reaction, cathodic protection, electroplating, or acid pickling. Some of the hydrogen atoms combine to form gaseous molecular hydrogen (H_2) on the metal surface and escape as gas bubbles. A portion of the atoms will enter into the metal and may cause problems, such as blistering, cracking, and hydrogen embrittlement. Certain substances, such as sulfide ions, phosphorus, and arsenic compounds, retard the formation of molecular hydrogen and thereby increase the entry of hydrogen into metal.

HYDROGEN BLISTERING

Hydrogen entry into low-strength steels can result in hydrogen blisters if there is a macroscopic defect in the steel, such as a lamination or inclusion. Any void in the steel provides a place for hydrogen atoms to combine, form hydrogen gas, and build sufficient pressure to cause blistering. This effect is illustrated by the hydrogen probes shown in **Figures 3.42A** and **3.42B**. This style hydrogen probe is constructed of a sealed, hollow steel tube with a pressure gauge attached to the top. When the probe is placed in a sour (H₂S) system and is allowed to corrode, the pressure gradually will increase as the result of hydrogen atoms diffusing through the walls of the tube and combining to form hydrogen gas molecules. The molecules are too large to diffuse back through the steel and the pressure increases as the number of hydrogen gas molecules increases. This is the phenomena that caused the blistering shown in **Figure 3.43**. In oilfield operations, hydrogen blistering is primarily a problem in sour environments. It most likely occurs in lower strength ductile steels with laminations (such as those used for some vessels and tanks [**Figure 3.44**]) and rarely results in a brittle failure, but it can cause rupture and leakage. The best defense against blistering is the use of a clean steel (low sulfur and low phosphorus) or control of the corrosion process.

B

A

Figure 3.42 A & B Hydrogen Probes—Atomic hydrogen from corrosion enters the tube through the steel wall where it combines to form hydrogen gas and is trapped. Pressure buildup is indicated on the gauge.
A. This probe is designed to be screwed directly into the pipe or vessel.
B. This probe is designed for use with an access fitting that allows installation and removal under pressure. Note it also has a thermometer so temperature as well as pressure may be recorded; thus, temperature variation may be compensated.

Figure 3.43 Hydrogen Blistering—Tubing cross section shows delamination by accumulated pressure of hydrogen gas forming at voids in the metal wall. The inset shows blisters. Note that this figure is susceptible to an optical illusion. The attack consists of raised blisters, not pits.

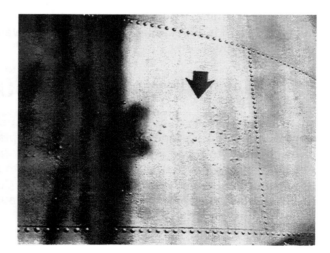

Figure 3.44 Hydrogen Blistering—Blisters on side of sour crude storage tank.

HYDROGEN EMBRITTLEMENT

Hydrogen entry into high strength steels can result in hydrogen embrittlement. In such an embrittled state, a material can fail in a brittle manner at stresses considerably below its yield strength. Limiting of this phenomena to high strength materials may be due to the fact that only such materials can have tensile stresses high enough to initiate the mechanism. Hydrogen leading to embrittlement may be entrapped during pouring of the molten metal, absorbed during electroplating or pickling, or generated by corrosive action.

If the metal is under a high tensile stress, brittle failure can occur. The path of failure may be either intergranular or transgranular, and it often is extremely difficult to distinguish failures caused by hydrogen embrittlement from stress corrosion cracking. Hydrogen embrittlement failures usually occur only with high-strength steels, generally those having yield strengths of 90,000 psi (620 MPa) or higher. The susceptibility to hydrogen embrittlement failure increases with increasing strength and hardness.

Failures due to hydrogen embrittlement do not always occur immediately after application of the load or exposure to the hydrogen-producing environment. Usually, there is a time period during which no damage is observed, followed by sudden, catastrophic failure. This phenomenon is referred to as delayed failure. The time period prior to failure is the "incubation" period during which hydrogen is diffusing to points of high triaxial stress. The time to failure decreases as the amount of hydrogen absorbed, applied stress, and strength level of the material increases.

Until a steel containing hydrogen actually cracks, there is no permanent damage. In many cases, the hydrogen can be baked out by suitable heat treatments, and the original properties of the steel can be restored. This is frequently done after electroplating of high strength steel parts. In early oilfield operations sour area sucker rod strings that had been experiencing brittle failures were at times left out of wells to "weather" or were "fired" before being run in another well.

SULFIDE STRESS CRACKING

Spontaneous brittle failures that occur in steels and other high-strength alloys when exposed to moist H_2S and other sulfide environments have been called by a number of names. Among these are H_2S cracking, sulfide cracking, sulfide stress cracking (SSC), sulfide corrosion cracking, and sulfide stress corrosion cracking. The possible explanation for the number of names is the number of theories about the mechanism of failure. These theories range from: sulfide stress cracking is a form of stress corrosion cracking (discussed later in this chapter) to that it is a form of hydrogen embrittlement. Regardless of the mechanism, the fact remains that SSC can cause catastrophic failures in sour oilfield environments. **Figure 3.45** shows some examples of SSC failures from the field. As the industry handles more sour gas around the globe, more materials are developed to be resistant to SSC. For this reason NACE Standard Materials Requirement, MR0175, "Sulfide Stress Cracking Resistant Metallic Materials for Oilfield Equipment," is updated annually.[7]

Figure 3.45 SSC—Tubing, coupling collar, carbon steel springs.

Although the mechanism of sulfide stress cracking is not completely understood, it is generally accepted that the following conditions must be present before cracking can occur:

- H_2S must be present.

- Water must be present—Even a trace amount of moisture is sufficient.

- A "high-strength" steel must be involved (the exact strength level varies with the composition and microstructure of the steel). [Although other materials are susceptible to SSC, this discussion is confined to steel.]

- The steel must be under tensile stress or loading (stress may be residual or applied).

If all these conditions are present, SSC may occur after some period of time. It is important to realize that SSC usually does not occur immediately after exposure to the sour environment but may take place after hours, days, or years of service. The susceptibility of a material to failure by this mechanism is primarily determined by the following variables:

1. Strength or Hardness—The hardness of carbon steels are proportional to strength. Thus, hardness has become a very important parameter for the susceptibility of steel to SSC. Carbon steels with hardness values of 22 HRC (hardness, Rockwell, C) or less are generally considered to be immune to sulfide stress cracking. Steels with hardness above this level are susceptible to cracking. The higher the hardness (strength), the shorter the time to failure. If steel is alloyed with other materials, such as nickel, failure can occur at hardness levels less than 22 HRC.[8] Conversely, certain heat treatments and steel composition can raise the maximum permissible hardness level above this value.

2. Stress Level (Either Residual or Applied)—The time-to-failure decreases as the stress level increases. In most cases, the stress results from a tensile load or from the application of pressure, or both. However, residual stresses and hard spots can be created by welding or by cold working the material (i.e., cold bending, wrench marks, etc.).

3. Hydrogen Sulfide Concentration—The time-to-failure increases as the H_2S concentration decreases. Delayed failures can occur at very low concentrations of H_2S in water (0.1 ppm) and at partial pressures as low as 0.001 (1 kPa) atmosphere, although the time-to-failure becomes very long. At high concentrations (5% to 10% in gas) of H_2S, the time-to-failure can be minutes. In early high H_2S exploration in areas of Wyoming and Canada, tubing strings were reported to crack and part while being run.

4. pH of Solution—Cracking tendency increases as the pH decreases. The tendency to failure can be drastically reduced if the pH of the solution is maintained above 9.0.

5. Temperature—There is a considerable amount of data indicating that cracking susceptibility decreases above approximately 150°F (66°C). Guidance on this is given in NACE Standard MR0175 (latest edition).[9]

HIGH TEMPERATURE ATTACK

At temperatures above 450°F (232°C), low-strength steels can be embrittled by exposure to hydrogen gas. At these temperatures, hydrogen reacts with iron carbides in the steel to form methane. The methane occupies a larger volume than the iron carbide and, therefore, will cause small cracks or voids. As a result, the steel can withstand very little deformation without cracking, that is, it becomes embrittled. The diffusion rate increases with an increase in hydrogen partial pressure and with temperature. Although, in oil and gas production, we seldom, if ever, see temperatures above 450°F (232°C), nor do we see large quantities of hydrogen gas in our produced streams. This is a hydrogen-induced failure; therefore, it is mentioned for thoroughness.

CORROSION FATIGUE

Metal fatigue is the cause of many costly failures in the petroleum production industry. Most of these failures occur in corrosive media, such as salt water, and are therefore more correctly described as corrosion fatigue failures. Corrosion fatigue has been recognized as the predominant cause of sucker rod and drill string failures for many years (**Figures 3.46** and **3.47**).

Figure 3.46 Corrosion Fatigue—Failed sucker rod. The most common cause of sucker rod breaks. Note the three areas of the failure: the smooth area where the cyclic action "peened" the surface, the grainy looking area where the crack opening was too fast for the "peening" to take place, and the final tip where the cross sectional area had been reduced to the point where the rod would handle the load and thus failed in a typical tensile failure fashion.

Figure 3.47 Corrosion Fatigue—Failed drill pipe. The circumferential crack proceeds until it reaches through the pipe wall resulting in a pressure leak that soon washes out into a hole through the wall.

FATIGUE OF METALS IN AIR

When metals are repeatedly stressed in a cyclic manner in air they will fail in a brittle mode at stresses far below the yield or tensile strength. There is, however, with some metals (notably steels), a stress below which the material may be cyclically stressed indefinitely without failure. This stress level is called the endurance limit and is always lower than the yield and tensile strengths. The performance of materials subjected to cyclic stressing is normally described by plotting the stress at failure against the logarithm of the number of cycles to failure for a series of stress levels. This type of plot is known as an S-N curve (**Figure 3.48**).

The endurance limit for ferrous metals usually is 40% to 60% of their tensile strengths, depending on the microstructure and heat treatment. Rapid quenched and tempered steels normally have better fatigue properties than slow-cooled carbon steels. Since the tensile strength of ferrous metals is roughly

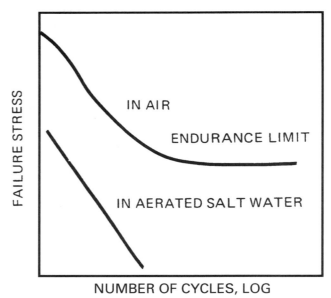

NUMBER OF CYCLES, LOG

Figure 3.48 Typical S-N curves for steel in air and in salt water. S-N curves are graphical presentations of cyclic stress data. Stress to failure is plotted against the logarithm of the number of cycles to failure.

proportional to hardness over a wide range, the endurance limit is also proportional to hardness over this range.

Fatigue cracks usually start at the metal surface, and the fatigue performance of any item is drastically affected by surface conditions. Notches, pits or metal inhomogeneities, such as inclusions or porosity, act as stress raisers, and the actual stress at the root of a notch may be many times the nominal applied stress. Heat treating processes can decarburize the surface of a metal part, and the fatigue strength is dependent on the strength of this lower carbon content surface layer.

THE EFFECT OF A CORROSIVE ENVIRONMENT ON FATIGUE LIFE

Corrosion fatigue is the most common cause of failure for sucker rods. The appearance of the break shown in **Figure 3.46** is very typical of such failures. Four distinct areas characterize this appearance. A pit or notch (which can be very small) on the surface serves as a stress riser to initiate the fatigue crack. The crack opens and closes as the rod cycles from compression on the downstroke to tension on the upstroke. As the crack grows through many cycles, the hammering together of the side of the crack produces a smooth area—this moon-shaped surface appears to have been peened. At some point in its life, the growth rate of the crack becomes too rapid for the peening to smooth the surface, and the fracture surface will appear grainy. This leads "old-timers" to state: "The rods parted because the steel crystallized." The last feature of the appearance occurs when there is too little rod cross section area remaining to support the load, and the rod pulls apart, leaving a tip typical of a tension failure.

Corrosion fatigue causes most sucker rod failures because the fatigue life of a metal is substantially reduced when the metal is cyclically stressed in a corrosive environment. The presence of the corrosive medium adds to the fatigue mechanism and shortens the time to failure. Hydrogen embrittlement can also contribute to fatigue failure in high strength steels—some sucker rod steels are more susceptible to corrosion fatigue than others. The critical characteristic of corrosion fatigue is that the metal no longer exhibits an endurance limit as it did in air **(Figure 3.48)**. Corrosion fatigue performance normally is characterized by the "fatigue limit," an arbitrarily defined quantity. The corrosion fatigue limit commonly is defined as the maximum value of stress at which no failure occurs after 10^7 cycles. (At a pumping speed of 15 strokes/minute 10^7 cycles is reached in approximately 463 days of pumping.)

TABLE 3.3 Corrosion Fatigue of Steel in Brine

DISSOLVED GAS	% DECREASE FROM AIR ENDURANCE LIMIT
Hydrogen sulfide (H_2S)	20
Carbon dioxide (CO_2)	41
Carbon dioxide + air	41
Hydrogen sulfide + air	48
Hydrogen sulfide + carbon dioxide	62
Air	65

In corrosion fatigue, the corrosiveness of the environment is extremely important. The presence of dissolved gases, such as H_2S, CO_2, or oxygen, causes a pronounced increase in corrosiveness and results in decreased corrosion fatigue life **(Table 3.3)**. Pitting or localized attack is most damaging from the standpoint of corrosion fatigue, but even slight general corrosion will substantially reduce fatigue life **(Figure 3.49)**.

A

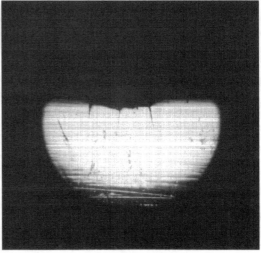

B

Figure 3.49 A & B Corrosion Fatigue—Fatigue cracks initiated by very small corrosion pits on the surface of a sucker rod.
A. Exterior surface of the failed rod.
B. Photomicrograph of fatigue cracks originating from the pits.

Hydrogen embrittlement can reduce the fatigue life in medium strength steels if outward diffusion of hydrogen is blocked or if the specimen is kept immersed in the corrosive fluid. Significant reduction in the fatigue life of high strength steels can result from hydrogen embrittlement. Other variables which affect corrosion rates also are important. The fatigue life of carbon steel in salt water or drilling mud with a pH above 11 has been shown to increase markedly.

The corrosion fatigue performance of carbon and low-alloy steels is independent of strength. This has been shown both for aerated fresh water and for brine containing H_2S, CO_2, air, or some combination. Hence, heat treatment and alloying are more important to corrosion resistance than to physical properties.

STRESS CORROSION CRACKING

Stress corrosion cracking (SCC) is caused by the "synergistic" action of corrosion and applied tensile stress; that is, the combined effect of the two is greater than the sum of the single effects. In the absence of stress, the particular metal would not corrode (in such a cracking manner), and in absence of corrosion, the metal easily supports the stress. The result of the combined effect is a brittle failure of a normally ductile metal.

The stress leading to SCC is always a tensile stress. It can be either applied or residual. Frequently, residual stresses are more dangerous because they may not be considered in evaluating the overall stresses. When a metal suffers SCC, metal loss from corrosion is generally very low, although pitting is frequently observed. In many cases, pitting precedes cracking, with stress corrosion cracks developing from the bases of the pits. The cracking may be either intergranular or transgranular, but is always in a direction perpendicular to the highest stresses. Sometimes crack growth will relieve stresses and change the direction of the highest stresses. The cracks will not be straight, but will continue at right angles to the highest stresses.

All alloys are subject to SCC, and only pure metals appear to be immune. In every case, however, stress corrosion results from exposure of a particular alloy to a particular corrosive; no one corrosive causes stress corrosion in all alloys, and most alloys are subject to attack in only a few specific corrosives.

In general, the time-to-failure and extent of cracking will vary with corrosive concentration, temperature, and stress intensity. Cracking tendency always increases with increasing stress level while time-to-cracking decreases. One approach to preventing failures is to minimize stresses. Areas that are particularly important are areas of stress concentration, differential expansion, forced mismatches, and other spots where local stresses would be high. In some cases, peening, burnishing, or rolling surfaces to induce compressive stresses will reduce cracking tendency.

Increasing solution concentration usually increases cracking tendency and decreases the time to cracking. This is most important in normally weak solutions that can become concentrated at local spots, such as liquid level lines, hot spots, and dead ends. For instance, type 304 stainless steel will crack in solutions containing only a few parts per million chloride, but the chloride concentration usually is found to be much higher at the point where cracking occurs. Oxygen can increase the chances of SCC even at low temperatures.

At higher temperatures, cracking tendency in many systems is greater and time-to-failure shorter. Failures will develop at local areas where the temperatures are higher than those of the system in general. SCC does not occur in dry gases due to absence of an electrolyte.

CARBON AND LOW-ALLOY STEELS

The most common corrosives causing SCC of mild steels are sodium hydroxide (NaOH) and nitrate solutions. Cracking in NaOH, known as caustic embrittlement, was once a very serious problem. However, enough is now known about the phenomenon that chemical inhibition and proper stress relief are widely used to avoid caustic embrittlement. Cracking by ammonium, calcium, and sodium nitrates are minimized by preventive measures, such as avoiding conditions that can cause localized concentration, controlling temperature, and reducing stresses. Since the use of these materials that can cause SCC is minimal in oilfield operations, this type of SCC is infrequent. However, certain CO/CO_2 combinations that can be encountered in inert gas flooding can cause cracking of carbon and low-alloy steels.

HIGH-STRENGTH STEELS

Cracking of high-strength steels is more widespread than that of mild steels. It occurs in salt solutions, moist atmospheres, and, with the ultrahigh strength steels, even in tap water. While many such failures are due to SCC, there is strong evidence that much of the cracking of high-strength steels is caused by hydrogen embrittlement. Cracking increases with the strength of steels, which accounts for the extreme susceptibility of the ultrahigh strength steels. Experience or actual tests are necessary to determine the corrosives and conditions that will cause cracking of these steels.

COPPER-BASED ALLOYS

Pure copper, like other pure metals, apparently is immune to SCC. Alloying with even small amounts of phosphorous, zinc, antimony, aluminum, silicon, or nickel makes it susceptible to serious intergranular SCC by ammonia and ammoniacal solutions. In some cases, cracking is both intergranular and transgranular. The presence of oxygen, in addition to ammonia, is necessary to cause cracking of the copper alloys, but even very small amounts of ammonia can be damaging.

In oil and gas systems, the most common use of copper-based alloys is in water handling, and ammonia is not usually present. The other common use is copper tubing for instrument or chemical injection lines. In most cases, SCC has not been a problem. Theoretically, some of the amines used in corrosion inhibitors could cause cracking. Experience and testing are necessary to verify the suitability of an alloy for a particular exposure.

ALUMINUM ALLOYS

SCC of aluminum is generally confined to high-strength alloys, such as the 20XX series (aluminum-copper) and the 70XX series (aluminum-zinc-manganese-copper). When heat treated for strength, these alloys sometimes contain precipitated phases in grain boundaries which make them susceptible to intergranular SCC in mild corrosives, particularly salt atmospheres. Most failures have been experienced where high strength-to-weight ratios are desired, such as in aircraft. In the process industries, aluminum is used more for corrosion resistance than for its strength-to-weight ratio, and nonsusceptible alloys can generally be chosen. Where susceptible alloys are used, coatings or some secondary protection are necessary. Since aluminum depends on an oxide film for its corrosion protection, and without oxygen it is susceptible to chloride pitting, its use in the production industry has been limited to temporary piping and special items where its protective oxide film is not in jeopardy. Aluminum drill pipe has been internally plastic coated.

NICKEL AND NICKEL-BASED ALLOYS

Nickel and nickel-based alloys are susceptible to stress corrosion cracking in a few specific corrosives, but generally have excellent resistance to all types of production environments.

TITANIUM AND TITANIUM ALLOYS

Because of their excellent corrosion resistance to a wide variety of environments, use of titanium alloys is rapidly increasing. However, titanium has been found to be susceptible to intergranular SCC in several environments. Often, however, titanium alloys that are resistant to cracking in a particular environment can be found, and in many cases have been used in oil patch heat exchangers.

LIQUID METAL EMBRITTLEMENT
(STRESS ALLOYING)

Another form of brittle failure that can result from corrosion is liquid metal embrittlement (stress alloying). The metal attacked reacts with another metal or a corrosion product which, under stress, penetrates the metal intergranularly. This intergranular phase is either much weaker or more brittle than the base alloy and, therefore, cannot support the load, or else melts at the temperature of service. Liquid metal embrittlement is another form of attack not usually found in oilfield operation, but it can occur.

Ambient temperature attack is limited to that caused by mercury on brass and other copper alloys and on high-strength aluminum alloys. The copper alloys are the more susceptible of the two, and whenever stressed brass or other copper alloys come in contact with mercury or mercury salts, serious cracking can result. With aluminum, only the higher strength alloys are severely affected and the severity of attack depends upon the heat treatment of the alloy. Although mercury is not commonly used in processes, instruments such as manometers and thermometers containing mercury are used. If such instruments break, mercury can be spread throughout a system. Mercury is produced with the gas in some producing areas, particularly Southeast Asia. Because of the relatively high vapor pressure of mercury and the fact that only a small amount can cause cracking failure, little mercury is required to create a rash of stress alloying failures. Mercury contamination also raises safety issues.

REFERENCES

1. R. J. Landrum, Fundamentals of Designing for Corrosion—A Corrosion Aid for the Designer (Houston, TX: NACE, 1989), p. 49.
2. R. M. Tuttle, private communication, October 1997.
3. C. P. Dillon, ed., Forms of Corrosion—Recognition and Prevention, NACE Handbook 1, Case History 2.2.2.6. (Houston, TX: NACE, 1982), p. 27.
4. R. M. Tuttle, private communication, October 1997.

5. NACE Standard MR0175 (latest edition), "Sulfide Stress Cracking Resistant Metallic Materials for Oilfield Equipment" (Houston, TX: NACE).
6. R. M. Tuttle, private communication, October 1997.
7. NACE Standard MR0175 (latest edition), Ibid.
8. NACE Standard MR0175-97, Ibid., p. 8.
9. NACE Standard MR0175 (latest edition), Ibid.

BIBLIOGRAPHY

Atkinson, J. T. N., and H. Van Droffelaar. *Corrosion and its Control—An Introduction to the Subject.* 2nd ed. Houston, TX: NACE, 1995.

Dillon, C. P., ed., *Forms of Corrosion—Recognition and Prevention,* NACE Handbook 1. Houston, TX: NACE, 1982.

Kaesche, H., *Metallic Corrosion—Principles of Physical Chemistry and Current Problems,* Trans. R. A. Rapp. Houston, TX: NACE,1985.

Szklarska-Smialowska, Z. *Pitting Corrosion of Metals.* Houston, TX: NACE, 1986.

CHAPTER 4

MATERIALS SELECTION—METALS

Since oil and gas production piping and facilities are constructed primarily of metals, it is important to understand some of the principles of metallurgy. The terminology, various microstructures, compositions, and physical properties and characteristics of metals used in the oilfield operations are reviewed in this chapter. Note: When specific metals are mentioned they will be identified by the appropriate Unified Numbering System (UNS) designator. Common names will be included where applicable. A detailed listing of UNS numbers and common names can be found in most engineering and metallurgy handbooks, including the NACE Corrosion Engineers Reference Book.[1]

BASIC METALLURGY
CRYSTALLINE STRUCTURE

Nearly all metals and alloys exhibit a crystalline structure. The atoms which make up a crystal exist in an orderly three-dimensional arrangement. **Figure 4.1** is a schematic representation of the unit cells of the most common crystal structures found in metals and alloys. The unit cell is the smallest portion of the crystal structure which contains all the geometric characteristics of the crystal. It can be considered the smallest building block of the crystal. The crystals, or grains, of a metal are made up of these unit cells repeated in three-dimensions. The crystalline nature of metals is not readily obvious.

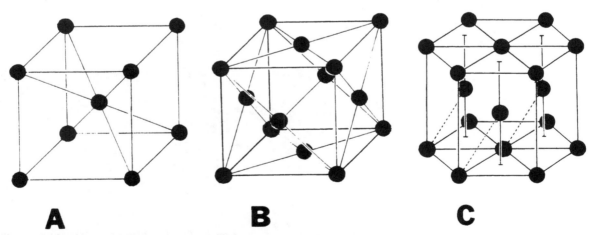

Figure 4.1 Schematic representation of unit cells of the most common crystal structures found in metals.
   A. Body centered cubic.
   B. Face centered cubic.
   C. Hexagonal close packed.

When a metal solidifies, the atoms, which are randomly distributed in the liquid state, arrange themselves into crystalline blocks. As the blocks of crystals or grains meet, there is a mismatch at their boundaries. When the metal has solidified and cooled, there will be numerous regions of mismatch between each grain. These regions are called grain boundaries. Since the most stable configuration of a metal is its particular crystal lattice, grain boundaries are high-energy areas and are more chemically active. Hence, grain boundaries are usually attacked slightly more rapidly than grain faces when exposed to a corrosive environment. In fact, metallographic etching depends upon just this effect to develop contrast between grains and grain boundaries, precipitates, twins and grains having different orientation with respect to the surface, etc.

Controlled etching with selected electrolytes will normally show the granular characteristics of metals and alloys. Normally, metal grains are so small they can only be observed with a microscope. The general range of grain size usually runs from 0.001 to 0.1 in. (0.025 to 2.5 mm) in diameter. To determine the grain size or microstructure (structure under the microscope) of a metal or alloy, it is usually necessary to prepare a sample for microscopic study by special grinding and polishing techniques. The polished surface is then reacted with a suitable etching reagent. The etchant attacks the grain boundaries and grains differently. This reveals the grain boundaries and the distinguishing features of the microstructure. Even though grains are very small, each is still made up of thousands upon thousands of unit cells. (Examples of etched samples showing various grain structures are shown in later photomicrographs such as **Figures 4.2** through **4.5**.)

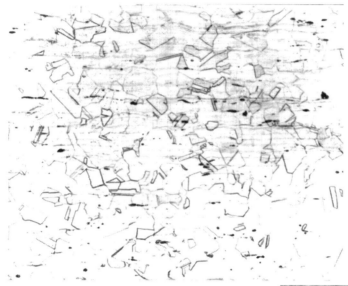

Figure 4.2 Photomicrograph showing the microstructure of austenitic stainless steel. (Photograph courtesy of Metallurgical Consultants, Inc., Houston, TX.)[2]

Figure 4.3 Photomicrograph of a martensitic structure. Note characteristic needle-like microstructure. (Photograph courtesy of Metallurgical Consultants, Inc., Houston, TX.)[2]

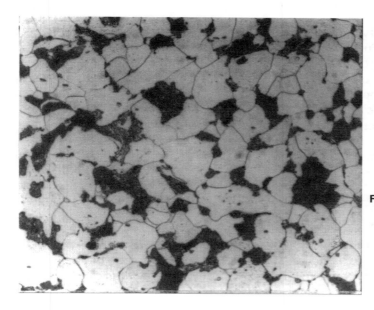

Figure 4.4 Photomicrograph of a ferritic and pearlitic structure. The ferrite grains are the light colored ones. The pearlite plates show up as the dark areas. (Photograph courtesy of Metallurgical Consultants, Inc., Houston, TX.)[2]

Figure 4.5 Detailed Photomicrograph of pearlitic structure. Insert shows typical iron—Fe_3C plates that make up the dark (pearlite) microelement in the larger photograph.

ALLOYS

Metals listed as pure or commercially pure actually contain a variety of impurities and imperfections. These impurities and imperfections are inherent causes of corrosion in an aggressive environment. However, high purity metals generally have low mechanical strength, and are rarely used in engineering applications. It is necessary, therefore, to work with metallic materials which are stronger and which are usually formed from a combination of several elemental metals. One metal usually serves as a major or base metal to which other metals or nonmetallic constituents are added. These metallic mixtures are properly called alloys. While alloys can exist in an almost unlimited number of combinations, only a portion are useful. The common alloys are those which have a good combination of mechanical, physical and fabrication qualities which tend to make them structurally, as well as economically, useful. Of course, an alloy's behavior in corrosion environments is also very important.

STEELS

As mentioned in Chapter 2, the majority of oil field equipment is constructed of steel, and steel is primarily an alloy of iron and carbon. Pure iron is a relatively weak, ductile material. When it is alloyed with small amounts of carbon (usually 0.2 to 1.0%), a much stronger material is created. However, as a result of reacting part of the iron with carbon, we now have a metal with two components: pure iron and iron carbide (Fe_3C), the product of the iron-carbon reaction. The iron carbide is distributed within the iron as microscopic islands, layers (platelets) or other shapes. The microstructure or morphology of the steel is dictated by the manner in which it was heated and cooled during its manufacture. This heating and cooling process is referred to as the heat treatment of the steel. Its primary purpose is to alter the mechanical properties of the metal, although it also may influence its corrosion resistance.

STRUCTURE OF STEEL

The microstructure (crystalline structure) of steel takes many forms. The most common, austenite, ferrite, martensite, and pearlite are defined in **Table 4.1**. Photomicrographs of these structures are shown in **Figures 4.2** through **4.4**.[2] The inset in **Figure 4.5** shows more detail of the pearlite platelet structure.

TABLE 4.1 Types of Microstructure of Steels

Austenite—The face-centered crystalline phase of iron-based alloys.
Ferrite—A body-centered cubic crystalline phase of iron-based alloys.
Martensite—A supersaturated solid solution of carbon in iron characterized by an acicular (needle-like) microstructure.
Pearlite—A mixture of ferrite and cementite (an intermetallic compound of iron and carbon, Fe_3C). Characterized by a microstructure of alternate plates.

NAMES FOR STEELS

Steels are often referred to by common names or descriptions. The chemical composition and microstructure are used to describe various steels. The common ones used in today's oil county literature are listed in **Table 4.2**.[3] Additional definitions of terms that are used in discussions of metals and metallurgy are given in **Table 4.3**.[3]

TABLE 4.2 Definitions of the Various Names Used for Steels in the Oil and Gas Industry
[As Defined in NACE MR0175-98, Section 2, Definitions]

Carbon Steel—An alloy of carbon and iron containing up to 2% carbon and up to 1.65% manganese and residual quantities of other elements, except those intentionally added in specific quantities for deoxidization (usually silicon and/or aluminum). Carbon steels used in the petroleum industry usually contain less than 0.8% carbon.
Low-Alloy Steel—A Steel with a total alloying element content of less than about 5%, but more than specified for carbon steel.
Austenitic Steel—A steel whose microstructure at room temperature consists predominately of austenite.
Duplex (Austenitic/Ferritic) Stainless Steel—A stainless steel whose microstructure at room temperature consists primarily of austenite and ferrite.
Ferritic Steel—A steel whose microstructure at room temperature consists predominately of ferrite.
Martensitic Steel—A steel in which a microstructure of martensite can be attained by quenching at a cooling rate fast enough to avoid the formation of other microstructures.
Stainless Steel—A Steel containing 10.5 % or more chromium. Other elements may be added to secure special properties.

TABLE 4.3 **Definitions Used When Discussing Metals and Metallurgy for Oil and Gas Production Tubing and Equipment**
[From NACE MR0175–98, Section 2, Definitions]

Age Hardening—Hardening by aging, usually after cooling or cold working.

Aging—A change in metallurgical properties that generally occurs slowly at room temperature (natural aging) and more rapidly at higher temperature (artificial aging).

Annealing—Heating to and holding at a temperature appropriate for the specific material and then cooling at a suitable rate, for the purpose of reducing hardness, improving machinability, or obtaining desired properties. (Also see Solution Heat Treatment.)

Case Hardening—Hardening a ferrous alloy so that the outer portion, or case, is made substantially harder than the inner portion, or core. Typical processes are carburizing, cyaniding, carbonitriding, nitriding, induction hardening, and flame hardening.

Heat Treatment—Heating and cooling a solid metal or alloy in such a way as to obtain desired properties. Heating for the sole purpose of hot working is not considered heat treatment. (See also Solution Heat Treatment.)

Lower Critical Temperatures—In ferrous metals, the temperatures at which austenite begins to form during heating or at which the transformation of austenite is completed during cooling.

Normalizing—Heating a ferrous metal to a suitable temperature above the transformation range (austenitizing), holding at temperature for a suitable time, and then cooling in still air or protective atmosphere to a temperature substantially below the transformation range.

Precipitation Hardening—Hardening a ferrous metal by austenitizing and then cooling rapidly enough so that some or all of the austenite transforms to martensite.

Quench and Temper—Quench hardening followed by tempering.

Solution Heat Treatment (Solution Anneal)—Heating a metal to a suitable temperature and holding at that temperature long enough for one or more constituents to enter into solid solution, then cooling rapidly enough to retain the constituents in solution.

Tempering—In heat treatment, reheating hardened steel or hardened cast iron to some temperature below the lower critical temperature for the purpose of decreasing the hardness and increasing the toughness. The process is also sometimes applied to normalized steel.

Tensile Strength—In tensile testing, the ratio of maximum load to original cross-sectional area (reference ASTM A 370). (Also called "ultimate strength.") *Like elasticity*

Transformation Ranges—Those ranges of temperature for steels within which austenite forms during heating and transforms during cooling. The two ranges are distinct, sometimes overlapping, but never coinciding.

Yield Strength—The stress at which a material exhibits a specified deviation from the proportionality of stress to strain. The deviation is expressed in terms of strain by either the offset method (usually at a strain of 0.2%) or the total-extension-under-load method (usually at a strain of 0.5%) (reference ASTM A 370).

HEAT TREATMENT OF STEELS

Plain carbon steels normally are found in one of four heat treatment conditions: Annealed, normalized, spheroidized, and quenched and tempered. Each of these heat treatments results in different microstructures and in different mechanical properties.

ANNEALING

Annealing involves heating steel to a temperature above its critical temperature of approximately 1,600°F (871°C) and slow cooling in the furnace. Cooling in this manner may take as long as 8 to 10 hours. The resulting microstructure is relatively coarse pearlite. It may be noted from **Figure 4.5** that the Fe_3C platelets in an annealed microstructure have significant thickness and are rather widely spaced.

NORMALIZING

A steel is normalized by heating it to a temperature above its critical temperature, then removing it from the furnace, and allowing it to cool in still, ambient air. Under such conditions, a piece of steel will likely cool to room temperature within 10 to 15 minutes. This somewhat more rapid cooling will produce Fe_3C platelets that are much thinner and are dispersed on a much finer spacing than for an annealed carbon steel. A normalized microstructure is usually described as "fine pearlite."

SPHEROIDIZING

Spheroidizing of carbon steel involves soaking the steel at a relatively high subcritical temperature [approximately 1,200°F (649°C)] for 24 hours or more. Under these conditions, the Fe_3C phase has an opportunity to coalesce into its most stable globular form. This is not a very common heat treatment and is not apt to be encountered in most major steel products used in the oil industry.

QUENCHING AND TEMPERING

A fourth heat treatment for oil industry products, is quenching and tempering. This is a two-step treatment in which the steel is heated to a temperature above its critical temperature, rapidly cooled by immersing in water or oil (quenched), and then heated at an elevated temperature below the critical temperature for periods of approximately one hour (tempered). The Fe_3C precipitated during the tempering operation is in the form of very fine particles.

CARBIDE DISTRIBUTION

Heat treatment has a rather striking effect on the distribution of the Fe_3C. As might be expected, this variation in distribution has an effect on the corrosion behavior of steel. While the effect is relatively small, it has been demonstrated that a platelet-type distribution of the carbide phase such as characterizes annealing or normalizing results in greater corrosion resistance than the globular or particulate carbide distribution, characteristic of the spheroidized or quenched and tempered steel. This somewhat superior corrosion resistance of carbon steels having platelet-type carbide distribution seems to be due to the fact that they tend to develop a nonreactive Fe_3C platelet barrier when the corrosion reactions extend to a significant depth within the steel.

LOCALIZED HEAT TREATMENTS

A piece of steel in the annealed condition and a similar piece of steel in the quenched and tempered condition, exposed to a similar corrosive environment, exhibit a relatively small difference in corrosion rates. Thus, from this standpoint, the effect of heat treatment is generally not of major consequence. There are circumstances, however, in which this difference becomes exaggerated and the net result is severe corrosion. Serious effects from heat treatment variations can be expected when marked differences of metallic structures produced by heat treatment exist within short distances of one another. Two results of this variation are ringworm and weld line corrosion. Examples of these types of corrosion can be found in Chapter 3.

Ringworm Corrosion. The term "ringworm corrosion" is used to describe the severe attack of tubular goods along a narrow band of demarcation between two heat treatments. A common example of this is found in upset tubing which has not been fully heat treated after up-setting. In this procedure, the tube is raised to an elevated temperature on both ends for the purpose of forging the upset. Where these heated regions run out into the body of the tube, marked variations in microstructure can develop. These bands of severe microstructural gradients, when exposed to corrosive environments, corrode at much more rapid rates than steel on either side of the bands **(Figure 3.31)**. The affected zones normally have more globular Fe_3C distributions than the normalized structures on either side. As noted in Chapter 3, full length normalizing after up-setting will provide a uniform microstructure and eliminate ringworm corrosion.

Weld Line Corrosion. A similar condition to ringworm corrosion's microstructural gradient can be observed at welds when the proper welding procedure was not used. Both the longitudinal seam of welded pipe and field joint circumferential welds can exhibit accelerated corrosion attack in the globularized microstructural gradient regions **(Figures 3.28** through **3.30)**. As discussed in Chapter 3, the corrosion may take place in the weld metal, the heat-affected zone (HAZ), or the base metal depending on the specifics of the situation. Adherence to the proper welding specifications by welders qualified to those specifications will provide the uniform microstructure necessary to avoid weld line corrosion.

In summary, the effect of heat treatment on corrosion resistance is generally of a low order of magnitude, and, normally, it can be ignored when selecting fully heat treated steels for corrosive environments. It is worth expending some effort to obtain uniform heat treatment of parts to be exposed in corrosive environments, thus avoiding ringworm and weld line type corrosion attack. It is also worthwhile, when dealing with materials for service in sour systems, to assure that the heat treatment results in the proper hardness as specified in NACE MR0175 (latest edition).[4]

ALLOYS

Alloys are mixtures of two or more metals or elements. Thus, carbon steel is an alloy since it contains iron carbide and minor amounts of other materials in addition to the major constituent, iron. However, the word "alloy" is normally reserved for materials other than carbon steels.

There are two general kinds of alloys—homogeneous and heterogeneous. Homogeneous alloys are solid solutions; that is, the components are completely soluble in one another, and the material has only one phase. An example of a homogeneous solid-solution alloy is 18-8 (type 300 series austenitic) stainless steel which consists of approximately 18% chromium, 8% nickel, a fraction of a percent carbon, and the balance iron. The iron, chromium, nickel, and carbon are dissolved completely (like milk in coffee), and the alloy has uniform composition.

Heterogeneous alloys are mixtures of two or more separate phases. The components of such alloys are not completely soluble and exist as separate phases. The composition and structure of these alloys are not uniform. Perhaps the most familiar examples of heterogeneous alloys are the carbon steels. Examination of the equilibrium phase diagram for iron-carbon alloys indicates that alloys with even a fraction of a percent carbon will be heterogeneous at ambient temperatures, and consist of a mixture of ferrite (a solid-solution of carbon in BCC iron) and cementite (iron-carbide, Fe_3C). In annealed steels, the carbide appears in lamellar form in a mixture with ferrite called pearlite **(Figure 4.5)**.

Therefore, in a heterogeneous alloy such as plain carbon steel, we have two distinct phases and thus a galvanic couple built right into our alloy. Fortunately, ferrite and iron carbide have electrode potential values sufficiently close together that the corrosion rate of plain carbon steel is ordinarily lower than that for a steel-brass galvanic couple. Alloys are usually divided into two major categories because of obvious commercial importance—ferrous and nonferrous alloys. The major component of ferrous alloys is iron, with significant quantities of other elements such as manganese, nickel, chromium, and molybdenum. "Nonferrous" alloys may still contain iron, but it is no longer the major constituent. Examples of nonferrous systems are aluminum alloys, brasses (copper), and superaustenitic stainless (nickel or cobalt).

The superaustenitic stainless, as well as the ferrous stainless, fall into a category of materials referred to as: "corrosion-resistant alloys" (CRAs). The CRAs have a wide range of corrosion-resistance, depending upon chemical composition, manufacturing method and heat treatment. The CRAs gain their strength by either heat treatment, cold working, or a combination of cold working and heat treatment.[5]

The corrosion control effectiveness of the CRAs depends upon the severity of the environment. H_2S partial pressure, temperature, chloride content, and the presence or absence of free-sulfur are critical factors in the final decision. These factors may affect both the SCC resistance and the crevice or pitting potential. Careful consideration of the anticipated environmental conditions should be made before the final decision is made. The cost factor compared to carbon steel may vary from 1.5 to 20 depending upon the alloy chosen.[5]

Many CRAs gain their strength through heat treatment. These alloys include 17-4 PH (UNS S17400) and A 286 (UNS S66286) stainless steels, and nickel base alloys 625 (UNS N06625), 718 (UNS N07718), 725 (UNS N07725) and 925 (UNS N09925). These alloys are often used for valve components, wellhead equipment, tubing hangers, bolting and other equipment items requiring both corrosion resistance and strength. The 17-4 PH stainless steel is only moderately corrosion-resistant, and is subject to SCC/SSC in the presence of high stresses and H_2S. The other heat treatable alloys are more corrosion-resistant and more immune to stress corrosion cracking (SCC).[5]

FERROUS ALLOYS

CARBON AND ALLOY STEELS

By far the largest single classification of metals used in oilfield equipment are carbon steels and alloy steels. They offer a wide variety of properties, are easily formed and fabricated, and, in general, are the least expensive metals commonly used. As defined in **Table 4.2**, straight carbon steels are those which contain up to about 2% carbon and only residual quantities of other elements (except those added for deoxidization as part of the smelting process). Thus, carbon steels may contain as much as 1.65% manganese and 0.60% silicon without being considered alloy steels. Alloy steels, on the other hand, are those containing significant quantities of alloying elements (other than carbon, manganese and silicon added for deoxidization, and sulfur and phosphorus present as residual elements). In common practice, steel is considered to be an alloy steel when the maximum content of the alloying elements exceeds one or more of the following limits: manganese 1.65%, silicon 0.6%, copper 0.6%—or when a definite range of any of the following elements is required: aluminum, boron, chromium, cobalt, columbium (niobium), molybdenum, nickel, titanium, tungsten, vanadium, zirconium, or other alloying elements added to obtain a desired effect. Frequently, steels will be referred to as low alloy, medium alloy, or high alloy steels. These designations are somewhat arbitrary, but low and medium alloy steels are generally regarded as those having 5% or less metallic alloying elements.

Above 5%, steels are considered high alloy steels, or are given other specific designations such as "stainless" steels. The mechanical properties of carbon and alloy steels cover the full range of properties used for oilfield equipment. The properties depend not only on composition but on other factors such as forming, fabrication, and particularly heat treatment. Alloying influences the corrosion resistance of steels as well as the response to heat treatment, formability, machinability, weldability, and other engineering properties. In addition, as would be expected, alloying increases the cost of the steel.

STAINLESS STEELS

The stainless steels are not one set of alloys, but they are a group of alloy systems with widely differing microstructure and mechanical properties. The one thing stainless steels have in common is corrosion resistance due to chromium. To be classed as a stainless steel, an alloy usually contains at least 10.5% chromium. With the various chemistries, microstructures, and mechanical properties of the stainless steel systems come variations in corrosion resistance. All stainless steels are not suitable for all services in all environments. It is extremely important that the specific stainless steel be specified for a specific service. Many types of stainless that are excellent in other industries should not be used in oil and gas production applications.

The corrosion resistance of stainless steels is associated with the ability of chromium to passivate the surface of the alloy. Chromium is a reactive element, but it and its alloys passivate in oxidizing environments and have excellent corrosion resistance. The passivation process is not completely understood, but is believed to be associated with the formation of an electrically insulating monolayer chromium-oxide film on the surface of the alloy.

The stainless steels may be divided into five distinct classes on the basis of their chemical content, metallurgical structure, and mechanical properties: martensitic, ferritic, austenitic, precipitation hardening and duplex.

Martensitic Stainless Steels. The martensitic stainless steels contain chromium as their principal alloying element. The most common types contain approximately 12% chromium; although for the different grades, the chromium may be as high as 18%. The carbon content ranges from 0.08% to 1.10%, and other elements such as nickel, columbium, molybdenum, selenium, silicon, and sulfur are added in small amounts for special purposes in certain grades. The most important characteristic that distinguishes these steels from other grades is their response to heat treatment. The martensitic stainless steels can be hardened by the same heat treatments used to harden carbon and alloy steels. As their name implies, the microstructure of these steels consists of martensite. All of the martensitic stainless steels are strongly magnetic under all conditions of heat treatment.

The martensitic stainless steels comprise part of the type 400 series of stainless steels. The most common of the martensitic stainless steels are types 410 (UNS S41000) and 420 (UNS S42000). Both types 410 and 420 nominally contain around 13% Cr. Type 410 fulfills the requirements of the standard for a material for tubes, and type 420 meets the requirements for a forging material.

Martensitic stainless steels have had the widest range of use of any of the available CRAs. Martensitic stainless steel may be manufactured, through heat treatment, into tubular products with acceptable yield strengths for downhole tubing. Many millions of feet of tubing (API grade L-80 type 13 Cr, maximum hardness of HRC 23) are in corrosive well service. L-80 type 13 Cr is considered the material of choice for many of the deep sweet gas wells, where the temperatures are < 300°F (<149°C) and salt water production is low. API grade L-90 type 13 Cr tubing has been used in sour environments up to about one psi H_2S partial pressure. The passivity of 13 Cr can be destroyed by chlorides.

Type 410 and similar martensitic cast products have been used extensively for valves and wellhead equipment. The lower strength (maximum hardness of HRC 22) martensitic stainless steels have been used for wellhead equipment without restriction on the H_2S content. When used as wellhead equipment in sour service great care must be exercised in manufacturing and inspection. Small departures in hardness levels above HRC 22 have resulted in rapid and explosive failures by SSC.

Ferritic Stainless Steels. The second class of stainless steels, the ferritic stainless steels, are similar to the martensitic stainless steels in that they have only chromium as the principal alloying element. The chromium contents of the ferritic stainless steels are, however, normally higher than those of the martensitic stainless steels, and the carbon contents are generally lower. The chromium content of the ferritic stainless steels ranges from about 13% to about 27%. They are not hardenable by heat treatment, and are used principally for their good corrosion resistance and high temperature properties. Ferritic stainless steels have limited use in oil and gas service.

The ferritic stainless steels are also part of the "400" series, the principal types being types 405 (UNS S40500), 430 (UNS S43000), and 436 (UNS S43600). The microstructure of the ferritic stainless steels consists of ferrite, and they are also strongly magnetic. Ferrite is simply body-centered cubic iron or an alloy based on this structure **(Figure 4.1)**.

Austenitic Stainless Steels. The austenitic stainless steels have two principal alloying elements—chromium and nickel—and their microstructure consists essentially of austenite. Austenite is face-centered cubic iron or an iron alloy based on this structure. They contain a minimum of 18% chromium and 8% nickel, with other elements added for special purposes, and range up to as high as 25% chromium and 20% nickel. The austenitic stainless steels have the highest general corrosion resistance of any of the stainless steels, but their strength is lower than that of the martensitic and ferritic stainless steels. They are not hardenable by heat treatment (although they are hardenable to some extent by cold work) and are generally nonmagnetic. The austenitic stainless steels constitute the "300" series, the most common ones used in oil field equipment are types 304 (UNS S30400) and type 316 (UNS S31600) (high Cr and Ni which may include Mo). Others used may include type 303 (UNS S30300) (free machining), and type 347 (UNS S44700) (stabilized for welding and corrosion resistance).

The austenitic stainless steels are used for items not requiring high strength. The highly alloyed austenitic stainless steels can be made to higher strengths and are more corrosion-resistant.

Precipitation Hardening (PH) Stainless Steels. Another type of stainless steel is a general class known as "precipitation hardening stainless steels," which contain varying amounts of chromium and nickel. They combine the high strength of the martensitic stainless steels with the good corrosion resistance of the austenitic stainless steels. Most of these stainless steels were developed as proprietary alloys, and there is a wide variety of available compositions. A common name that may show up in field equipment is "17-4 PH stainless steel" (UNS S17400)—an approximately 17% chromium, 4% nickel alloy. The distinguishing characteristic of the precipitation hardening stainless steels is that by certain specified heat treatments, at relatively low temperatures, the steels can be hardened to various strength levels. Most can be formed and machined before final heat treatment, with the finished product being hardened. Thus, the most common application of these stainless steels is in corrosion-resistant/wear resistant parts for equipment.

Duplex Stainless Steels. The latest development in the types of stainless steels for use in the oil patch is the class known as "duplex stainless steels." The duplexes have a microstructure that is a mixture of austenite and ferrite **(Figure 4.6)**. They were developed in an attempt to provide a material with the corrosion resistance of the austenitic stainless steels and with the higher strengths of the ferritic stainless steels. Although more expensive than 13 Cr or other corrosion-resistant alloy materials used in oil and gas production, duplex stainless has found a place in severely corrosive or high risk operations. Duplex is being used in downhole tubing, flowlines, facilities piping and pressure vessels. Most duplexes have compositions in the range of 20% to 29% chromium and 3% to 7% nickel.

Figure 4.6 Photomicrograph showing the microstructure of duplex stainless steel. The light areas are austenite, the darker areas are ferrite. (Photograph courtesy of Metallurgical Consultants, Inc., Houston, TX.)[2]

The duplex stainless steels and many of the CRAs gain high strength through cold working. The yield strengths can be as high as 110,000 to 125,000 psi (760 to 860 MPa), which makes these products useful for deep well tubular goods.

Cold-worked duplex stainless steel has been used as downhole tubing in a number of sweet corrosive wells. Duplex tubing has also been used in wells containing as much as 1.5 psi (10 kPa) H_2S partial pressure. Annealed duplex has been used as line pipe, and in surface facilities. Forty miles (64 km) of welded annealed duplex line pipe have been affective in wet CO_2 service for several years. The annealed duplex stainless is more resistant to H_2S than the cold-worked versions.

CAST IRONS

Cast iron is a family of alloys in which the carbon content is such that most of the carbon is not in solution in the iron as it is in steel. Therefore, there is free carbon in the microstructure. As the name implies, equipment made of cast iron is cast to shape rather than being hot or cold formed. The cast irons as a family have very low ductility as compared to steels, and the strength is generally lower than that of the higher strength carbon and alloy steels. The big advantage of cast iron is the variety of shapes that can be made from them and a relatively low cost. There are several types of cast iron such as gray cast iron, white cast iron, malleable cast iron, nodular cast iron, which differ in composition, heat treatment, microstructure, and properties. Some operators do not allow the use of the less ductile cast irons in hydrocarbon service because of the chance of a brittle failure in case of an accident.

IRON-NICKEL-CHROMIUM ALLOYS

The iron-nickel-chromium alloys can be considered an extension of the austenitic stainless steels. The austenitic stainless steels contain at least 50% iron and most contain 75% or more. The iron-nickel-chromium alloys contain more iron than any other single element, which meets the current ASTM definition for ferrous alloys.

NONFERROUS ALLOYS

Although the great majority of materials used in the oilfield are steels and ferrous alloys, large amounts of other alloys are used for special purposes.

NICKEL-BASED ALLOYS

Increasing the nickel to above 50% gives the nickel-based alloys, most of which also contain significant amounts of chromium and iron. While most of these alloys can be specified by UNS numbers or ASTM standards, they are commonly referred to by trade names. These alloys are not widely used in oil and gas producing equipment except for applications involving very severe conditions.

Another widely used family of nickel base alloys are the nickel-copper alloys. There are several types that vary in composition to achieve different properties, such as better machinability and hardenability. These alloys have good resistance to a wide variety of corrosives and especially to waters of all types. In oil and gas production, they are often used for pump parts and other specialty items.

COPPER-BASED ALLOYS

Unalloyed copper is widely used because of its good corrosion resistance, mechanical workability, and thermal conductivity. Its most general application in corrosive services is in handling waters of various compositions.

Copper may be alloyed with any of several other metals to improve certain properties. The most common copper-based alloys are the brasses, which contain zinc as the principal alloying element. The big advantages of brasses compared to copper alloys are their improved mechanical properties and their greater resistance to impingement. However, the brasses are sensitive to certain types of corrosion, such as dezincification and stress corrosion cracking. As with unalloyed copper, the brasses find their widest use in applications handling water. Zinc-less bronzes such as aluminum bronze (UNS C61300 and C61400) also are widely used in injection water service.[6]

Another class of copper alloys is the copper-nickel alloys. These are alloys containing 10–30% nickel and the balance copper. The more common alloys have designations such as: 90/10 copper-nickel (UNS C70600) and 70/30 copper-nickel (UNS C71500). These alloys, in general, have better corrosion resistance in certain environments than the other copper alloys, and resist stress corrosion cracking better than the zinc alloys. The copper-nickels are used for raw seawater piping in seawater water floods and similar applications.

ALUMINUM AND ALUMINUM ALLOYS

The most outstanding property of aluminum and aluminum alloys is their light weight, and consequently, their high strength-to-weight ratio. Aluminum is a very reactive metal, and like chromium, it gets its corrosion resistance from a tenacious oxide layer. Therefore, it is most useful in aerated and atmospheric situations. Unlike chromium, aluminum finds most application in corrosive environments at a pH level between 5 and 7, and undergoes rapid corrosion under either highly acidic or highly alkaline conditions. Aluminum is alloyed mainly to improve its mechanical properties. In oilfield applications, aluminum is most likely to be found as temporary water lines handling aerated fresh water, specialty equipment, and heat transfer (such as the fins on the tubes in fin-fan coolers).

SPECIFICATIONS AND STANDARDS

In general, oilfield equipment is ordered to specifications which include all properties of the materials of manufacture, as well as the dimensional details. A number of technical organizations issue specifications or standards covering various facets of manufacture and service conditions. Some standards cover only the chemical composition of metals, others only the mechanical properties of the raw material, while still others include standardized dimensions or permissible conditions for safe use of the finished product. Although overlap is common, one seldom finds contradictions or incompatibility.

There are many standards organizations around the world. Most countries have their own national standards bodies. The big push in standardization is to develop international standards. This work, which will take many years, is being done through The International Organization for Standardization[7] (ISO). The American National Standards Institute[8] (ANSI) represents the USA. The USA effort for the oil and gas industry involves many people from American Petroleum Institute[9] (API) and NACE (from the corrosion control standards standpoint).

SPECS and STANDARDS—They Are Not the Same!

The terms "specifications" and "standards" are sometimes confused. They do not necessarily mean the same thing, By definition, a specification[12] is, "A detailed statement of particulars, especially one prescribing materials, dimensions, and quality of work for something to be built, installed, or manufactured." A standard[13] by definition is "An acknowledged basis for comparing or measuring; criterion." or "A degree or level of requirement, excellence, or attainment." For all practical purposes, a specification is a purchase document. As such a specification may contain or require that one or more standards be followed. For example: The specification for a particular pump to be used in sour service could state that the materials must conform to NACE Standard Materials Requirement MR0175, latest revision.

Until international standards are available, the standards most frequently quoted in oilfield specifications are:

- The API Standards for various types of equipment for oilfield service,

- The ASTM (American Society of Testing and Materials[10]) Standards for metals and for the broad field of material properties, compositions, dimensions, and test methods,

- ASME (American Society of Mechanical Engineering[11]) Code Specifications which cover materials, manufacturing, and operating limitations (particularly the pressure vessel and piping codes) and,

- NACE publications which are concerned particularly with prevention of failures associated with corrosion.

REFERENCES

1. R. S. Treseder, ed., R. Baboian, and C. G. Munger, co-eds., NACE Corrosion Engineer's Reference Book, 2nd ed. (Houston, TX: NACE, 1991), p. 153–155.
2. Metallurgical Consultants, Inc., private communication, October 1997.
3. NACE Standard MR0175-98, "Sulfide Stress Cracking Resistant Metallic Materials for Oilfield Equipment" Section 2, Definitions, (Houston, TX: NACE, 1997), p. 5–8.
4. NACE Standard MR0175 (latest edition), Ibid.
5. R. M. Tuttle, private communication, October 1997.
6. NACE Standard RP0475-91, "Selection of Metallic Materials to be Used in All Phases of Water Handling for Injection Into Oil-Bearing Formations" (Houston, TX: NACE, 1991).
7. The International Organization for Standardization, various publications, Geneva, Switzerland.
8. American National Standards Institute, various publications, New York, NY.
9. American Petroleum Institute, various standards and specifications, Washington, D.C.
10. American Society of Testing and Materials, various standards and specifications, West Conshohocken, PA.
11. American Society of Mechanical Engineering, various codes and specifications, New York, NY.
12. The American Heritage Dictionary, 3rd ed. (Boston, MA: Houghton Mifflen, 1996), p. 783.
13. The American Heritage Dictionary, Ibid, p. 793.

BIBLIOGRAPHY

B. D. Craig, *Practical Oilfield Metallurgy and Corrosion*, 2nd ed. Tulsa, OK: PennWell Publishing Co., 1993.

NACE Publication 1F192 (latest edition), "Use of Corrosion-Resistant Alloys in Oilfield Environments." Houston, TX: NACE, 1993.

NACE Publication 1F196. "Survey of CRA Tubular Usage." Houston, TX: NACE, 1996.

CHAPTER 5

MATERIALS SELECTION— NONMETALLICS

INTRODUCTION

The term "nonmetallic materials," when mentioned for the oil patch, usually brings to mind the terms "plastic" or "fiber-reinforced plastic (FRP)." Generally that's a good reference, however, the subject is broader than that. To be complete, wood, concrete (cement) and mortars, cement asbestos, and tile must be mentioned.

WOOD

Early flowlines and pipelines were made of wood staves and wrapped with wire or banded similar to wooden barrels. Petroleum products, such as kerosene, were shipped around the world in wooden barrels. Presumably this is why oil has been measured in barrels rather than drums or some other standard volume. Long after wooden barrels and pipelines were abandoned, wooden tanks were still in use in severely corrosive areas, particularly in sour fields. **Figure 5.1** shows a wooden tank battery.

Wooden tanks performed well in sour service. However, they fell out of favor, not because coated

Figure 5.1 Wooden tank battery in a western Kansas oil field producing sour gas, crude, and water. The taller vessel—called a "gun barrel"—serves as a free-water knockout. (Photo circa 1970.)

steel tanks were better, but because steel tanks became more economical. The manufacture, construction, erection, and maintenance of wooden tanks is quite manpower intensive, and as the craftsmen who made wooden tanks faded away, such tanks became uneconomical. Even if the costs could be reduced, today's environmental regulations would preclude their use. In order to work properly, the wood staves must remain moist and swollen; thus, they are designed to weep or seep.

CEMENT AND CONCRETE

Cement materials show up in several forms, from reinforced concrete offshore structures and foundations for pumping units, injection pumps, compressors, and other heavy equipment, to cement linings for tank bottoms, internal pipe coatings (discussed in Chapter 6), and concrete secondary containment basins.

Concretes are basically resistant to seawater and brines. The main problem with reinforced concrete is corrosion of the reinforcing steel bars (rebar) or mesh. Normally concrete provides excellent protection to steel—the highly alkaline portland cement in concrete allows a stable, corrosion-mitigating passive oxide film to form on the steel. If the film does not form, or is destroyed, corrosion can occur. Chlorides and oxygen are the major causes of such corrosion. Corrosion of rebar leads to cracking and/or spalling of the concrete (due to the effect of the corrosion product requiring more volume than the steel), and can eventually lead to structural failure **(Figure 5.2)**.

Reinforcing steel corrosion can be minimized by selecting a concrete formulation that is the least permeable and is low in contaminants (*e.g.*, chlorides), designing the structure to have several inches of concrete encasing the rebar, coating the rebar with protective coatings (*e.g.*, fusion bonded epoxy [FBE]), and installing cathodic protection. NACE RP0187 (latest edition), "Design Considerations for Corrosion Control of Reinforcing Steel in Concrete,"[1] addresses these issues. NACE RP0395 (latest edition), "Epoxy-Coated Steel Reinforcing Bars,"[2] covers procedures for coating rebar with FBE applied by the electrostatic spray method. NACE RP0290 (latest edition), "Cathodic Protection of Reinforcing Steel in Atmospherically Exposed Concrete Structures,"[3]

Figure 5.2 Concrete deterioration and spalling due to corrosion of steel imbedded in the concrete on an offshore facility. As the steel components corrode, the corrosion product (rust) that has more volume than the steel, causes cracking and spalling of the concrete. The same phenomena causes concrete to fail when the reinforcing bars corrode.

presents guidelines for the use of impressed current cathodic protection on new or existing installations. On the other hand, NACE Standard RP0390 (latest edition), "Maintenance and Rehabilitation Considerations for Corrosion Control of Existing Steel Reinforced Concrete Structures,"[4] has guidelines for the repair of deteriorating/deteriorated structures. Because of the tremendous amount of reinforced concrete in the world's infrastructure, corrosion control of rebar is an area receiving continuing attention and development.

Concrete floors and foundations exposed to corrosives may deteriorate with time unless coated with protective coatings specifically formulated for that purpose. Secondary containment structures also may be coated with similar materials to seal them to prevent seeping.

CEMENT-ASBESTOS

When water flooding and salt water disposal system technology was first being developed, cement-asbestos pipe was a favored material for gravity and low pressure gathering and distribution lines. This material was very resistant to attack both externally and internally. It was manufactured from a homogeneous material of Portland cement, asbestos fibers, and silica. Some manufacturers plastic coated the pipe internally to provide resistance to specific chemicals for special applications. Although health considerations have removed cement-asbestos from the market, many of the 1960s and 1970s installations are still in place, particularly some of the older water disposal systems.

CERAMIC TILE

Although not widespread, some ceramic tile pipe (similar to the ceramic sewer pipe) has been used for gravity-type water gathering system piping. The tile was very resistant to attack both externally and internally. However, just as with sewers, the joints had a habit of seeping.

PLASTIC (POLYMERIC) MATERIALS

Although plastics are the most widely used nonmetallic materials in today's oilfield operations, they are probably the most underused corrosion control option. That is, plastics are often overlooked when considering corrosion control for a specific field application. Unfortunately, plastics have often been misapplied or mishandled by assuming that they were a noncorroding, direct substitute for steel. Properties such as thermal expansion, long-term creep, temperature limits, and resistance to specific chemicals were overlooked when a material was selected for a particular application. However, with today's design information and cumulative experience, plastics are quite satisfactorily used for downhole

Figure 5.3 FRP tubing is not a new product, as can be noted in this 1963 photograph showing FRP tubing being run into a water injection well.

tubing, flowlines, facilities piping, tanks, and the internals for water handling vessels such as tanks, deaeration towers, or filters (**Figure 5.3** through **5.11**). The key to successfully engineering with plastics is to select the proper material for the application. There are many plastics available with different physical, chemical, and mechanical properties.[5]

A plastic is by definition, a nonmetallic compound usually synthetically produced from organic compounds by polymerization. Plastics fall into the following two (broad) categories:

- Thermoplastic materials are those that can be melted, reformed, molded, or extruded with little or no change in their properties. They have lower temperature limits and are generally used for less severe service than the thermosetting materials.

- Thermosetting materials are cured to develop cross linking and cannot be remelted. Since they do not melt, they have higher service temperature limits than the thermoplastics. Cross linking provides more severe service ability.

THERMOPLASTICS

The common thermoplastics used in production operations are: polyvinyl chloride (PVC), polyethylene (PE), low density PE (LDPE), high density PE (HDPE), and polypropylene (PP). These plastics are used for low-pressure line pipe (**Figures 5.4** and **5.5**), pipe liners (new and reclamation), and as chemical storage drums for some types chemicals. **Table 5.1** presents service considerations for the three. Dimensions, materials, physical properties, and service factors for PE line pipe are covered in the American Petroleum Institute's (API) Standard Specification 15LE. **Table 5.2** lists API Standards Concerning Nonmetallic Materials Used in Oil and Gas Production Operations (including 15LE).

TABLE 5.1 Service Considerations for Thermoplastic Materials

THERMOPLASTIC	SATISFACTORY	NOT SATISFACTORY
Polyvinyl chloride (PVC)	0°F (-17.8°C) to 140°F (60°C)	Prolonged high temperature
	Alkalis Oxidizing acids Aliphatic hydrocarbons Water and brines	Fatty acids Acetic acid Solvents Aromatic hydrocarbons Sunlight
Polyethylene (PE)	0°F (-17.8°C) to 140°F (60°C) Hydrocarbons <100°F (<38°C) Acids Alkalis Water and brines	Oxidizing acids Hydrocarbons >100°F (>38°C) Solvents >120°F (>49°C) Aromatic hydrocarbons Sunlight without stabilizers
Polypropylene (PP)	0°F (-17.8°C) to 200°F (93°C) Hydrocarbons <100°F (<38°C) Alkalis Acids Water and brines	Same as PE

All three of these thermoplastic materials are made into pipe by heating the raw powdered or pelletized materials to the melting point for fusion and extruding through dies for shaping into pipe. The soft, hot pipe is immediately cooled and thus rehardened.

Figure 5.4 Polyvinyl chloride (PVC) plastic flowline on a sucker rod pumping well.

Figure 5.5 FRP pipe and thermoplastic pipe (the darker color). Oilwell flowlines bring well fluids to a central battery location. Note that the manifold is steel.

CORROSION CONTROL IN PETROLEUM PRODUCTION

THERMOSETTING

Thermosetting plastics are usually found in production operations as materials known as "FRP." These materials are also known as "fiberglass-reinforced plastic," because the most common fiber for oil field FRP is fiberglass. This type of material, that is, one made by intimately melding two entirely different materials into a single material, falls into a broad category known as "composites." Like the FRP used to make boats, automobile bodies, and other consumer products, the FRP used for production is basically high-strength fibers embedded in a thermosetting resin. The most common use of FRP is for tubular goods, tanks, and internal fittings in water handling service (**Figures 5.5** through **5.9**).

Figure 5.6 FRP piping in a water flood plant.

Figure 5.7 FRP pipe used as a water injection line in a water flood. Note the individual well cartridge filter.

Figure 5.8 FRP internals in a vacuum tower feaerating seawater for water flood supply water. Note the vessel wall is internally plastic coated.

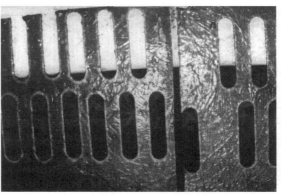

Figure 5.9 FRP spreader plate in a seawater deaeration tower in a water flood. Note the polypropylene packing below the FRP plate.

Fiberglass reinforced pipe is manufactured either by filament winding or centrifugal casting. In filament winding, the glass fibers are saturated with the resin material and wound on a mandrel at carefully controlled angles with relation to the axis of the pipe. The winding process continues until enough layers of glass fibers are wound to give a specified wall thickness. In centrifugally cast pipe, the glass fibers saturated with resin material are cast against the inside of a mandrel by centrifugal force. FRP tanks are made in a similar manner.

Several different resins with different properties are used in manufacturing FRP pipe and tanks. Most are epoxy or polyester resins. It is very important that the material match the intended service. When ordering FRP pipe or tanks, the vendor needs to know what the item will be used for, or the product may fail. Just taking any FRP tank from the warehouse will not do. For example, no money is saved (nor points made) if the solvent in an oilfield chemical dissolves the resin from the glass in a tank used to store the chemical (a true story). Thus, for specific applications, particularly for chemicals other than produced fluids, the chemical and FRP pipe or vessel supplier should be consulted. Data on the resistance of nonmetallic materials to various chemicals, solutions, and solvents can be found in a NACE book, "Corrosion Data Survey—Nonmetals Section."[6] This also covers thermoplastics. A companion book on metals, "Corrosion Data Survey—Metals Section,"[7] covers alloy performance with many chemicals. Data on chemical resistance is also available in the NACE COR•SUR™ and COR•SUR 2™ software, which cover metals and nonmetals, respectively.

NONMETALLIC PIPE

As indicated, both thermoplastic and thermosetting are used to make oilfield pipe or tubulars. Not only do they have different properties, but they may require different joining methods to go with the different applications.

JOINING METHODS

The methods used to join various types of nonmetallic pipe include: heat welding, solvent welding, and threads.

Heat Welding. Both polyethylene and polypropylene plastic pipes can be joined by heat welding. This method uses a heating element to soften the ends of the joints, which are then butted together and held in position until the joint cools and rehardens. A slight amount of upsetting occurs, but this is usually not objectionable. The heating and joining procedures for the particular plastic, size, and thickness of pipe must be carefully followed if the new line is to be leak-free.

Solvent Welding. (Some times referred to as "gluing" or "glued joints.") Solvent welding can be used on PVC. This method usually consists of a two-solution application—first the solvent is applied, and then the glue is applied, to the pin and collar ends. The joints are quickly pushed together, allowing the pin end to fuse inside the collar.

The collars are the most important part of the solvent welded joint. There are basically two types of collars, molded and tapered extruded. The tapered collar, which is the superior of the two, is usually machined to the desired taper. However, at least one manufacturer inserts a heated tapered plug into the extruded collar. There is no advantage of one tapered collar over the other, provided that the collars have the proper taper. An inferior joint can result if the collars are not properly tapered.

Sometimes FRP pipes are joined by solvent welding. The piping installer needs to be familiar with the solvent welding procedures for the particular pipe being joined. As usual on any construction job, quality assurance is required to assure a satisfactory installation.

Threaded Connections. Threads can be used on most nonmetallic pipe and provide good joints if the wall thickness is great enough. Schedule 80 is usually specified for threaded thermoplastic pipe. In threaded and coupled thermoplastic pipe, the working pressure rating is normally reduced 50%. For FRP pipe, the threads are either cut in an upset end or molded onto standard pipe so there is no reduction in wall thickness.

APPLICATION OF NONMETALLIC PIPE

In the application of nonmetallic piping, three primary factors must be considered:

- Chemical resistance.
- Mechanical properties.
- Economics.

Chemical Resistance. In oilfield operations, chemical resistance to oilfield fluids or gases and commonly used treating chemicals are of primary concern. All plastic pipe materials discussed are resistant to attack from most oilfield fluids; they have been used successively over the years in these environments. However, that does not mean they are totally unaffected. Some of these materials will be weakened by these products due to absorption over a long period. Therefore, an environmental or service factor should be considered for long-term installations. As noted in **Table 5.2**, service factors are included where appropriate in the API documents.

TABLE 5.2 American Petroleum Institute (API) Standards Concerning Nonmetallic Material Used in Oil and Gas Production Operations

API Spec 15HR, Specification for High Pressure Fiberglass Line Pipe, Second Edition, Apr. 1, 1995.

Covers fiberglass line pipe and fittings rated for operating pressures greater than 1000 psi. Quality control tests, dimensions, and performance requirements are included.

API Spec 15LE, Specification for Polyethylene (PE) Line Pipe, Third Edition, Apr. 1, 1995.

Provides standards for PE line pipe suitable for use in conveying gas, oil and nonpotable water in underground service for the oil and gas producing industries. Dimensions, materials, physical properties, and service factors are included.

API Spec 15LR, Specification for Low Pressure Fiberglass Line Pipe, Sixth Edition, Sept. 1, 1990 (ANSI/API Spec 15LR–1992).

Covers glass fiber reinforced thermosetting resin line pipe suitable for use in conveying gas, oil, or nonpotable water in the oil and gas producing industries at a maximum rating of 1,000 psi.

API Spec 15LT, Specification for PVC Lined Steel Tubular Goods, First Edition, Jan. 1, 1993 (ANSI/API Spec 15LT–1992).

This specification provides standards for PVC lined steel pipe or tubing suitable for use in conveying water and/or oil in the petroleum industry.

API RP 15TL4, Recommended Practice for Care and Use of Fiberglass Tubulars, First Edition, Oct. 1, 1993.

RP15TL4 provides information on the transporting, handling, installing, and reconditioning of fiberglass tubulars in oilfield usage. Appendices are also included to cover adhesive bonding, repair procedures, and inspection practices.

API Spec 12P, Specification for Fiberglass-Reinforced Plastic (FRP) Tanks, Second Edition, Jan. 1, 1995.

Covers minimum requirements for material, design, fabrication, and testing of FRP tanks.

API Bull 6J, Bulletin on Testing of Oilfield Elastomers—A Tutorial, First Edition, Feb. 1, 1992 (ANSI/API Bull 6J-1992).

This document is a tutorial for the evaluation of elastomer test samples of actual elastomeric seal members intended for use in the oil and gas industry. It is also a review of the testing criteria, environments, evaluation procedures, guidelines for comparisons, and effects of other considerations on the evaluation of elastomeric seal materials and members.

Mechanical Properties. The two major physical properties that dictate selection of nonmetallic piping materials for a specific application are the pressure and temperature ratings. The pressure rating is usually dependent on the service temperature and the amount of time which the material is exposed to service conditions. Normally, the higher the temperature, the lower the permissible working pressure.

It should also be noted that pressure ratings must be reduced when pressure surging is anticipated. It is not uncommon to encounter surge pressures 10 to 15 times the normal operating pressure in long lines, especially when control valves are used. In addition, maximum working pressures must be adjusted for temperature.

TYPICAL APPLICATIONS OF PIPE

Some typical applications of nonmetallic pipe in oil and gas operations are:

Thermoplastics:

- Flow Lines—Used principally for carrying produced fluid of oil or oil and water from the well to separating equipment and tank batteries.

- Gathering Lines—For oil and water or low pressure gas.

- Salt Water Lines—Primarily disposal systems and drains.

- Liners—For steel pipe in high pressure operations. API Spec 15LT, Specification for PVC Lined Steel Tubular Goods, **(Table 5.2)** covers standards for this application. Considerable work continues developing procedures for rehabilitation of corrosion damaged lines with thermoplastic linings.

- Fuel Lines—For gas engines.

FRP:

- Used—For all of the above applications.

- Tubing—For injection and disposal wells.

ADVANTAGES AND DISADVANTAGES OF NONMETALLIC PIPE

It is fairly obvious that nonmetallic piping systems will be very attractive when they are capable of meeting the technical requirements at a cost equal to or less than a comparable steel system with corrosion protection. However, it is essential that the user be aware of the major advantages and disadvantages inherent in nonmetallic piping.

Advantages:

- Nonmetallic materials are immune to corrosion by water.

- They are lightweight, resulting in lower freight costs and easy handling.

- Nonmetallic pipe is quickly and easily joined and installed.

- No external corrosion protection, such as coating, wrapping, or cathodic protection, is required.

- The smooth internal surface results in lower fluid friction loss.

Disadvantages:

- Nonmetallic pipe has limited working temperature and pressure.

- These limits are difficult to predict with assurance. The pressure and temperature limitations are often interrelated (*i.e.*, the higher the temperature, the lower the permissible working pressure). Furthermore, physical properties change with time under normal conditions.

- Careful handling is required in loading, unloading, and installation. (But that is also true to get the maximum from any material, even steel.)

- Plastic pipe should be buried to protect it from sunlight (which will cause deterioration with time), mechanical damage, freezing, and fire.

- Weeping can occur in low quality FRP pipe.

- Nonmetallic pipe has very low resistance to vibration and pressure surging. Both reinforced epoxy and PVC piping is commonly down-rated 30% to 50% from the manufacturers' recommended maximum working pressure to allow for pressure surging.

FIBERGLASS (FRP) TANKS

FRP tanks and vessels are used in many services in production related operations. Probably the most numerous are relatively small tanks used for oilfield chemical and other chemical storage. (**Figure 5.10** and **5.11** show FRP tanks in chemical storage service.) However, many are used in water injection (water flood and salt water disposal) systems and as lease crude tankage. As was noted earlier, manufacturing of FRP tanks uses similar techniques to FRP pipe manufacturing. In many cases the FRP tanks will be made up of multiple layers with different resins and possibly different glass thicknesses in each layer. In such cases, the inside layer is designed to be resistant to the substance stored in the tank, inner layers are structural, and the outer layer would be designed for atmospheric protection including ultraviolet protection. API Spec 12P **(Table 5.2)** covers the requirements for materials, design, fabrication, and testing of FRP tanks.

Figure 5.11 A FRP tank used for chemical storage. Note the secondary containment walls.

Figure 5.10 FRP chemical storage tank.

FIBERGLASS (FRP) SUCKER RODS

When FRP sucker rods first hit the market, they were considered a corrosion-resistant rod; the FRP rod body is corrosion-resistant. However, the connections are steel and in some rod string designs it has been necessary to run a number of steel sucker rods or weight bars to provide sufficient string weight for proper pumping action. Thus, corrosion inhibition programs have continued to protect the metal parts of the rod string and the steel tubing. FRP sucker rods do have their use; however, they need to be justified for mechanical reasons, not to eliminate or reduce inhibition costs. FRP rods are recognized as viable additions to rod pumping equipment and API's Spec 11B, "Specification for Sucker Rods,"[8] and RP 11BR, "Recommended Practice for the Care and Handling of Sucker Rods,"[9] include FRP rods in their coverage.

ELASTOMERS

Another class of polymeric materials related to plastics are the elastomers. The most common uses are as seals and packing. For example, most O-rings are made from elastomers. Another use of elastomers (in sheet form) is as tank linings. Although not directly involved in corrosion control, the selection of the proper elastomer can have an impact on failures and downtime of equipment. Furthermore, the integrity of seals is the key to being able to operate systems oxygen free, as discussed in the chapter on controlling the corrosive environment.

SEALS AND PACKING

The common seal resins for oil field use are: nitrile (Buna-N), EPDM (ethylene-propylene-diene-monomer), fluorocarbon, and HSN (Highly Saturated Nitrile). Each material has specific uses. Some perform satisfactorily in water, but not oils; others may be used with oil, as long as there is no H_2S, and many are sensitive to high pressure gases. **Table 5.3** presents some examples of environments and elastomers. By no means is this table complete. As with other materials, for proper seal selection, it is essential that the equipment vendor knows the service environment—especially in critical situations. Detailed, up-to-date information on elastomer properties may be obtained from seal vendors. Basic elastomer property information maybe found in the book, NACE Corrosion Engineers Reference Book, Second Edition.[10]

TABLE 5.3 Examples of the Selection of Elastomeric Seals for Different Environments

Water use:
EPDM—To 275°F (135°C) without oil present.
HSN, nitrile, fluorocarbon—to 180°F (82°C) with oil.
Crude oil use:
Fluorocarbon, nitrile—to 250°F (121°C) without H_2S.
HSN—to 250°F (121°C) with H_2S.
Carbon dioxide (CO_2).
EPDM, nitrile—to 275°F (135°C).

Both API and NACE have standards dealing with the testing of elastomers. API Bull 6J, Bulletin on Testing of Oilfield Elastomers, A Tutorial, is described in **Table 5.2**. NACE test methods on elastomers include:

- TM0187, Evaluating Elastomeric Materials in Sour Gas Environments.
- TM0192, Evaluating Elastomeric Materials in Carbon Dioxide Decompression Environments.
- TM0196, Chemical Resistance of Polymeric Materials by Periodic Evaluation (applies to plastics as well as elastomers).
- TM0296, Evaluating Elastomeric Materials in Sour Liquid Environments.

TANK LINERS

The lining of tanks with sheet elastomers is more common in the process industries than in oil and gas production. However, this approach has been used in oil field operations. Common liner materials include: Neoprene (polychloroprene), Butyl, EPDM, and Nitrile. The same service limits and remarks made above on seals also applies to liners. Successful tank lining requires an experienced applicator who will use procedures that assure lap joint integrity, proper cure, and adhesion, while avoiding or at least minimizing bubbles, softening and swelling.

REFERENCES

1. NACE Standard RP0187 (latest edition), "Design Considerations for Corrosion Control of Reinforcing Steel in Concrete" (Houston, TX: NACE).
2. NACE Standard RP0395 (latest edition), "Epoxy-Coated Steel Reinforcing Bars" (Houston, TX: NACE).
3. NACE Standard RP0290 (latest edition), "Cathodic Protection of Reinforcing Steel in Atmospherically Exposed Concrete Structures" (Houston, TX: NACE).
4. NACE Standard RP0390 (latest edition), "Maintenance and Rehabilitation Considerations for Corrosion Control of Existing Steel Reinforced Concrete Structures" (Houston, TX: NACE).
5. N. E. Hamner, ed., Corrosion Data Survey—Nonmetals Section, 5th ed. (Houston, TX: NACE, 1975). Also see NACE Nonmetal Selection Software: COR•SUR 2™.
6. D. L. Graver, ed., Corrosion Data Survey—Metals Section, 6th ed. (Houston, TX: NACE, 1985). Also see NACE Metal Selection Software: COR•SUR™.
7. R. S. Treseder, ed., R. Baboian, and C.G. Munger, co-eds., NACE Corrosion Engineer's Reference Book, 2nd ed. (Houston, TX: NACE, 1991), p. 153–155.
8. API Specification 11B, "Specification for Sucker Rods" (latest edition) (Washington, D.C.: American Petroleum Institute).
9. API PR 11BR, "Recommended Practice for the Care and Handling of Sucker Rods" (Washington, D.C.: American Petroleum Institute).
10. R. S. Treseder, Ibid., p. 230–233.

CHAPTER 6

PROTECTIVE COATINGS

INTRODUCTION

As the name implies, a "protective coating" is a coating that is applied to a surface to protect the surface from the surrounding environment. Coatings that are applied for decorative or aesthetic purposes are usually referred to as "paints." Obviously, there is some overlap—the coating used to protect the outside of a steel tank can be decorative, since it improves the appearance of the tank. Likewise, one of the functions of the paint selected for the wood trim on your house is to protect the wood from deterioration. For the purposes of this chapter, the word "coating" will refer to protective coatings and/or coating systems (most of the liquid applied coatings used in production will be multi-coat "systems"). **Figures 6.1** and **6.2** show the coated exteriors and interiors of tanks.

Figure 6.1 Externally coated water injection plant.

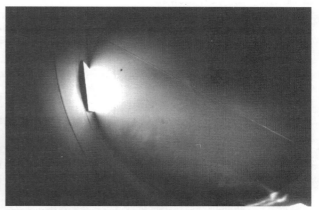

Figure 6.2 Looking through the thief hatch into a newly coated tank.

By definition, a coating is any relatively thin material, usually applied as a liquid or powder that, on solidification, is firmly adhered to the surface to be protected, and keeps the environment from contacting the surface. In addition to controlling corrosion, an internal coating may be applied to increase the capacity of pipelines by reducing friction, to minimize deposition, or to prevent product contamination.

To protect against corrosion for a practical period of time, it is necessary that coatings possess flexibility, resistance against impact, chemical resistance to the environment to which exposed, resistance to permeation by moisture, good adhesion and cohesion, and resistance to the temperature to which they are exposed. Economics should be considered when developing a coating program. For example, it may be more economical to invest in a premium (more expensive—long life) coating system, than to select a less expensive system that will require periodic maintenance and re-coating. Of course, as discussed in the final chapter, economic decisions must be based on the way a company looks at its finances.

The first part of this chapter will discuss coatings topics such as classifications, chemistry, properties, surface preparation, application, and inspection in general. The latter part will discuss coating specific production equipment. Appendix 6A is a listing of NACE International's Standards on coatings that can have application for production facilities and lines. For more information on coatings, a bibliography of additional reading is included at the end of this chapter just after the references.

Except as otherwise noted, the coatings discussed in this chapter are liquid applied materials.

Many of the traditional coatings used in production operations are being reformulated to meet environmental regulations restricting the level of volatile organic compounds (VOC) that can be released into the atmosphere. This is an evolving situation; therefore, some coatings mentioned in this chapter may not be available at a later date. Coatings manufacturers will, of course, be supplying materials that meet regulations.

COATING CLASSIFICATION OR TYPE

Coatings may be classified or categorized in many ways. One important breakdown is by service environment (*i.e.*, atmospheric service, immersion service, and external pipe service). Each of these environments has different requirements for the coating and each can be further subdivided. For example, atmospheric environments may be housed or open—where the same coating system could require different surface preparation. Coatings are also categorized by the equipment that's coated—such as internal vessel coating and internal tubing coating which may be quite different—yet both call for immersion coatings. Coatings may be referred to as "thick film" or "thin film" coatings, based on the thickness of the coating film after it has cured (dried). More recently, coatings have been categorized as "original construction coatings" and "maintenance coatings." Of course, coatings are classed by chemical composition. They may be classed by curing method—air dry, forced cured, baked on, or fusion bonded. Another category being used more frequently in tank and vessel repair and rehabilitation are the reinforced coatings or linings.

SERVICE ENVIRONMENT

Since the first thing to be decided when selecting a coating is the service, a convenient way to classify coatings is by the intended service. Atmospheric, internal, and underground/submerged environments have their own considerations and requirements for coatings.

Atmospheric coatings are those used on the external surfaces of facilities. The exposure may be the open atmosphere or may be housed inside a building. Most oil production equipment will be in the open (outdoors) unless it is located in a harsh climate such as the arctic. Coating systems for atmospheric service are designed to handle ever changing environments and must be resistant to sunlight (ultraviolet rays [UV]), alternate wet/dry conditions, temperature changes, physical damage and atmospheric contaminants. The selection of the specific coating system will depend on the severity of the atmospheric environment as discussed in Chapter 1. These are usually air dried coatings, which cure due to the evaporation of solvents or reaction products of two component coatings. The surface preparation is more critical for coatings exposed to the weather than for those coatings in housed conditions.

Immersion coatings are basically internal coatings that are immersed in liquid all (or at least much) of the time. These are the coatings used inside vessels, tanks, pipes, and oil country tubular goods (OCTG). Immersion service may be a very demanding service, depending on the fluids in the tank, vessel, pipes or tubulars. Air dry, force cure, baking, and fusion bonded materials are all available for immersion service. Surface preparation and application techniques are critical for these internal coatings.

Underground (or buried) coatings are often referred to as "pipeline coatings." In addition to being resistant to the corrosive soil environments, pipeline coatings must survive stresses in the soil, and be resistant to damage by rocks or by "cathodic disbondment" from cathodic protection systems. These coatings may be similar in chemistry to other coatings (such as fusion bonded epoxy—FBE), but generally they will be quite different. Some are applied as tapes, others are extruded onto the pipe. Some of these same coatings also may be used on offshore (subsea) pipelines. Pipeline coatings and coating systems are discussed in more detail in the latter part of this chapter.

COATING THICKNESS

The dry film thickness of a coating is of importance from several standpoints. The optimum thickness range for a specific coating depends on the coating. Most of the materials have limits to the allowable thickness. If the coating is applied too thick, the cohesive forces within the coating may be stronger than the adhesive forces that hold the coating on the surface. The result is that the too thick coating will disbond. On the other hand, too thin a coating will not provide a proper barrier, and the metal surface will corrode. The required coating thickness will also determine the desirable anchor pattern to be obtained by surface preparation blasting.

Thin film coatings specifications for production equipment usually call for a 5 to 8 mil (0.13 to 0.2 mm) dry film thickness. On the other hand, because of the different compositions and requirements, a thin film pipeline coating could be 20 to 100 mils (0.5 to 2.5 mm).

Thick film coatings for production equipment are often those with dry film thickness of 12 to 25 mils (0.3 to 0.6 mm). Specifications usually allow a 5 to 6 mil (0.13 to 0.15 mm) tolerance. Thick film pipeline coatings may be any of those over 100 mils (2.5 mm).

CHEMICAL COMPOSITION

Coatings are available in two general chemical categories: organic and inorganic. The organic and inorganic coatings for vessels, tanks, piping, and tubing are basically liquid applied coatings that are sprayed onto the surface and allowed to dry. **Table 6.1** is a listing of some of the chemical types that are or have been used in production facilities. The other inorganic coatings, metallic, ceramic, and other specialty materials are placed on the surface by plating, spraying, or casting techniques.

TABLE 6.1 Typical Liquid Applied Protective Coatings

THE MOST COMMON CHEMICAL TYPES OF LIQUID APPLIED COATINGS ARE:	
PRIMARY RESIN (BINDER)	TYPICAL USE (SERVICE)
Acrylics	External
Alkyds & modified alkyds	External—weathering
Chlorinated rubber	External—chemical resistant
Coal-tar epoxy	Immersion
Epoxy—catalyzed (two part epoxy)	Immersion
Epoxy ester (one part epoxy)	External—housed
Phenolic (baked)	Internal—vessel, tubing
• Epoxy modified (baked)	Internal—vessel, tubing
• Oil modified	External—marine
Polyesters & fiber reinforced polyesters	Immersion—tank/vessel
Silicones	High temperatures
Urethane	
• Oil modified (uralkyd)	External—weathering
• Moisture cured	External—concrete
• Converted (catalyzed)	
Vinyl	External—internal
Vinyl acrylic	External—weathering
Zinc—rich	—
• Inorganic, post-cure, water-based	External—primer
• Inorganic, self-cure, water-based	External—primer
• Inorganic, self-cure, solvent-based	External—primer
• Organic, one package	External—primer
• Organic, two package	External—primer
• Organic, three package	External—primer

Organic coatings are the most common materials used to protect oil and gas production facilities and equipment. The basic components in organic coatings are organic resins. Generically, many are the same resins and polymers mentioned in Chapter 5. These include the various epoxies, vinyls, phenolics, and urethanes.

Inorganic coatings is a term used to classify any coating that is not an organic. This broad category includes metallic coatings applied to protect carbon steel. Metallic coatings may be either sacrificial such as galvanizing with zinc or a corrosion-resistant barrier such as electroless nickel or chromium plating used on valve, pump, and related equipment components. Liquid applied inorganic coatings usually have a silicon-based vehicle, which may carry a pigment (*e.g.*, the inorganic zinc silicate primers). (There are also organic zinc primers.) Other inorganic coatings include cement linings used in water injection piping systems and ceramic coatings. While ceramic coatings can protect against corrosion, they are more often used for erosion and wear resistance.

CURING METHODS

The terms "curing" or "drying" of coatings refers to the mechanism of the coating converting from the wet as-sprayed film to the hardened final protective film. Different coatings have different curing procedures.

Air dried is the most common form of curing, particularly for atmospheric coatings. Solvents or reaction products evaporate from the coating at ambient temperature. The drying time is unique to a specific formulation, and the application specification should emphasize the importance of following the coating manufacturer's instructions.

Force cured is most likely to be used for internal tank or vessel coating. Force curing is related to air dried, except the vessel is heated (usually with hot air) to speed the drying time. This approach is not applicable to all coatings because if the surface is dried too fast, the evaporation will not be complete and the coating will not be properly cured. Force curing temperatures may be as high as 175°F (80°C) for some materials. Once again, it's very important to abide by the manufacturer's recommendations.

Baked coatings are actually baked in an oven at temperatures around 400°F (205°C) to reach proper cure. The epoxies, phenolics and similar internal tubing coatings are baked coatings as are some vessel coatings. These materials are usually applied in very thin, multiple, coats and receive intermediate bakes at lower temperatures after each coat.

Fusion-bonded coatings are a special type of material that are applied as a solid powder to a heated metal surface. The melting particles adhere to the hot metal and fuse together to form the coating film. The most common material of this type are the fusion-bonded epoxies (FBE) used as pipe coatings. Original equipment manufacturers of valves and other oilfield equipment will be using more of the powder coatings in the future because of the very low VOC emitted by these materials.

REINFORCED COATINGS

Polyester or epoxy coatings reinforced with fiberglass or with flaked glass particles are used to provide thicker, stronger linings for rehabilitating and restoring damaged or leaking tank or vessel bottoms.

COATING FORMULATION

The material that comes in the can called a "coating" is not just a single material—not just an epoxy or polyurethane or vinyl resin. Rather, it is a combination of materials, each of which is important to achieve the properties desired from that particular formulation. The two basic components in a coating are the pigment and the vehicle. In the most general terms, these are the solid and the liquid portions of the coating.

PIGMENT

The pigment is often thought of as just the coloring agents in the coating. However, they are much more than that. **Table 6.2** lists a number of reasons that pigments are used in coatings. To accomplish these tasks, many formulations will contain several types of pigments—inhibitive pigments (only in primers), inert and reinforcing pigments, and color pigments. Each pigment has its own function in the final coating.

TABLE 6.2 Typical Reasons Why Pigments are Used in Protective Coatings

PIGMENTS ARE USED IN PROTECTIVE COATING FORMULATIONS:

- To provide rust inhibiting characteristics.
- To decrease the permeability of the coating film.
- To hide the surface underneath.
- To provide color.
- To protect the film from the effects of ultraviolet light and weather.
- To perform self-cleaning and controlled chalking.
- To decrease gloss and increase the bond of subsequent coats.
- To assist in drying the coating binder.
- To provide specific surface finishes.
- To aid storage properties of the coating.
- To increase the coating consistency so that thicker film may be applied.

The primary function of a primer's inhibitive pigment is to provide a passive surface or cathodic protection (the overall aspects of the primer are discussed later in this chapter). The inert and reinforcing pigments are often added to improve the density, chemical resistance, toughness, adhesion, and bonding, as well as to increase the dry film thickness. Additionally, they may be used to contribute to the viscosity, thixotropy, and overall workability of the coating in its liquid stage. Color pigments are used to impart opacity, to hide the underlying surface, to protect from UV ray deterioration, as well as provide color.[1]

VEHICLE

The vehicle consists of the various resins, solvents, and plasticizers in the coating formulation.

The resin(s), known as the "binder," has a number of functions including binding the pigments together to make a homogenous film. The binder also wets the metal (or previous coat) to provide adhesion, serves as the primary barrier to the environment, and maintains its integrity in a corrosive environment. While the binder in many coatings is composed of only one resin, many others have more than one compatible resin. The combination imparts specific properties.[1] Many different generic resins are available and are used in coatings for production equipment (Table 6.1).

The solvents, as the name implies, are the fluids that dissolve the binder and create a useable liquid. Many binder resins are solids until dissolved in an appropriate solvent. As the coating cures, or dries, the solvents evaporate and are not part of the dry film. Traditionally, most solvents in protective coating formulations have been mixtures of various organic materials, such as aliphatic and aromatic hydrocarbons, ketones, esters, alcohols and ethers. Water is used as the solvent in some formulations but, until recently, most water base coatings have been for commercial rather than industrial use (with the exception of the inorganic zinc silicates). With the worldwide concern for air quality, many locations have tight limits on the release of VOC. These restrictions have impacted the use of many coating formulations. Coatings industry research is continually reformulating coatings to reduce or eliminate the VOC content. Water base formulations, as well as solvent free powder coatings, are receiving much of the attention. Coating users must continue to stay abreast of the latest developments as new coating formulations are substituted for some of the old standbys.

Plasticizers make up the third type of material that may be used in the vehicle of some coatings. They are in the formula to provide flexibility, extendibility, and toughness.

COATING SYSTEMS

Protective coatings should be referred to as "coating systems," because they are normally not single coats of material. Atmospheric coatings are usually two- or three- coat systems—a primer coat and a topcoat or a primer coat, intermediate coat, and a topcoat—each having its own purpose. When the terms "two coat" or "three coat" are used, this refers to the different types of coatings with different functions—not the actual number of times the structure was sprayed

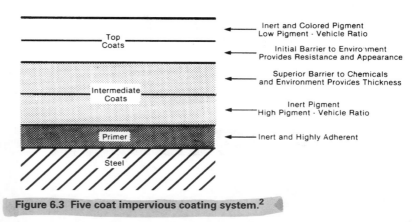

Figure 6.3 Five coat impervious coating system.[2]

with coating. Some systems may have as many as five coats. **Figure 6.3** shows a five-coat system, and indicates the purpose of each of the three different kinds of coats.[2] Baked on immersion coatings may have even more individual sprayings—very thin multiple coats with intermediate bakes between coats.

PRIMERS

The primer is required for all anticorrosion coatings and is considered to be a most important part of the coating system. **Table 6.3** lists the primary purposes of a primer.

TABLE 6.3 Purposes of the Primer in a Coating System

PRIMER COAT:

1. Provides an effective bond to the metal substrate (superior to the bond other coats would have to the metal).
2. Provides a tie (inter-coat bond) to subsequent coat.
3. May provide a strong resistance to corrosion and chemicals as a barrier.
4. May provide corrosion protection as an inhibitor (inhibitive primer).
5. May provide corrosion protection with sacrificial metal (zinc-rich primer).

When equipment or facilities are fabricated, the surfaces may be prepared and the primer coat applied before the equipment is shipped. It may be weeks or even months before the final coat(s) are applied. Thus, the primer may have to prevent atmospheric rusting for an extended period. There are three basic types of primers—barrier, inhibitive, and sacrificial (or galvanic or cathodic). All three types provide the bonds to the metal substrate and the next coat.

Barrier primers are often variations on the formulations of the other coats (*i.e.*, the resin may be the same). This is the usual type primer for immersion coating systems. Barrier primers rely on inert characteristics and very strong adhesion.

Inhibitive primers are formulated with inhibitive pigments that will suppress rust in atmospheric service. Originally, the most widely used inhibitive pigment was red lead; however, health and safety regulations are requiring alternative materials. Pigments containing phosphates or similar nontoxic compounds are among those in use today.

Sacrificial primers contain a high concentration of zinc dust. The zinc acts as a sacrificial anode to protect the bare steel when the coating is damaged. Available as both inorganic zinc primers and organic zinc primers, the choice depends on the service and the topcoat material. The zinc-rich primers are sometimes used without a topcoat. Although similar in action to galvanizing, the zinc-rich primers can be easily topcoated with most resins, whereas galvanizing requires special treatment in order to be successfully topcoated. **Figure 6.4** is an example of improper conditioning of a galvanized railing before top coating. The topcoat disbonded and came off in sheets.

Zinc-rich primers are normally used with atmospheric coatings. Most marine/offshore coating systems use zinc-rich primers **(Figure 6.5)**.

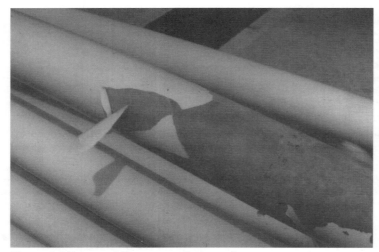

Figure 6.4 Topcoat failure on an improperly prepared galvanized railing.

Figure 6.5 Off-shore platform coated with inorganic zinc primer.[2]

INTERMEDIATE COATS

The intermediate coat(s) in three or more coat systems is also called the "barrier coat" or "body coat." **Table 6.4** lists the primary purposes of the intermediate coats.[3]

TABLE 6.4 **Purposes of the Intermediate Coat in a Coating System**[3]

INTERMEDIATE COAT:
1. Provides thickness for the total coating.
2. Provides strong chemical resistance.
3. Provides resistance to moisture vapor transfer.
4. Provides increased coating electrical resistance.
5. Provides strong cohesion (strength within the coating film).
6. Provides a strong bond to the primer and to the topcoat.

The intermediate coat is a very critical coat in many aggressive environments. That is why many offshore facilities are coated with three coat systems.

TOPCOATS

The topcoat, sometimes referred to as the "finish coat," is the first line of defense against chemicals, water, and the environment. **Table 6.5** lists the common functions of the topcoat.[3]

TABLE 6.5 Purposes of the Topcoat in a Coating System[3]

> TOPCOAT:
>
> 1. Provides a resistant seal for the coating system.
> 2. Forms the initial barrier to the environment.
> 3. Provides resistance to chemicals, water, and weather.
> 4. Provides a touch- and wear-resistant surface.
> 5. Provides a pleasing appearance.

Although many of the topcoat's functions are similar to the intermediate coat, the topcoat will normally have a lower pigment to vehicle ratio. Often the topcoat will be a different color than the intermediate coat, so the coater and inspector can judge the amount of coverage.

COATING APPLICATION

The term "coating application" is an all inclusive term standing for the three main portions of the application—surface preparation, coating the structure, and inspection. An old adage in the coating industry goes as follows: "A poor coating material properly applied will outperform the very best coating material improperly applied." In spite of the many advances in coating technology over the years, that statement is still true.

DESIGN FOR COATING

Regardless of the structure to be coated—offshore structure, vessel internals, piping internally and externally, etc.—the design must allow the surfaces to be properly cleaned and prepared, coated, and inspected. Such features as sharp edges, skip welds, blind areas, crevices and similar design faults spell "coating failure" even before the coating job starts. **Table 6.6**[4] provides a list of items to consider and include in design specifications to assure that the structure or equipment is amenable to coating. **Figures 6.6** through **6.8** illustrate the results of overlooking some of these design items. Other design considerations will be mentioned as appropriate in the discussion on coating of specific production equipment.

Figure 6.6 Sharp edges, torch cuts, and welds not ground smooth. Note rust breakthrough along edges of beams.

TABLE 6.6 Designing for Protective Coating
(Adapted from Fundamentals of Designing for Corrosion Control[4])

STEPS TO ASSURE THAT THE DESIGN OF STRUCTURES AND EQUIPMENT IS AMENABLE TO COATING:

1. Eliminate sharp corners.
2. Use butt welding instead of lap welding.
3. Remove weld splatter.
4. Specify that welds are to be continuous, no skip welding.
5. Avoid designs that will collect or hold water and debris.
6. Provide drainage in recessed zones.
7. Specify the removal of roughness and surfaces defects by grinding.
8. Specify the rounding of all corners.
9. Eliminate hard to reach places.
10. Specify that surfaces be easily accessible.
11. Provide a continuous and even surface to allow complete bonding of the coating to the metal surface.
12. Eliminate intricate construction that would be difficult to coat. Use pipe construction or other simple design.
13. Specify that irregular surfaces, such as threads, be cleaned and caulked.
14. When a thick plate is to be joined to a thinner plate, design the surface to be coated to be flat.
15. Locate stiffeners or structural supports for tanks on the outside of the tank.
16. Specify that baffles and other vessel internals be removable so the internal surface of the shell can be properly coated.
17. Do not incorporate crevices or pockets in the design. Where crevices can not be avoided, specify that they be welded and welds be ground prior to the application of the coating.
18. Ascertain that mill scale be removed from the steel surface.
19. Provide tanks, vessels or piping, with easy access for coating and inspection.
20. When dissimilar metals are required for vessel internals they should be electrically isolated from the coated shell.
21. All nozzles on internally coated vessels should be 2 in. or greater I.D. for proper surface preparation and coating.

Figure 6.7 Poor weld not properly ground.

Figure 6.8 Poor design—beam stiffener positioned to form a water trap. The atmospheric coating must serve as an immersion coating.

Several of the NACE Standard Recommended Practices listed in **Appendix 6A** contain design tips for specific pieces of equipment. In **Appendix 6B**, "Fabrication Requirements for Internally Coated Production Vessels and Tanks," **Figures 6B.1** through **6B.15**, illustrate examples of "acceptable" and "not acceptable" fabrication.

SURFACE PREPARATION

Surface preparation involves two areas—preparing a clean smooth surface and preparing an anchor pattern. Each is important.

Cleaning the surface may be as simple as washing the surface with solvent to remove dirt, oil, and grease. Or it may involve grinding to remove weld splatter, to grind out defects in the surface, and to smooth rough welds. The final step in cleaning the surface is the grit blast to remove rust and mill scale and to prepare the anchor pattern. The importance of proper surface preparation is illustrated in **Figure 6.9**.[5] Improper surface preparation can shorten the life of a coating. **Figures 6.10** and **6.11** show blistering of the coating that can occur when the metal surface is not properly cleaned.

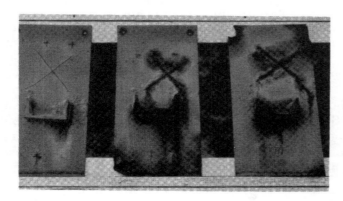

Figure 6.9 The effects of surface condition on coating life—Corrosion at scribes in the same coating (three-coat vinyl system) applied over sandblasted steel [left], rusted steel [middle], and intact mill scale [right], exposed for 9 years in a marine environment.[5]

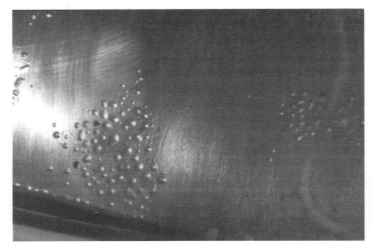

Figure 6.10 Poor surface preparation can cause blistered coating.

Figure 6.11 Another example of blistered coating.

Blast cleaning is the most common method of surface preparation used for production equipment and facilities. Commonly referred to as "sand blasting," blast cleaning may use a number of different materials. Health/safety concerns have brought on regulations in many places concerning the use of sand. Currently, blast material selection varies from garnet, slag, and shot, to agricultural materials such as walnut shells. The choice depends upon the cleaning/anchor pattern required, cost, and local regulations.

There are many blast standards available worldwide. The most common in North America have been NACE International Standards and the Society of Protective Coatings, formerly known as the Steel Structures Painting Council (SSPC) standards. In 1994 the two organizations issued revised Joint Surface Preparation Standards. These Standards provide for four basic degrees of cleanliness, usually referred to by their common names: White Metal, Near White Metal, Commercial, and Brush-Off. The White Metal being the most stringent (cleanest) and brush-off being the least stringent. A digest of the requirements would be:

- NACE No. 1/SSPC-SP 5 White Metal Blast Cleaning—When viewed without magnification, the surface shall be free of all visible oil, grease, dust, dirt, mill scale, rust, coating, oxides, corrosion products, and foreign matter.[6]

- NACE No. 2/SSPC-SP 10 Near-White Metal Blast Cleaning—When viewed without magnification, the surface shall be free of all visible oil, grease, dust, dirt, mill scale, rust, coating, oxides, corrosion products, and foreign matter except for random staining limited to 5% of each unit area approximately 88 mm x 88 mm (3 in. x 3 in.).[7]

- NACE No. 3/SSPC-SP 6 Commercial Blast Cleaning—When viewed without magnification, the surface shall be free of all visible oil, grease, dust, dirt, mill scale, rust, coating, oxides, corrosion products, and foreign matter except for random staining limited to 33% of each unit area approximately 88 mm x 88 mm (3 in. x 3 in.).[8]

- NACE No. 4/SSPC-SP 7 Brush-Off Blast Cleaning—When viewed without magnification, the surface shall be free of all visible oil, grease, dust, dirt, loose mill scale, loose rust, and loose coating, tightly adherent mill scale, rust and coating may remain on the surface.[9]

A complete definition of the cleanliness requirements is given in each Standard. The Standards also cover procedures before and after blasting (immediately prior to coating and lining), blast cleaning abrasives, blast cleaning methods and operation, and inspection requirements. Appropriate comments and explanatory notes are included so that the document can easily be part of the specification for a coating job.

Visual standards and comparators are available for use in evaluating the cleanliness on the job. For example, SSPC-Vis 1-89 provides color photographs for the various grades of cleanliness as a function of the preblast condition of the steel. Sand abrasive-blasted comparison panels that consist of encapsulated steel panels blasted to NACE grades 1, 2, 3, and 4 are available commercially **(Figure 6.12)**.[10]

Figure 6.12 Visual comparator for various degrees of surface cleanliness from brush blast to white metal blast. (Photograph courtesy of KTA-Tator, Inc., Pittsburgh, PA.[10])

Another type of visual comparator is NACE's Visual Comparator for Surface Finish of Welds Prior to Coating **(Figures 6.13A** and **6.13B)**.[10] This plastic weld replica was molded from 14 actual welds with various degrees of surface finish and illustrates the written requirements in NACE RP0178.[11]

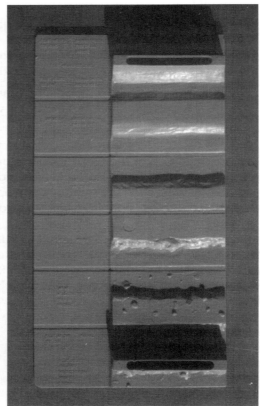

Figure 6.13 A & B NACE visual comparator for surface finish of welds prior to coating.

    A. Butt welds reflecting different conditions, top to bottom:
- Ground flush and smooth, free of all defects.
- Ground flush.
- Ground smooth, free of all defects.
- Ground smooth and blended.
- Minimal.
- Weld condition prior to grinding.

    B. Fillet and Lap Weld, top to bottom:
- Fillet welded tee joint—ground smooth, free of all defects.
- Fillet welded tee joint—ground smooth and blended.
- Lap joint—ground smooth, free of all defects.
- Lap joint—ground smooth and blended.
- Lap joint—minimal.
- Lap joint—weld condition prior to grinding.
- Fillet welded tee joint—minimal.
- Fillet welded tee joint—weld condition prior to grinding.

These photographs may give an optical illusion. The welds are raised, not grooves.
(Photograph courtesy of KTA-Tator, Inc., Pittsburgh, PA.[10])

Anchor pattern is the term used to describe the profile of the metal's surface roughness. It is a measure of an average distance between the peaks and valleys created by blast cleaning. Having the proper anchor pattern is a necessary step in achieving satisfactory coating performance. Too small an anchor pattern (too low a profile) can lead to unsatisfactory adhesion between the coating and the metal. Too large an anchor pattern (too high a profile) and the coating will not cover the peaks.

Anchor patterns vary depending on many factors including the type and size of the blast material. The anchor pattern requirement is primarily a function of the coating thickness and will usually be specified by the coating manufacturer for a specific formulation. **Table 6.7** can be used as a general guide to the relationship between coating thickness and anchor pattern on mild steel.[12]

TABLE 6.7 Relationship Between Coating Thickness and Anchor Pattern[12]

DRY FILM COATING THICKNESS	ANCHOR PATTERN
125–200 μm (5–8 mils)	20–25 μm (1–2 mils)
200–500 μm (9–20 mils)	50–75 μm (2–3 mils)
500 μm or more (over 20 mils)	75–125 μm (3–5 mils)

The anchor pattern can be verified on the job by the replica tape method. NACE RP0287 covers the details of this method.[13] **Figure 6.14** Illustrates a method of measuring a surface profile using replica tape.[14] Visual comparators that also may be used to confirm the depth of the anchor pattern are commercially available **(Figure 6.15)**.

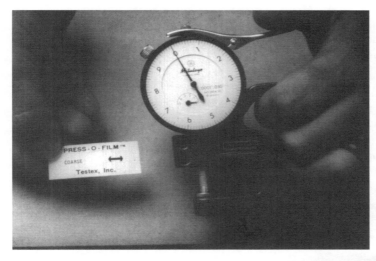

Figure 6.14 Surface profile with replica tape. (Photograph courtesy of KTA-Tator, Inc., Pittsburgh, PA.[14])

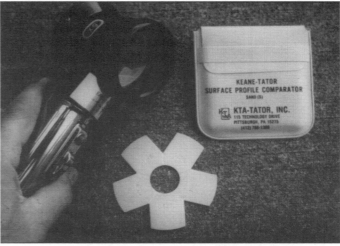

Figure 6.15 Surface profile visual comparator. (Photograph courtesy of KTA-Tator, Inc., Pittsburgh, PA.[14])

COATING THE STRUCTURE

When the surface preparation is complete, the next step is the actual application of the coating. Spray coating is the most common method and the most practical with today's anticorrosion coating technology. Two types of spray equipment are available—conventional air spray and airless spray. The former atomizes the coating with compressed air. The latter forces the coating through the nozzle under high pressure, achieving atomization by the pressure drop at the nozzle orifice.

It is very important that the applicator follow the manufacturer's instructions for each specific coating material in the system. Items such as coating viscosity, thinners, mixing (two component coatings), time between coats, and application temperature limits are all critical for a successful coating job. **Table 6.8** lists some examples of the application problems that occur if specifications and instructions are not followed closely.

TABLE 6.8 Potential Coating Application Problems

THE COATING JOB WILL NOT BE SUCCESSFUL IF THE COATING IS:
Too Viscous in Spray Pot:
• May not spray properly.
• The cure time will be improper.
• The solvent may be trapped in the film.
Too Fluid in Spray Pot:
• May not spray properly.
• May not build required wet film thickness.
• Extra coats may be required for dry film thickness.
Too Thick on Substrate:
• The cure time will be improper.
• Runs, sags, cracks may occur.
• The solvent may be trapped in the film.
• May disbond from previous coat or substrate.
Too Thin on Substrate:
• May have rust bleed-through.
• May allow premature failure.
Too Long After Abrasive Blast Cleaning:
• Surface rusting may have started.
• The coating may not properly bond to the surface.
• Coating will prematurely fail.
Too Soon After Previous Coat:
• May result in solvent entrapment and improper cure.
• Can lead to defects—wrinkling, blistering, delamination.
Too Long After Previous Coat:
• May not bond properly if previous coat completely cured.
• May not adhere to previous coat due to surface contamination.
Too Cold Substrate:
• May slow or prevent cure.
• May not have adequate anticorrosive properties.
Wrong Component or Ratio (Two Component Coating):
• Will not cure or will over-cure and fail.
Wrong Thinner:
• May react and effect spraying.
• May prevent cure.

The spraying technique is another very important aspect of coating application. Factors including spray gun pressures, spray pattern, spray gun to structure distance, and coverage area can make the difference between an excellent coating job and a poor coating job.

INSPECTION

The final general subject for consideration when discussing protective coatings is inspection. The role of the coating inspector is a continuing one throughout a coating project. Ideally, the inspector will start at the prejob conference with the applicator and will continue until the final cure inspections are complete. Large coating jobs may be handled by third party inspectors, smaller ones by user company personnel. In all cases, the qualifications of the inspector are critical. NACE has a coating inspector training/certification program that is widely recognized. Many coating project specifications require a NACE-Certified Coating Inspector on the job. The primary duty of the inspector is to verify that specifications are met throughout the project. The inspector must have the authority to enforce the specifications, and if necessary, to see that any variations are satisfactorily resolved. The inspector will run whatever tests are required to evaluate and verify conditions and results. NACE RP0288, "Inspection of Linings on Steel and Concrete," summarizes inspection requirements, equipment, and reference standards.[15] Although the title specifically spells out immersion service, the document can essentially be used for atmospheric coatings as well. The coating specification should include the details of inspection and other quality control issues. An example is given in Section 8 of the owner company coating specification presented in Appendix 6C.

INSPECTION TIMING

Initial inspections should take place before the surface preparation begins to ascertain the condition of the structure. Environmental conditions such as metal temperature, ambient weather, and atmospheric contaminants will be important concerns at each step in the project. Surface preparation efforts include verifying that the specifications for cleanliness and anchor pattern requirements are met. During application, the inspector will assure that the various manufacturer's recommendations are met to avoid the items listed in **Table 6.8**, as well as determine the wet and dry film thicknesses. As appropriate, the dried coats will be holiday checked for voids or damaged places. **Table 6.9** lists suggested inspection check points. Although this table was adapted from an immersion coating standard (NACE RP0181–94[16]), the same points apply to atmospheric coating projects as well.

TABLE 6.9 Coating Job Inspection Check Points[12]

INSPECTION CHECK POINTS SHOULD BE ESTABLISHED AS FOLLOWS:
1. Pre blast cleaning.
2. After blast cleaning.
3. After each coat is applied.
4. After final cure.
5. Final completion inspection (Includes damage inspection after scaffolds removed).

INSPECTION TOOLS

In addition to comparators for surface cleanliness-grade and surface profile/anchor pattern evaluation, and routine inspection equipment (mirrors, magnifiers, depth gages, etc.), film thickness (wet and dry) gages and holiday detectors are required.

Film thickness gages are used to evaluate both the wet film thickness before curing and the dry film after curing. Several different types of each are available commercially. **Figure 6.16** shows a notch type wet film thickness gage. The appropriate edge of the gage is pressed into the wet film. The thickness of the film will be between the last wet notch and the first dry notch. By knowing the amount of shrinkage during cure, the manufacturer can specify the wet film thickness to obtain the specified dry film. Thus, the applicator or inspector can tell if the correct amount of coating has been applied.

Figure 6.17 shows an example of a magnetic pull-off type gage used to measure dry film. Thickness is determined by the amount of "pull" required to lift a magnet off the coating. The thickness is read on the moveable dial. It is probably the most common thickness gage in use today since it is lightweight and one of the easier type gages to calibrate and use. Other types of dry film thickness include electronic and electromagnetic styles **(Figure 6.18)**.

Figure 6.16 Notch type wet film thickness gage. (Photograph courtesy of KTA-Tator, Inc., Pittsburgh, PA.[14])

Figure 6.17 Magnetic pull-off dry film thickness gage. (Photograph courtesy of KTA-Tator, Inc., Pittsburgh, PA.[14])

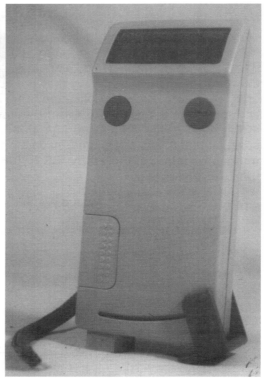

Figure 6.18 Electronic dry film thickness gage. (Photograph courtesy of KTA-Tator, Inc., Pittsburgh, PA.[14])

Holiday detectors are used to inspect a coating to locate discontinuities in a coating film. A holiday may be a void, crack, thin spot, foreign inclusion, or contamination in the coating that significantly lowers the dielectric strength on the coating.[17] Since the dielectric strength is an important parameter, electrical techniques are used to locate the discontinuities. Holiday testers are available in two principal types—low-voltage wet sponge type and high-voltage spark type.

The low-voltage wet sponge holiday detector is applicable for thin-film coatings **(Figure 6.19)**. The unit that supplies the low-voltage DC is grounded to the metal structure and connected to the wet sponge. As the sponge is passed over the coating, the water will penetrate the holidays and damaged places, completing the circuit and sounding an audible alarm. The water used in the sponge should be tap water with a low sudsing wetting agent. Salt should not be used in the water. Salty water could lead to erroneous indications, and even more important, residual salt on the coating could interfere with the adhesion of additional coats. The sponge speed should be slow enough to detect the holidays (1 ft/s [0.3 m/s] is recommended).[18]

For thick-film coatings, a high-voltage spark type holiday detector should be used. The high-voltage unit uses a metal wire whisk or spring assembly (exploring electrode) to contact the coating, rather than the wet sponge. When the electrode reaches a holiday, a spark will jump the air gap to complete the circuit and trigger the alarm. To avoid burning holes in the coating, voltage and current must be controlled for the film thickness involved. The manufacturer can supply the figures for the maximum voltage for the specific coating. NACE RP0188-90 gives suggested voltages based on dry film thickness.[19]

Figure 6.19 Coating inspection with the wet sponge holiday detector. (Photograph courtesy of KTA-Tator, Inc., Pittsburgh, PA.[14])

It is recommended that the dry film thickness be measured before selecting the holiday detector. If the coating film exceeds 20 mils (0.5 mm), the high-voltage procedures should be used.[17]

COATING OF PRODUCTION FACILITIES AND EQUIPMENT

The preceding parts of this chapter presented the basic principles that apply to the various uses of the liquid applied coatings. The remainder of this chapter will look at considerations or issues in the use of coatings for specific equipment and facilities. While coatings are not the total answer to oil and gas corrosion problems, they, by themselves and combined with other control methods, are viable, economical approaches to corrosion control.

ATMOSPHERIC PROTECTION

Except for appearance, exterior protection of structural steel, tanks, vessels, and piping is usually only necessary along the sea coast, in marine environments, or in industrial areas where acid gases are present. In moist atmospheres, especially in marine and coastal regions, a coating system using a sacrificial primer, such as the organic or inorganic zinc-rich coatings is advisable. In other areas it is quite common to use galvanized structural steel and tanks without a topcoat. As mentioned earlier in this chapter, if the galvanizing is to be topcoated, the zinc surface requires special treatment for the topcoat to properly adhere. Use the treatment recommended by the topcoat manufacturer. Housed facilities may be externally coated to protect equipment, steel decks, or concrete floors from attack due to spills.

VESSELS AND TANKS

Internal coatings are used in all types of field vessels and tanks, anywhere that free-water (liquid water) can collect or be condensed from gas. Separators, free-water knockouts, heater treaters, water handling vessels, lease tankage or stock tanks may be coated where corrosive conditions merit protection. Types of coatings include baked phenolics, epoxy-modified phenolics, or ambient temperature-cured and force-cured-catalyzed coatings such as amine, amine adduct or polyamide-cured epoxies, amine-cured epoxy-modified phenolics, amine- or polyamide-cured coal-tar epoxies, hot-applied asphalt and coal-tar pitch enamels, or solvent release polyesters and epoxies. Depending on the coating material, these are applied either in an applicator's shop or by an applicator after erection in the field. The coating choice depends on the service requirements, economics, and coating applicators available. If cathodic protection is to be used in addition to coating, a coating system resistant to cathodic disbonding will be necessary.

Regardless of the coating system selected, the vessel or tank must be designed for coating. The examples of acceptable design given in **Appendix 6B** should be reviewed to assure the coatability of any vessel or tank. The requirements in NACE Standards for immersion coatings, RP0178[20] and RP0181[21] (latest editions), may be used as guidelines for planning coating projects. They also can be incorporated in whole or part in the coating specifications for a particular project.

Appendix 6C, "Coating Specification Internal Tank Coating—Application of Thin Film Coatings," is an example of a detailed coating specification. Obviously, it is designed to provide for several different approved coatings.

Although in most production vessels, the only areas to require coating are the free-water section or along the bottom and the gas section; many times it is more economical to coat the entire shell than to selectively coat portions. Large storage tanks, however, are more likely to have coating on the underside of the deck and down the sides to the working oil level, and on the bottom and sides up 18 to 24 in. (0.5 to 0.6 m).

Obviously, the best time to coat a vessel or tank is before it is placed in service; however, used vessels and tanks are often coated to extend their lives. Surface preparation is very critical since all the oil, grease, scale and corrosion product must be removed. Shallow pits will blast clean. Sharp edged or deep pits should be ground smooth before blasting if they are to be properly cleaned.

If the tank bottoms are corroding through from internal or external corrosion, fiberglass reinforced resin linings or concrete may be used to repair and to minimize further attack.

Bolted tanks present a coating challenge due to the design. The bolts and the gasket make it difficult to obtain a uniform, continuous coating film. Special treatment is required. NACE RP0181 (latest edition) presents one approach—undercutting the gaskets, and caulking gaskets and bolt heads. Covering the seams and bolts with fiberglass and resin also has been used effectively. Note the resin and the coating must be compatible and the manufacturers' directions must be followed to assure proper adhesion and sealing between the two materials.

When the final coating holiday inspection is completed, holiday repair may be required. Some specifications call for all holidays to be repaired. A typical holiday repair procedure is detailed in the **Appendix 6C** sample specification, paragraph 7.9.6.

For maximum benefit from a coating system, once the vessel has been placed in service, care must be taken not to damage the coating. Operations and maintenance personnel should be aware that a vessel has internal coating. **Figure 6.20** shows one approach to keeping everyone informed. One common example of mistreating a coating is welding on the back side of a coated vessel wall. **Figure 6.21** shows the results of welding burning a coating.

Figure 6.20 An example of labeling a vessel so all personnel are aware of the vessel's internal coating.

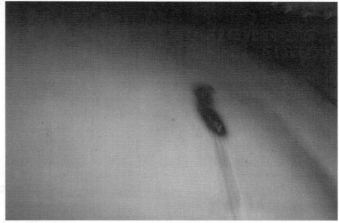

Figure 6.21 An illustration of coating damage caused by welding on the back side of the vessel wall.

TUBULAR GOODS

Internal coating of tubing and other downhole equipment is an established method for controlling corrosion in high-pressure gas condensate wells, flowing oil wells, gas lift oil wells and water injection wells. The most common coatings are organic resin coatings very similar to the immersion coating used in vessels and tanks (cement-lined tubing also may be used in water injection service). The term internally plastic coated (IPC), is often used to designate tubular goods (*e.g.*, tubing, casing, line pipe, and drill pipe) and accessories (*e.g.*, couplings, valves, packers, etc.) **(Figure 6.22)**.

Figure 6.22 Internally plastic coated drill pipe.

As noted in **Appendix 6A**, NACE has several standards covering IPC tubulars. Of particular importance to anyone using IPC materials are RP0191 and RP0291, which respectively cover the application of IPC and its care, handling, and installation.

Several materials are available for inhole use. Basically all are the so called "high bake" materials (oven baked in the 400°F [204°C] range to achieve the proper cure). The coatings for hydrocarbon service are usually classed as "thin film coatings," less than 250 μm (10 mils) dry film thickness (DFT).[22] Water service IPCs are more likely to be "thick film coatings," 250 to 760 μm (10 to 30 mils) DFT.[22]

When the use of IPC tubing is being evaluated, the tubing connection must be considered. Many premium connections are considered uncoatable. That is, the design precludes coating the connection in a manner that assures that no bare metal is exposed when the connection is made-up properly. For example, thread systems that seal by metal-to-metal shoulder contact are not coatable, because the coating cannot extend on to the sealing surface. However, many connections are considered coatable. For instance, EUE 8RD, 8RD long casing threads, connections that use a "corrosion barrier" ring—often referred to as a CB ring—and tubing buttress threads are considered coatable. These connections allow the coating to extend around the nose of the pin to mate with the coating or CB ring in coupling. When these connections are made-up, the net effect is continuous coating throughout the tubing.

It is extremely important to match the coating material to the service. That is, do not use a coating designed for water system service in an oil or gas well—it will fail. Do not use a coating above its temperature limits.

Quality control and inspection at the coating plant are extremely important to a successful coating job. Purchasing company or third party inspectors should always be present when tubing or wellhead equipment is being coated.

Another important consideration is the proper care and handling of coated materials—in transportation, running into the well, and while in service. Any pipe can be damaged by improper handling—coated pipe takes just a little more care. Basically, these coatings can be damaged by direct impact onto the coating (so protect the pin ends) and will be damaged if the steel is permanently deformed.

NACE RP0291 presents guidelines for the care and handling of coated tubing. Such items as the use of slings rather than hooks in the ends, leaving thread protectors in place until the joint is in the derrick, use of stabbing guides, etc. will reduce the odds for a premature failure. **Figure 6.23** illustrates the types of damage that can result from removing thread protectors too early. Even though the coating is tough and damage can be tolerated in many wells, minimizing damage and prolonging the tubing life is good operating practice.

The most likely time for coating damage in a well is, of course, when wire-lining. While excessive wire-lining can cause damage, coatings can take quite a bit of abuse. **Figures 6.24A** and

Figure 6.23 Internally plastic coated tubing. Note that the tubing is racked without thread protectors and the chipped coating at the lip.

6.24B show a sample of coated tubing from a well that had numerous wireline operations. Note that, although the coating is worn, bare metal is not showing, nor is there corrosion. This example is typical of the condition of the coated tubing from this well. No special care had been exercised during wireline operations because the well record did not show coated tubing. When the well was pulled, it was discovered that the lower portion was coated and the upper was bare pipe.

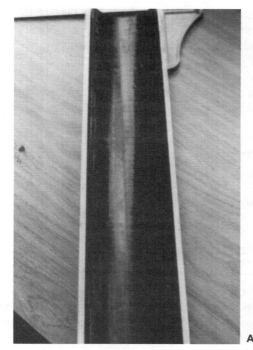
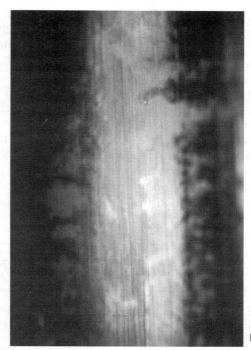

Figure 6.24 A & B Internally plastic coated (ipc) tubing that had numerous wireline runs.
  A. Overall view of the split joint.
  B. Close-up of the worn area.
Note that, although the coating is worn, bare metal is not showing nor is there corrosion. This
  example is typical of the condition of the coated tubing from this well. No special care had been
  exercised during wireline operations because the well record did not show coated tubing. When
  the well was pulled it was discovered that the lower portion was coated and the upper bare pipe.

MISCONCEPTIONS—Old Wives Tales

Discussions about coated tubing and damages to the coating often bring up statements such as:

  —"Corrosion will be accelerated at holidays and damaged places in coating; therefore, we are better off with bare pipe!"

or —"Wireline damaged coating is worse than no coating at all!"

Neither statement is true! Certainly, it is not when talking about coated tubing in oil field operations.

The reason these are not true has to do with the geometry of the corrosion cell—the cathode/anode areas. As discussed in **Chapter 3**, the rate of corrosion in a particular environment is related to the area of the anode (which is corroding) and the area of the cathode. For a given system, if there is a large cathode area and a small anode area, current flow will be high and corrosion will be accelerated. However, if there is a large anode area related to a small cathode area, corrosion will be reduced.

Now then—refer back to **Figure 3.26** in **Chapter 3**, the wireline cut bare pipe illustrating "wear-corrosion." The wireline wore a bright spot in the metal, which was anodic to the rest of the steel and corrosion was accelerated due to the large cathode-small anode (most of the pipes surface area—the wireline cut) relationship.

Now coat that same joint and cut through the coating with the wireline exposing the same line of bright steel to serve as an anode—but what about a cathode? The large cathode area from the bare pipe is now isolated with coating. All anodes and cathodes will have to form on the bare metal exposed by the wireline wear—thus, only small anode-small cathode. Corrosion will not be accelerated—in fact, it could be reduced. There could be less corrosion on damaged coated tubing than on bare tubing.

Even though the coating is tough, it can be damaged by wirelining. Too high wireline speeds can cause the tools to "rattle" and pound on the coating—particularly as they pass through couplings and connections. To minimize damage, tools should have rounded corners, and whenever possible, be coated. Wireline speeds should be held to less than 30m (100 ft) per minute.[23] Wireline operations can damage coatings, but when the use of IPC tubing is justified, the possibility of future wireline work should not affect the decision to use IPC. See the sidebar, "Misconceptions—Old Wives Tales."

As an insurance measure, some companies have justified the use of inhibitors to supplement the coating for critical, high cost/high risk areas (such as high pressure, offshore, remote, urban, and high corrosion rate areas).

Why use both coatings and inhibitors? This is simply a technique to approach complete corrosion control. Furthermore, if relying on inhibitors alone, if the program fails for some reason, massive corrosion would weaken the pipe, requiring a costly fishing job. If the pipe is coated and the supplementary inhibition fails, there may be a hole in the pipe—but structural integrity is maintained—and pulling and replacement costs are held to a minimum.

FLOWLINES, GATHERING SYSTEMS, INJECTION LINES, AND PIPING

From the standpoint of external corrosion control, the various surface piping systems (whether produced fluids, or oil, or gas, or water) are treated much alike. That is, aboveground atmospheric protection follows the same guidelines discussed earlier in this chapter. Buried and subsea (submerged) systems rely on the so called "pipeline" coating reviewed in a later section. Depending on the environment and stakes, coatings may be used by themselves or in combination with cathodic protection.

Most oil well and gas well flowlines and gathering systems depend upon inhibitors rather than internal coatings. In extremely corrosive gas well, systems resistant alloys are also used. Immersion coatings would be more competitive except for the joining problems. Since most flowlines and gathering lines are high pressure systems, they are welded. Welding destroys the coating at each joint. A number of proprietary joining systems have been developed, but most have had limited specialized use.

One approach that allows the use of liquid applied organic immersion coatings to welded lines is "in-place" coating—also called "in-situ" coating. The cleaning and surface preparation is the greatest challenge for in-place coating. This highly specialized technique has been most successfully used to coat new lines. New, uncorroded pipe is relatively clean, and stands the best chance of a successful coating application. In spite of the problems with getting a good job in old systems, inplace coatings have successfully reduced the number of failures, and extended the life of some severely corroded piping systems.

Rehabilitating lines inplace with prefabricated liners is becoming more widely used than in-situ coating. As mentioned in the chapter on nonmetallics, both thermoplastic and thermosetting pipe have been and are being used as liners to rehabilitate older corroded lines. As with other materials, the liners must be matched with the service environment for satisfactory performance. Rehabilitation of corroded piping is a subject of continuing research, particularly in the gas industry. Spinoffs from that research will undoubtedly have application in production piping.

On the other hand, the problem of coating long lengths of welded joints is not a concern in facilities piping systems, since they can be flanged. Flanged piping can be coated if it is designed for coating. **Appendix 6B** has a drawing that shows acceptable and nonacceptable design. The key to coatable piping is accessibility—accessibility of the surfaces to be coated—accessibility for grinding of welds, surface preparation, coating application, and inspection. A rule of thumb is: "the pipe piece should have only one change of direction (ell)—all surfaces must be visible."

The same coating materials and techniques as discussed under immersion service are used inside piping. Most piping systems can be coated at an applicator's shop where conditions are easier to control than in the field.

Water system gathering, injection, and plant piping is often internally protected. Cement linings and plastic liners have been the most widespread for new construction. Cement linings are usually centrifugally cast in the pipe joints. **Figure 6.25** shows a joint of cement lined pipe. Techniques involving heat-resistant gaskets that allow welding cement lined pipe were developed over 30 years ago.

Figure 6.25 Cement lined pipe for a water injection system. Note extruded external coating.

OFFSHORE PLATFORMS

Chapter 1 discussed the various corrosion zones of an offshore platform: submerged zone, splash zone, and atmospheric zone. The environmental differences in each zone has caused the industry to develop different control approaches for each zone.[24] NACE RP0176 covers corrosion control of fixed offshore production platforms for each of these zones. Cathodic protection in the submerged zone is discussed in the next chapter of this book. This chapter will briefly cover splash zone protection, and discuss the use of coatings in the atmospheric zone.

Splash zone areas are alternately wet-dry. Thus, cathodic protection is not a practical method of corrosion control. Yet, the splash zone has the highest corrosion rates on a platform's structure. A corrosion allowance in the form of wear plates (additional steel thickness) is usually provided in the splash zone.[25] The wear plates are normally protected with coating or sheathing. Corrosion-resistant nickel-based and copper-based alloys may be welded over the steel. Other materials such as high-build fiberglass or glass flake coatings, rubbers, heat shrink sleeves, flame sprayed aluminum, and a number of proprietary materials have been used to protect this critical area.

Atmospheric zone environments on offshore platforms are considered by many as the most severe of the atmospheric environments. The coating of platforms has evolved from the original painting schemes adopted from the shipping industry (including frequent "chipping and repainting") to today's sophisticated multi-coat systems.

Platform coating is often broken into two categories—original construction and maintenance.[26] Original construction coating is done onshore at the fabrication yard and involves the latest techniques of surface preparation, application, and inspection. Usually, the three to five coat systems described earlier in the chapter are used. Maintenance coating, as the name implies, is a program of periodic inspection and repair or touch-up. The objective is to have preventative maintenance, rather than waiting until the coating approaches total failure, then attempting a costly repainting in the marine atmosphere.[26]

Different operators have different preferences and different specifications for their offshore coating systems. **Table 6.10** presents some typical systems for atmospheric zone coating.

& submerged zone.

TABLE 6.10 Typical Coating Systems Used in the Atmospheric Zone[1]

COATING SYSTEM	THICKNESS	
	μm	mils
Wash Primer	13	0.5
Vinyl, intermediate and topcoats (three to four coats)	200 to 250	8 to 10
Wash Primer	13	0.5
Chlorinated rubber, intermediate and topcoats (three to four coats)	200 to 250	8 to 10
Inorganic zinc-rich self-cured primer	75	3
Epoxy intermediate coat	125	5
Vinyl acrylic or polyurethane topcoat	50	2
Inorganic zinc-rich self-cured primer	75	3
Epoxy intermediate and topcoat (two coats)	250	10
Inorganic zinc-rich self-cured primer	75	3
Vinyl high-build intermediate coat	100 to 150	4 to 6
Vinyl topcoat (two coats)	50	2
Inorganic zinc-rich post-cured primer	75	3
Epoxy intermediate coat	125	5
Vinyl acrylic or polyurethane topcoat	50	2
Inorganic zinc-rich post-cured primer	75	3
Epoxy tie-coat	50	2
Epoxy intermediate coat	100 to 150	4 to 6
Vinyl acrylic or polyurethane topcoat	50	2
Inorganic zinc-rich post-cured primer	75	3
Co-polymer tie-coat	50	2
Vinyl high-build topcoat	150 to 250	6 to 10
Inorganic zinc-rich self-cured primer	75	3
Epoxy tie-coat	50	2
High-build polyurethane	150 to 200	6 to 8

(1)   The specified number of coats and the thickness may vary among operators and manufacturers.

The criteria for the selection of a coating system is outlined in NACE RP0176 (latest edition).[27] Because real-time testing takes a number of years of onsite exposure, several accelerated tests are presented. NACE Standard Test Method TM0184[28] is one of the several accelerated tests listed.

Individual companies specifications may be very detailed and specify different coating systems for each piece of equipment. **Appendix 6D**, "Excerpts from a Specification for External Coatings for Offshore and Severely Corrosive Environments," illustrates one offshore operator's approach.

PIPELINE COATINGS

With a few exceptions, the materials used for external coatings on buried and submerged pipelines are different materials than those discussed in previous chapters. Most pipeline coatings would be classed as very thick coatings.

While many pipelines were welded together and then coated "over the ditch," today's oil and gas production flowlines, gathering, and injection systems are primarily made from shop coated pipe. The only field coating is at the joints or to repair holidays from damage while laying.

NACE RP0169-96, "Control of External Corrosion on Underground or Submerged Piping Systems,"[29] is the basic document on the subject. It is cited in many rules and regulations around the world. Although usually thought of as a cathodic protection document, NACE RP0169 covers external coatings as well. Much of the information is by reference to other documents that detail specific tests, materials, or procedures. Included in the references list are the other NACE standards listed in **Appendix 6A**'s section on external pipeline coatings.

Figure 6.26 Pipeline coating—Coal tar enamel with wrapper. Note that this pipe is cement-lined for a water injection project.

Figure 6.27 Pipeline coating—Tape coating applied on corroded pipe. Note the tape has conformed to the pipe surface, is overlapped for a seal.

The common pipeline coatings covered in NACE RP0169 are the hot applied coal tars (enamels and tapes); wax coatings (hot and cold applied and tapes), detailed in NACE RP0375[30]; prefabricated films (tapes), detailed in NACE MR0274[31]; fusion-bonded epoxy coatings (FBE), detailed in

NACE RP0394[32]; and extruded polyolefin coatings (polyethylene and polypropylene jacketed), detailed in NACE RP0185.[33] **Figures 6.26** through **6.29** show examples of some of these coatings.

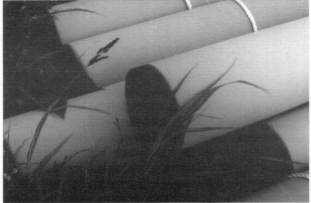

Figure 6.28 Pipeline coating—FBE coating.

Figure 6.29 Pipeline coating—Extruded polyethylene coating.

Probably the most common external pipe coatings in production operations are the extruded coatings. Typically, the system has a layer of about 250 μm (10 mil) mastic, covered and compressed by a 875 to 1,000 μm (53 to 40 mil) polyethylene or polypropylene jacket. These tough abrasive resistant coatings are used for new installations and for partial replacements when repairing leaking lines. The extruded poly coatings are used both onshore and offshore. FBE coatings are being more widely used in new construction.

Field joints are commonly coated with shrink sleeves or one of the self-adhesive tape coatings. They also may be coated with FBE with techniques using an induction heater.[34]

Field applied plastic tapes can be used with care; that is, unless the tape is properly applied with the proper tension, overlap, and mastic or adhesive, it will fail to protect the pipe. Sometimes hand (manual) wrapping will be attempted, usually with poor results, because the tension will not be constant. Manual application will be necessary for some of the materials used as protective coatings for valves, fittings, and joints (such as those covered in NACE RP0190[35]).

External pipeline coatings require the same attention to specifications for surface preparation, application and inspection as other coating services. Holiday inspection of pipeline coatings is covered in two NACE Standards: RP0274[36] (for general pipeline applications), and RP0490[37] (specifically for FBE pipeline coatings). **Figure 6.30** shows the use of a ring type holiday detector scanning a pipeline.[38]

Figure 6.30 Holiday detection—High voltage ring type holiday detector inspecting a pipeline coating. (Photograph courtesy of KTA-Tator, Inc., Pittsburgh, PA.[38])

REFERENCES

1. C. G. Munger, Corrosion Prevention by Protective Coatings (Houston, TX: NACE, 1984), p. 73.
2. C. G. Munger, Ibid, p. 66.
3. C. G. Munger, Ibid, p. 68.
4. R. J. Landrum, Fundamentals of Designing for Corrosion Control (Houston, TX: NACE, 1984), p. 317.
5. C. 125125
G. Munger, Ibid, p. 209.
6. NACE Standard RP0494-94, "Joint Surface Preparation Standard—NACE No. 1/SSPC-SP 5 White Metal Blast Cleaning" (Houston, TX: NACE, 1994), p. 1.
7. NACE Standard RP0594-94, "Joint Surface Preparation Standard—NACE No. 2/SSPC-SP 10 Near-White Metal Blast Cleaning" (Houston, TX: NACE, 1994), p. 1.
8. NACE Standard RP0694-94, "Joint Surface Preparation Standard—NACE No. 3/SSPC-SP 6 Commercial Blast Cleaning" (Houston, TX: NACE, 1994), p. 1.
9. NACE Standard RP0794-94, "Joint Surface Preparation Standard—NACE No. 4/SSPC-SP 7 Brush-Off Blast Cleaning" (Houston, TX: NACE, 1994), p. 1.
10. KTA-Tator, Inc., private communication.
11. NACE Standard RP0178-95, "Fabrication Details, Surface Finish Requirements, and Proper Design for Tanks and Vessels to be Lined for Immersion Service" (Houston, TX: NACE, 1994), Appendix C.
12. NACE Standard RP0181-94, "Liquid-Applied Internal Protective Coatings for Oilfield Production Equipment" (Houston, TX: NACE, 1994), p. 4.
13. NACE Standard RP0287 (latest edition), "Field Measurement of Surface Profile of Abrasive Blast Cleaned Steel Surfaces Using Replica Tape" (Houston, TX: NACE, 1994).
14. KTA-Tator Inc., Private communication.
15. NACE Standard RP0288 (latest edition), "Inspection of Linings on Steel and Concrete" (Houston, TX: NACE, 1994).
16. NACE Standard RP0181-94, p.5.
17. NACE Standard RP0188-90, "Discontinuity (Holiday) Testing of Protective Coatings" (Houston, TX: NACE, 1990), p.1.
18. Ibid, p. 2.
19. Ibid, p. 4.
20. NACE Standard RP0178 (latest edition), "Fabrication Details, Surface Finish Requirements, and Proper Design for Tanks and Vessels to be Lined for Immersion Service" (Houston, TX: NACE).
21. NACE Standard RP0181 (latest edition), "Liquid-Applied Internal Protective Coatings for Oilfield Production Equipment" (Houston, TX: NACE).
22. NACE Standard RP0191-96, "The Application of Internal Plastic Coatings for Oilfield Tubular Goods and Accessories" (Houston, TX: NACE, 1996), p. 1.
23. NACE Standard RP0291-96, "Care, Handling, and Installation of Internally Plastic-Coated Oilfield Tubular Goods and Accessories" (Houston, TX: NACE, 1996), p. 4.
24. NACE Standard RP0176-94, "Corrosion Control of Steel Fixed Offshore Platforms Associated with Petroleum Production" (Houston, TX: NACE, 1994), p. 1.
25. NACE Standard RP0176-94, p.16.
26. J.R. Coke, "Protective Coatings for Offshore Equipment and Structures," MP, 29, 5, (1990): p. 35–38.
27. NACE Standard RP0176-94 (latest edition).
28. NACE Standard TM0184 (latest edition), "Accelerated Test Procedures for Screening Atmospheric Surface Coating Systems for Offshore Platforms and Equipment" (Houston, TX: NACE).
29. NACE Standard RP0169-96 (latest edition), "Control of External Corrosion on Underground or Submerged Piping Systems" (Houston, TX: NACE).
30. NACE Standard RP0375 (latest edition), "Wax Coating Systems for Underground Piping Systems" (Houston, TX: NACE).
31. NACE Standard MR0274 (latest edition), "Material Requirements for Polyolefin Cold-Applied Tapes for Underground or Submerged Pipeline Coatings" (Houston, TX: NACE).
32. NACE Standard RP0394 (latest edition), "Application, Performance, and Quality Control of Plant-Applied, Fusion-Bonded Epoxy External Pipe Coating" (Houston, TX: NACE).
33. NACE Standard RP0185 (latest edition), "Extruded Polyolefin Resin Coating Systems with Soft Adhesives for Underground or Submerged Pipe" (Houston, TX: NACE).
34. D. Drake, private communication, October 1997.

35. NACE Standard RP0190 (latest edition), "External Protective Coatings for Joints, Fittings, and Valves on Metallic Underground or Submerged Pipelines and Piping Systems" (Houston, TX: NACE).

36. NACE Standard RP0274 (latest edition), "High-Voltage Electrical Inspection of Pipeline Coatings Prior to Installation" (Houston, TX: NACE).

37. NACE Standard RP0490 (latest edition), "Holiday Detection of Fusion-Bonded Epoxy External Pipeline Coatings of 250 to 760 μm (10 to 30 mils)" (Houston, TX: NACE).

38. KTA-Tator, Inc., private communication.

Appendix Reference

6B-1. ARCO Exploration and Production Technology Co., private communication, January 1997.

APPENDIX 6A

NACE INTERNATIONAL PROTECTIVE COATING STANDARDS THAT MAY BE USED IN PETROLEUM PRODUCTION FACILITIES AND LINES

NACE International issues three categories of Standards: Recommended Practice (RP), Test Method (TM) and Material Requirement (MR). In the area of protective coatings NACE and the SSPC (Society of Protective Coatings, formerly known as Steel Structures Painting Council) issue some joint standards that are published by and can be obtained from both organizations. The following list groups the standards by service categories or environments.

GENERAL—SURFACE PREPARATION

NACE No. 1/SSPC-SP 5	White Metal Blast Cleaning (RP0494-[1] **)
NACE No. 2/SSPC-SP 10	Near-White Metal Blast Cleaning (RP0594-**)
NACE No. 3/SSPC-SP 6	Commercial Blast Cleaning (RP0694-**)
NACE No. 4/SSPC-SP 7	Brush-Off Blast Cleaning (RP0794-**)
NACE No. 5/SSPC-SP 12	Surface Preparation and Cleaning of Steel and Other Hard Materials by High- and Ultrahigh-Pressure Water Jetting Prior to Recoating (RP0595-**)

GENERAL—INSPECTION

RP0287-**	Field Measurement of Surface Profile of Abrasive Blast Cleaned Steel Surfaces Using a Replica Tape
RP0188-**	Discontinuity (Holiday) Testing of Protective Coatings
RP0288-**	Inspection of Linings on Steel and Concrete

Atmospheric Service

RP0176-**	Corrosion Control of Steel Fixed Offshore Platforms Associated with Petroleum Production
RP0281-**	Method for Conducting Coating (Paint) Panel Evaluation Testing in Atmospheric Exposure
RP0487-**	Considerations in the Selection and Evaluation of Interim Petroleum-Based Coatings
TM0184-**	Accelerated Test Procedures for Screening Atmospheric Surface Coating Systems for Offshore Platforms and Equipment

---

[1] Latest edition.

Immersion Service

RP0178-**   Fabrication Details, Surface Finish Requirements, and Proper Design Considerations for Tanks and Vessels to be Lined for Immersion Service

RP0181-**   Liquid-Applied Internal Protective Coatings for Oilfield Production Equipment

RP0184-**   Repair of Lining Systems

TM0174-**   Laboratory Methods for the Evaluation of Protective Coatings and Lining Materials in Immersion Service

External Pipeline Service

RP0169-**   Control of External Corrosion on Underground or Submerged Metallic Piping Systems

RP0274-**   High-Voltage Electrical Inspection of Pipeline Coatings Prior to Installation

RP0375-**   Wax Coating Systems for Underground Piping Systems

RP0675-**   Control of External Corrosion on Offshore Steel Pipelines

RP0185-**   Extruded Polyolefin Resin Coating Systems with Soft Adhesives for Underground or Submerged Pipe

*

RP0190-**   External Protective Coatings for Joints, Fittings, and Valves on Metallic Underground or Submerged Pipelines and Piping Systems

RP0490-**   Holiday Detection of Fusion-Bonded Epoxy External Pipeline Coatings of 250 to 760 μm (10 to 30 mils)

RP0394-**   Application, Performance, and Quality Control of Plant-Applied, Fusion-Bonded Epoxy External Pipe Coating

MR0274-**   Material Requirements for Polyolefin Cold-Applied Tapes for Underground or Submerged Pipeline Coatings

*

Internal Tubing Service

RP0191-**   The Application of Internal Plastic Coatings for Oilfield Tubular Goods and Accessories

RP0291-**   Care, Handling, and Installation of Internally Plastic-Coated Oilfield Tubular Goods and Accessories

TM0183-**   Evaluation of Internal Plastic Coatings for Corrosion Control of Tubular Goods in an Aqueous Flowing Environment

TM0384-**   Holiday Detection of Internal Tubular Coatings of Less than 250 μm (10 mils) Dry Film Thickness

TM0185-**   Evaluation of Internal Plastic Coatings for Corrosion Control of Tubular Goods by Autoclave Testing

TM0186-**   Holiday Detection of Internal Tubular Coatings of 250 to 760 μm (10 to 30 mils) Dry Film Thickness

Concrete and Rebar Coating

RP0376-**   Monolithic Organic Corrosion-Resistant Floor Surface

RP0187-**   Design Considerations for Corrosion Control of Reinforcing Steel in Concrete

RP0591-**   Coatings for Concrete Surfaces in Nonimmersion and Atmospheric Services

RP0395-**   Epoxy-Coated Steel Reinforcing Bars

APPENDIX 6B

FABRICATION REQUIREMENTS FOR INTERNALLY COATED PRODUCTION VESSELS AND TANKS

The following drawings are from a specification used by an owner company to assure that a vessel, tank, or piping is "coatable" (*i.e.*, the design, materials, and surfaces are suitable for the application of coatings).[6B-1]

ACCEPTABLE	NOT ACCEPTABLE
INSIDE NO SHARP PROJECTIONS	SCABS, ROLLOVERS, LAMINATIONS, ETC. MUST BE CORRECTED
PLATE DEFECTS	
ROUND BOTTOM	VEE BOTTOM
LAYOUT MARKS	
PITS OPENED, ROUNDED BOTTOM	CANNOT CLEAN OR COAT PITS
PITTING	

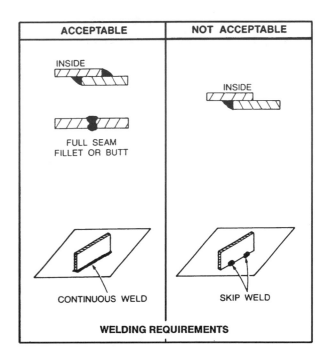

WELDING REQUIREMENTS

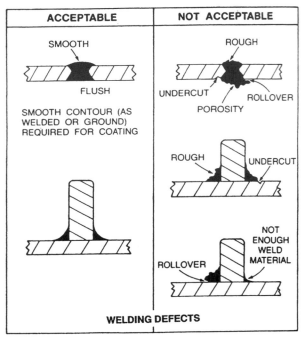

WELDING DEFECTS

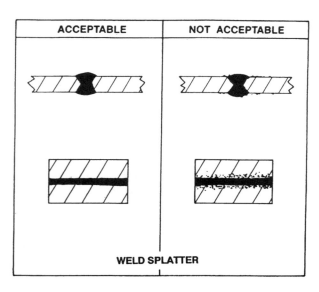

WELD SPLATTER

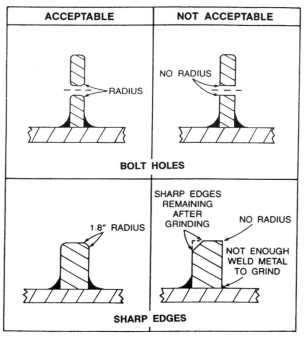

BOLT HOLES

SHARP EDGES

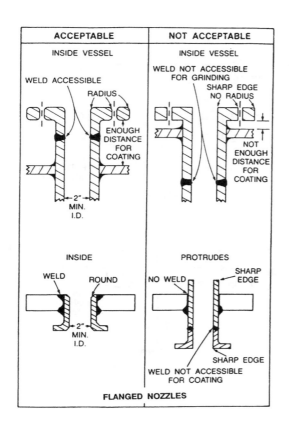

FLANGED NOZZLES

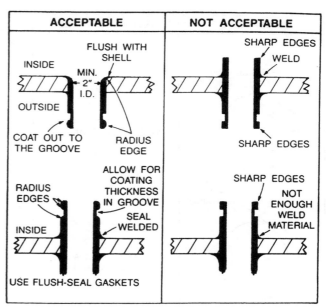

VICTAULIC CONNECTIONS

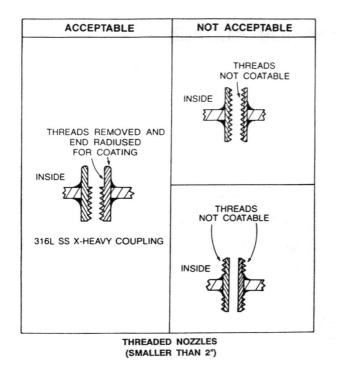

**THREADED NOZZLES
(SMALLER THAN 2")**

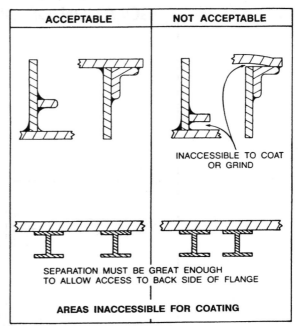

AREAS INACCESSIBLE FOR COATING

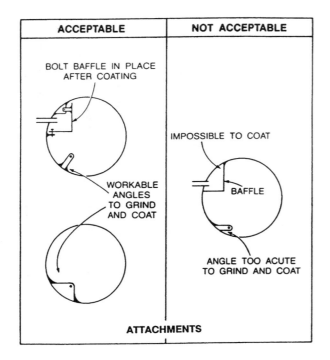

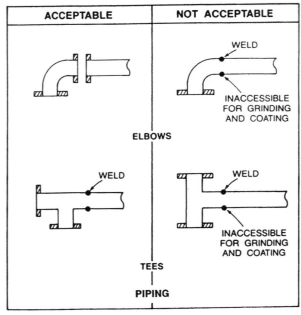

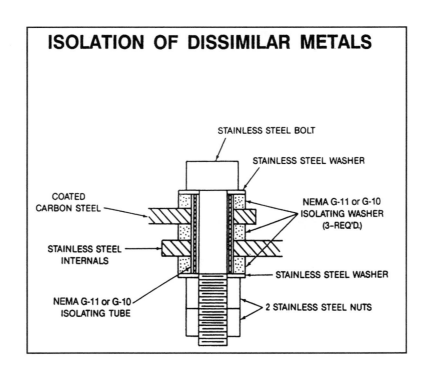

ISOLATION OF DISSIMILAR METALS

APPENDIX 6C

COATING SPECIFICATION INTERNAL TANK COATING— APPLICATION OF THIN FILM COATINGS

Appendix 6C shows a reproduction of a generic specification used by an owner company as part of their coating contracts.

Note:

- The header "Section" is blank so that the appropriate section in a contract may be listed.
- The owner company's name has been removed.
- The coating vendor's name in the tables have been replaced with letter deisgnations.
- The specification begins with page 45, becasue the first 44 pages involve standard contractual information.
- The trade names have been removed.

This specification is included to serve as a model and to show the detail required for a comprehensive coating specification. The items that are covered are listed in the Specification Table of Contents.

TABLE OF CONTENTS

Section	Subject
	INTERNAL TANK COATING— APPLICATION OF THIN FILM COATINGS

REVISION RECORD				APPROVAL SIGNATURES	
Rev	Date	Status	Remarks	Initiator	Approval
A	06/06/96	Draft			

Section	Subject **INTERNAL TANK COATING— APPLICATION OF THIN FILM COATINGS**

1.0—SCOPE

1.1 This specification covers the surface preparation, coating application, and coating inspection requirements for the internal lining of steel tanks with epoxy or epoxy phenolic coating for immersion service.

1.2 The term "tank" used in this document shall be taken to mean any steel tank, vessel, storage container, or other equipment intended for immersion service.

1.3 "Owner" as used in this specification means Owner Company and its affiliates. "Contractor" means a company or individual under contract to perform specific work or services for Owner.

1.4 In case of conflict between this specification, the inquiry or purchase order, the accompanying data sheets and drawings, and any other supplemental specifications, the Contractor shall notify OWNER for resolution.

2.0—CODES AND STANDARDS REQUIREMENTS

2.1 Except as amended by this specification, the latest approved editions of the following codes and standards shall form an integral part of this specification.

- NACE International, RP0178: "Recommended Practice for Fabrication Details, Surface Finish Requirements, and Proper Design Considerations for Tanks and Vessels to be Lined for Immersion Service"
- NACE International, RP0188: "Recommended Practice for Discontinuity (Holiday) Testing of Protective Coatings," Section 3.0—Low Voltage Wet Sponge Testing
- Steel Structures Painting Council, SSPC - SP 1: "Solvent Cleaning"
- Steel Structures Painting Council, SSPC - SP 5: "White Blast Cleaning"
- Steel Structures and Painting Council, SSPC - VIS 1: "Visual Standard for Abrasive Blast Cleaned Steel"

2.2 In case of conflict between documents, contact OWNER for resolution.

3.0—REFERENCED SPECIFICATIONS

See Attachments

Section	Subject
	INTERNAL TANK COATING— APPLICATION OF THIN FILM COATINGS

4.0—GENERAL REQUIREMENTS

4.1 The Contractor shall furnish all labor, materials, and equipment necessary for the cleaning, blasting, coating, curing, and inspection of surfaces to be coated.

4.2 It is the responsibility of the Contractor to meet the requirements of this specification, to use equipment capable of meeting these requirements, and to perform all inspections necessary to insure compliance.

4.3 In addition to the Contractor's inspections, OWNER or Owner's designated representative(s) may perform any inspection to verify compliance with this specification. Inspection may include any and all work, equipment, inspection equipment, materials or procedures and may be conducted at any time OWNER chooses.

4.4 The Contractor shall correct any work which OWNER has determined not to comply with the requirements of this specification. Corrections shall be made without additional cost to OWNER.

4.5 It is the responsibility of the Contractor to perform all work in a manner consistent with all applicable health and safety regulations.

4.6 The Contractor shall notify OWNER at least three weeks prior to beginning the coating job. A pre-job meeting shall be held. Representatives of the Contractor, OWNER, and the coating manufacturer shall be present.

4.7 The failure of OWNER or OWNER's representative to discover or reject defective work or materials does not constitute acceptance of such work or materials by OWNER.

4.8 The Contractor must have a proven procedure to document and maintain accurate records. Records must be kept on all aspects of the coating job including the results of all quality control testing outlined in Section 8.0. These records shall be made available for audit at OWNER's request. Contractor must submit copies of inspection forms to OWNER for approval prior to beginning job.

4.9 The area of the tank to be internally coated will be defined on the purchase order, data sheet, or accompanying specification. Contact OWNER if you have any questions concerning the scope of work.

Section	Subject **INTERNAL TANK COATING— APPLICATION OF THIN FILM COATINGS**

5.0—MATERIALS

5.1   Tank

      5.1.1   All tanks must be designed and fabricated in accordance with OWNER specifications. The surface area intended for internal lining must also conform to NACE RP0178 requirements.

      5.1.2   Contractor shall inspect the surface to be coated and confirm that it meets NACE RP0178. Notify OWNER prior to beginning the job if the surface does not conform to NACE RP0178 or if any other problems exist. OWNER may require grinding, or other repair, if the surface condition is inadequate.

5.2   Coating

      5.2.1   Coating material shall be as specified by OWNER from those coating systems listed in Appendix B. The service chart given in Appendix C is provided as a reference to OWNER. Substitution of materials by the Contractor is not permitted. All thinners, catalyzing agents, and other additives shall be as specified by the coating manufacturer for use with the specified coating system. Use of special curing accelerators is not allowed.

      5.2.2   Approved caulking materials are also included in the list of coating materials given in Appendix B. Caulking material shall only be used when specifically directed by OWNER.

      5.2.3   The Contractor shall supply all coating materials, catalysts, and thinners unless other arrangements have been made and approved by OWNER.

      5.2.4   Store coating materials in their original containers with their original labels visible and readable. Storage conditions shall be as specified by the manufacturer's data sheet. Use each material within its shelf life as defined by the manufacturer.

      5.2.5   Do not use coatings which have exceeded their shelf life or which have deteriorated in storage. Deterioration is indicated by formation of a surface skin, by gelling, or by settling of solids which cannot be mixed into a smooth consistency.

      5.2.6   Contractor shall obtain copies of the manufacturer's product data sheet and MSDS for each product. This information must be available at the job site.

5.3   Abrasive Materials

      5.3.1   Abrasive shall be either sharp steel grit, a mixture of steel grit and steel shot, coal slag, garnet, or aluminum oxide and meet the following requirements:

          • contain less than 1% free silica.

          • be free of harmful quantities of toxic metals.

          • contain less than 125 ppm water soluble chlorides.

APPENDIX 6C

Section	Subject **INTERNAL TANK COATING— APPLICATION OF THIN FILM COATINGS**

- contain less than 200 ppm water soluble sulfates.

- be free of clay, limestone, shells, undersize and oversize particles, organic material and other detrimental foreign material.

Contractor must obtain certification from the abrasive supplier that the abrasive meets the above requirements. A copy of the certification shall be submitted to OWNER prior to abrasive blasting.

5.3.2 No substitution of blasting media shall be made without written approval of OWNER.

5.3.3 The abrasive must be of proper size to achieve the cleanliness and anchor profile requirements of this specification.

5.3.4 Reclamation and reuse of blast media shall not compromise surface cleanliness or surface profile as required in this specification.

5.3.5 Surfaces which are abrasive blasted using a non-approved abrasive shall be re-blasted with the proper abrasive at no additional cost to OWNER.

5.3.6 "Wet or Dry" type abrasive paper must be used where hand sanding (abrading) is required. Abrasive paper must not leave a residue.

6.0—SURFACE PREPARATION

6.1 Contractor shall provide sufficient lighting to permit the blast operators to see their work and to permit thorough and accurate inspection of blasted surfaces.

6.2 Contractor shall visually inspect surface to insure it meets requirements of Section 5.1. Contractor shall remove all weld slag, weld spatter, and smooth rough surfaces as needed in the area to be coated. This requirement includes original construction as well as any subsequent repairs.

6.3 Before abrasive blasting, all surfaces to be coated shall be cleaned in accordance with SSPC SP-1 to remove all oil, grease, cutting oils, dirt and other contaminants. The extent of cleaning shall include the area intended for coating plus a minimum of 1 ft. (300 mm) beyond this area. Cleaning may include solvent cleaning or steam cleaning with detergent. Steam cleaning with detergent must be followed by fresh water steam or wash to remove all traces of detergent residue.

6.4 After the tank has been cleaned, no contamination is permitted. All people entering the tank shall wear gloves, sweat bands, and clean gum-soled shoes or over-boots. Street shoes are not permitted. Footwear worn during painting must not cause contamination of the tank surface and must not be affected by the coating solvents. A clean area shall be provided at the tank entry. Footwear worn in the tank shall be stored in the clean area when not in use. There shall be no eating, drinking or smoking in the tank or in the clean area.

Section	Subject
	INTERNAL TANK COATING— APPLICATION OF THIN FILM COATINGS

6.5 The area to be coated shall be cleaned according to SSPC SP-5 using dry abrasive blasting. The extent of blasting shall include the area intended for coating plus a minimum of 6 in. (155 mm) beyond this area. The anchor profile must be as listed in Appendix B. Verify profile using (May specify manufacturer and brand by name) replica tape, follow manufacturer's instructions. Verify cleanliness using SSPC VIS-1.

6.6 Air used in abrasive blasting must be free of oil and water as determined by a blotter test performed at least daily. Perform blotter test according to Section 8.7.3.

6.7 Use only venturi type carbide blast nozzles 3/8 in. or 7/16 in. long (9.5 or 11 mm). Air pressure must be 85–100 psi (5.9–6.9 bar) at the blast nozzle. All other blasting equipment must be sized to maintain this pressure at the blast nozzle.

6.8 Blast abrasive shall be as specified in Section 5.3.

6.9 The temperature of the steel must at least than 5°F (3°C) warmer than the dew point of the air during blasting. Condensation shall not be permitted at any time during the blasting process or during the time between blasting and the application of the first coat. Blasted surfaces shall not be exposed to rain or weather.

6.10 All surfaces to be coated shall receive full surface preparation. This includes the interior surface of the tank, nozzle bores, clips, internal piping, and attachments. Nozzle bores must be blasted through the internal bore and up around the flange face as shown in Appendix B.

6.11 Stainless or other corrosion-resistant alloy items connected to the tank shall also be prepared for coating if they are within the area of the tank designated to be coated. Stainless Steel items that are electrically isolated from the tank shall be excluded from this requirement.

6.12 Remove all visible blasting residue from the surface to be coated using, as appropriate, shovels, brooms, soft brushes, and vacuum cleaners.

6.13 If additional defects such as slivers and laminations are discovered in the surface to be coated after abrasive blasting, grind smooth with an oil-free grinder. Alternatively, the repair of these newly discovered defects may be delayed until after application of the first coat. However, after the first coat is dry, these defects must be ground out using an oil-free grinder and the coating must be repaired prior to the second coat according to Section 7.9.6, Steps 1–5.

Section	Subject
	INTERNAL TANK COATING—
	APPLICATION OF THIN FILM COATINGS

7.0—COATING APPLICATION

7.1 Coating materials shall be applied to properly prepared surfaces before any sign of oxidation is visible. The surface to be coated must meet the requirements of SSPC-SP 5 just prior to coating application, see Section 6.0.

7.2 Contractor must provide adequate and safe ventilation of the work area.

7.3 Mix coating materials by first mixing each component to break up all solids and to produce a smooth uniform liquid. After each component is fully mixed, combine components and thinners as specified on the manufacturer's data sheet and blend thoroughly. Use only air driven or explosion proof electric power mixers. Mixing will comply with the manufacturer's data sheet unless specific alternate written instructions have been provided by OWNER. Do not split kits. Mixing of partial kits is not allowed.

7.4 Do not apply coatings when the air temperature, steel temperature or relative humidity is outside the range permitted on the manufacturer's data sheet. Do not apply coating unless the steel is at least 5°F (3°C) warmer than the dew point of the air. Do not apply coating if dew point is near this limit and falling. The surface temperature must be maintained at least 5°F (3°C) above the dew point during application, drying, and curing of the coating.

7.5 Do not apply coatings if the surface will be rained on or will collect condensation before the coatings can properly cure. OWNER may stop coating application when weather conditions may cause damage to the coatings.

7.6 Extent of Coating

The area to be coated shall be defined by OWNER prior to the job as explained in paragraph 4.10. Within the defined area to be coated, the following shall apply:

7.6.1 Coat all internal surfaces, nozzle bores, flange gasket sealing surfaces, bolts, bolt holes, and carbon steel internals unless otherwise specified. Bolt holes need not be holiday free.

7.6.2 Completely coat all stainless steel nozzles, clips, flanges, or other items connected to the tank and extending inside the tank. Exceptions to this requirement include items outside the area to be coated and items electrically isolated from the tank. (Note: Coated carbon steel nozzles, clips, flanges, etc. are desirable. When possible, attach stainless steel internals by bolting and electrically isolate them from the tank.)

7.6.3 Coat all threaded stainless steel connections welded to the tank up to the threads. Use of any stainless steel or threaded connection must be approved by OWNER prior to installation.

7.6.4 Stainless steel internals that are electrically isolated and bolted to the tank need not be coated.

7.6.5   Internally coat nozzles that are welded to tanks and extend outside the tank. Coating shall include the internal nozzle bore a portion of the connected flange face as shown in Appendix A. Note that coating of seal surface of raised face flange depends on service and pressure.

7.6.6   All areas not coated, such as threads and metal-to-metal seal areas, shall be protected from blasting and from buildup of coating or coating over-spray.

7.6.7   If in doubt about what surfaces are to be coated, Contractor shall contact OWNER for clarification.

7.7   Application Equipment

7.7.1   Coatings may be applied with either conventional or airless spray equipment. Application equipment must be according to the coating manufacturers recommendations.

7.7.2   A 360° spray nozzle on a lance must be used to internally coat all tank nozzles that are from 3 in. (76 mm) up to 16 in. (400 mm) in diameter when the nozzle length exceeds 0.5 times the diameter. A 360° spray nozzle on a lance must also be used on nozzles larger than 16" (400 mm) diameter if the length of the nozzle exceeds 1.0 time the diameter. Brushing and/or swabbing is allowed for nozzles 3 in. (76 mm) and smaller when necessary to obtain a quality application within specified thickness limits. Use only high quality brushes and materials that will not leave debris in the coating film.

7.8   Caulking

Caulking materials shall be used only when specifically required by OWNER. When required, apply caulk as follows:

Step 1:   Abrasive blast areas to be caulked per Section 6.0 to a SSPC-SP 5 cleanliness.

Step 2:   Apply caulk to rivets, seams, and elsewhere as directed by OWNER in accordance with the manufacturer's instructions.

Step 3:   After it has hardened, roughen the caulk with abrasive paper or sweep blast prior to application of the first coat of the coating system. Contractor may choose to perform this sweep blast while abrasive blasting the remaining area."

7.9   Coating Application Procedure

7.9.1   Prior to coating application, all surfaces must be prepared according to Section 6.0 of this specification.

7.9.2   Inspect the surface to verify that the cleanliness satisfies SSPC SP-5. Areas found not to comply must be re-cleaned per Section 6.0.

7.9.3   First Coat

Step 1:   Brush apply a thin coat of the specified coating material to all welds, corners, edges, rough areas, and attachments. Thin using one part coating to three parts of the appropriate thinner. Stir frequently to prevent settling.

Step 2:   Using multiple crossing passes (or multiple lance passes in nozzles), apply a coat of the specified material to all surfaces to be coated. Thin only as needed and as recommended by the coating manufacturer. Dry film thickness (DFT) shall be as specified in Appendix B.

Step 3:   Air dry the first coat as specified in the "Time Between Coats" column of Appendix B. Appendix B provides the minimum time, or time range, required at corresponding temperatures for drying between coats. The entire coated surface of the tank must comply with the time and temperature limits listed. Where a temperature range is not provided, maximum time between coats shall not exceed manufacturer's recommendations.

Maintain continuous air flow through the tank to prevent settling of solvent vapors. The minimum time/temperature information in Appendix B is based on adequate ventilation. If ventilation is not adequate, drying may take longer than the minimum listed. In all cases, do not proceed to Step 4 until the coating is hard enough to walk on without damaging it.

Step 4:   Check the dry film thickness throughout the tank as specified in Section 8.7.6. Areas found to be in excess of the specified range shall be hand sanded to conform to the specified thickness. Use 200-400 grit "wet or dry" type abrasive paper.

Step 5:   Check the coating for blisters, runs, sags, and dry over-spray. Also inspect for trash, sand, or any other foreign material. Areas containing these shall be hand sanded to remove the defects and/or to loosen the debris. Use caution to avoid exposing bare steel on welds, clips, and other irregular surfaces.

Step 6:   Remove all sanding residue and debris by wiping, brushing, or vacuuming as needed.

7.9.4 Second Coat

Step 1: After all sanding residue and debris have been removed from the tank, repeat Steps 2 and 3 in Section 7.9.3.

Step 2: After the material has air dried as specified in Appendix B, check all of the coated surfaces for blisters, runs, sags, and over-spray and trash, sand, or other foreign material. Coating containing such defects shall be repaired as directed in Step 3b below.

Step 3: Check the dry film thickness throughout the tank as described in Section 8.7.6. All coating not in compliance as defined in Section 8.7.6 shall be corrected prior to final cure.

a) Any area with coating less than the specified minimum thickness shall be corrected by applying additional material according to this specification.

b) Any area with coating in excess of the specified maximum thickness and any area containing blisters, runs, sags, or any foreign material shall be corrected as follows:

1. Sand areas down by hand using 120–180 grit wet or dry abrasive paper. The coating thickness after sanding shall be at least 1 mil (25 μm) below the acceptable maximum (and greater than the acceptable minimum).

2. Remove all sanding residue and debris by wiping, brushing, or vacuuming as needed.

3. Brush apply a thin coat of the specified coating to the sanded areas. The coating shall be thinned using one part coating to three parts thinner. Brush application is preferred, but spray application may be used on very large areas.

7.9.5 Holiday Inspection

After all coating in the tank has dried, and all thickness corrections have been made, perform a complete holiday inspection of all coated surfaces according to Section 8.7.8. All holidays found after the second coat (except those in bolt holes) shall be repaired according to Section 7.9.6 before final cure.

7.9.6 Coating Repair

Repair all holidays and coating damage using the following procedure:

Step 1: For pinpoint holidays, use a ¹/₈ inch diameter grinding device to crater the holiday down to bare metal. The grinding stone shall roughen the steel and feather into the surrounding coating. For larger repairs use

(Specific name) stone or equivalent to prepare the surface. Surface must meet original cleanliness and anchor profile requirements. Feather at least 1" into existing sound coating in all directions.

Step 2: Remove all grinding residue and debris by wiping, brushing, or vacuuming as needed.

Step 3: Apply a coat of the specified coating to the prepared area using conventional air spray, roller, or brush based on size and location of repair. A small artist brush shall be used on pinpoint holidays. Over-lap feathered area around repair. Thin coating only as needed and according to manufacturer's recommendations.

Step 4: Air dry as specified in Appendix B. Correct excess thickness and slightly roughen the repair areas by carefully hand sanding the repair area using 200-400 grit "wet or dry" type abrasive paper. Use caution to avoid exposing bare steel on welds, clips, and other irregular surfaces.

Step 5: Remove all sanding residue and debris by wiping, brushing, or vacuuming as needed.

Step 6: Apply a second coat of the specified coating to the repair area using brush, roller, or spray as mentioned in Step 3 above. Again, thin coating only as needed and according to manufacturer's recommendations. The coating thickness of the repair area must comply with Section 8.7.6. Multiple coats may be applied to achieve the specified thickness.

Step 7: Air dry as specified in Appendix B.

Step 8: Repeat holiday inspection according to Paragraph 7.95. and Section 8.7.8.

7.10   Curing

7.10.1 Air Cure

Cure the coating as specified in the "Final Cure" column of Appendix B. Continuous air flow through the tank shall be maintained to prevent settling of solvent vapors. Appendix B specifies the minimum time required at corresponding temperature for curing. The temperature used for table reference shall be the lowest measured on the tank wall in the coated area. The temperature shall not exceed the maximum or fall below the minimum given in Appendix B for the coating specified.

7.10.2 Force Cure

7.10.2.1 Force curing, if required, shall be performed by raising the metal temperature at a maximum rate of 40°F (22°C) per hour to the

Section	Subject
	INTERNAL TANK COATING—
	APPLICATION OF THIN FILM COATINGS

temperature shown in Appendix B. The cure temperature shall be maintained for the time specified in Appendix B.

7.10.2.2 Force curing shall not begin until after the last coating applied in the tank has experienced the minimum time / temperature requirements for between coats given in Appendix B. Continuous air flow through the tank shall be maintained throughout the curing process to prevent settling of solvent vapors.

7.10.2.3 The coating may be force cured by installation of external insulation and introduction of heated air. Adequate air movement shall be provided in order to minimize temperature variation, maximize ventilation of the solvents, and avoid dead air space in the tank. The specific procedures using this method shall be approved in advance by OWNER.

7.10.2.4 All fuels used shall be clean gas (natural gas, propane, or butane). Complete combustion shall be ensured to prevent sooty deposits.

7.10.2.5 After the material has been force cured, all coated surfaces shall be inspected for blisters. Blistered coating will be rejected. The coating in these areas must be totally removed and re-coated according to this specification.

7.11 Coating damage occurring after the final cure either as a result of mechanical damage, welding repair, anode installation, or other cause must be repaired by the Contractor. The repair shall be according to Section 7.9.6. Coating surrounding the repair must be feathered and roughened to promote adhesion.

8.0—QUALITY CONTROL AND INSPECTION

8.1 The Contractor is responsible for the quality of all work performed and for assuring compliance with these specifications. Contractor is responsible to stop operations and promptly notify OWNER when conditions develop which could adversely affect the quality of the completed work.

8.2 OWNER may inspect any work, equipment, material storage or any other aspect of the project. OWNER's inspectors shall have safe access to all work and storage areas.

8.3 The Contractor is to provide all inspection and calibration equipment needed to perform the quality control and testing functions outlined in this specification. The equipment needed shall include, but not be limited to the following:

- Surface Sensing Thermometer
- Sling Psychrometer with Psychrometric Tables
- Materials to Perform Blotter Test per Paragraph 8.7.3

Section	Subject
	INTERNAL TANK COATING— APPLICATION OF THIN FILM COATINGS

- Surface Cleanliness Comparators, SSPC-VIS 1
- Replica Tape and Spring Micrometer
- Surface Profile Comparator
- Wet Film Thickness (WFT) Gauge
- Dry Film Thickness (DFT) Gauge
- National Institute of Standards and Technology (NIST) Certified Coating Thickness Calibration Standards for Non magnetic Coating on Steel.
- Wet Sponge Holiday Detector

Specific information on the above items and their use is given in Section 8.7. In all cases equipment shall be as specified or approved equivalent.

8.4   The Contractor must record the results of all quality control checks and testing, including but not limited to those listed in Section 8.7. Contractor must submit sample copies of inspection forms to OWNER for approval prior to beginning job. Records shall include the identification of the tank and any physical inspection results, such as replica tape, etc. An example set of acceptable inspection forms are attached as Appendix D

8.5   The quality control inspections and tests specified in this Section 8.0 are considered to be a minimum. Further testing may be required to follow-up when inspection results are not acceptable or when other problems arise.

8.6   Work not meeting the material or quality requirements of this specification, as determined by OWNER, must be repaired or redone at Contractor's expense.

8.7   Required Inspections

Contractor shall perform the inspections listed below and record the results on the inspection forms. OWNER representative will confirm results.

8.7.1   Coatability

All surfaces to be coated shall be inspected for coatability prior to blasting and coating. All defects shall be corrected before proceeding with the coating application.

8.7.2   Ambient Conditions

The steel surface temperature, ambient air temperature, humidity, and dew point shall be checked and recorded at least every 8 hours during all blasting, coating, drying, and curing procedures. Steel temperature must be monitored continuously and recorded during forced curing. Readings must comply with this specification at all times.

Measure air temperature, relative humidity, and dew point with any suitable sling psychrometer and corresponding psychometric tables, or approved meter.

Measure steel temperature with any suitable surface sensing thermometer such as (Brand and model number) or other approved meter and recording device if required.

8.7.3   Compressed Air Supply

Perform a blotter test by directing a strong stream of compressed air at a clean white absorbent material and at a smooth plastic or metal surface. No oil, water or discoloration is to be visible in either case. Test the air at a point downstream of oil traps and dryers. This test must be performed at least daily and more often if deemed necessary.

8.7.4   Surface Cleanliness

Inspect the surface cleanliness after blasting and prior to coating application using visual comparators according to SSPC-VIS 1. The surface must meet the requirements of SSPC-SP 5, White Metal Cleanliness.

8.7.5   Surface Profile

The surface profile of blasted surfaces shall be inspected prior to the application of the coating using replica tape. Use according to the manufacturer's instructions. The profile depth must be as specified in Appendix B. The density of the blast peaks and valleys and the appearance of the blasted surface must be comparable to that of the Surface Profile Comparator. Report results and attach replica tape to inspection report.

8.7.6   Dry Film Thickness

Determination of dry film thickness (DFT) shall be based on a sufficient number of spot measurements needed to verify compliance with the requirements listed in Appendix B. OWNER reserves the right to make as many measurements as needed to determine compliance. As a minimum, one spot measurement per 20 ft^2 (2 m^2) is required to assure compliance.

A spot measurement is defined as the average of three gauge readings taken in close proximity. The gauge readings must be no closer than 0.5 in. (12 mm) and no further apart than 3 in. (75 mm). Each gauge reading shall be at least 80% of the specified minimum thickness and less than 120% of the specified maximum. The average of the three gauge readings constitutes a spot measurement. The spot measurement must fall within the specified DFT range given in Appendix B.

Thickness measurements must be made with a magnetic type dry film thickness gauge for ferrous substrates such as (list acceptable instruments), or other as approved by OWNER. The gauge must be calibrated according to the gauge manufacturer's instructions using the National Institute of Standards and Technology (NIST) Certified Coating Thickness Calibration Standards for Non magnetic Coating on Steel.

Calibrate gauge before and after each use as a minimum. If calibration has drifted, contractor must repeat measurements until data agrees with previous measurements.

8.7.7   Coating Integrity

The coating shall be examined for blisters, runs, sags, dry spray, and foreign material after the last coat has dried and before it has cured. No coating containing blisters, runs, sags, dry spray, or foreign material shall be accepted.

8.7.8   Holiday Inspection

Conduct holiday inspection of the entire coated area after the final coat has dried and before the coating is cured. Use the Low Voltage Wet Sponge technique specified in NACE RP0188. All coated surfaces except bolt holes shall be 100% holiday free.

Use a (Brand and Model No.) wet-sponge holiday detector or equivalent. The exploring probe shall consist of a cellulose sponge, approximately 2 in. x 2 in. x 6 in. (50 mm x 50 mm x 150 mm). Dampen the sponge using a solution of tap water with 1 oz. / gal. (7.8 ml / L) of (Brand name) wetting agent, or approved equivalent. The detector shall have a voltage of 67.5 volts with a sensitivity of 80,000 ohms. A resistance of 80,000 ohms or less in the external circuit shall actuate the signal device. Calibrate as described in NACE RP0188.

8.7.9   General Cleanliness Inspection

A cleanliness inspection shall be performed prior to each application of coating and prior to final cure to ensure that the tank is free of all visible foreign materials. All tape, polyethylene floor covering, padding, masking material, etc., must be removed prior to beginning the final cure.

8.8   Inspection Hold Points

The following is a list of inspection hold points. Contractor must cease operations on a particular structure at these hold points and obtain the approval of the on-site OWNER representative before proceeding. The inspection hold points are:

- Verification of surface cleaning before abrasive blasting
- Verification of cleanliness after abrasive blasting and prior to any coating application
- Verification of coating quality and thickness after each coat of material prior to application of additional coats.

At the hold points listed above the OWNER representative will confirm that the Contractor has made the proper inspection and that the results of that inspection conform with this specification. The existence of these hold points do not release the

Contractor from conducting the necessary inspections. Other required hold points may be determined later at OWNER's discretion.

8.9 Cleanliness

8.9.1 Personnel

After the tank to be coated has been cleaned to remove oil and grease, no person shall enter the tank or touch the surfaces to be coated unless wearing the following protective clothing:

- Clean gum-soled shoes, over-boots, or tennis shoes.
- Clean overalls.
- Clean head covering, including sweatband.
- Clean gloves.

Protective clothing shall be replaced when soiled or wet. Protective clothing that is to be worn inside the tank, including shoes, shall not be worn outside the tank. Clothing must be put on and removed in the immediate area of the tank entrance. That area shall be kept free of abrasives and other debris that may be tracked into the tank.

8.9.2 Cleanliness of Equipment

a) No equipment, including blasting hoses, coating hoses, scaffolding, etc., shall be taken into tanks without being cleaned thoroughly. Do not drag equipment across coated surfaces.

b) All spray equipment, including guns, hoses, pots, etc., shall be cleaned thoroughly after each use and between work shifts. Before applying any coating, the spray equipment shall be flushed with the thinner specified for use with that coating. Contamination of any coating with another coating, with an improper thinner, or with residues in the spray equipment is not permissible.

c) Brushes used to apply thinned coating or to make repairs must be new or thoroughly cleaned with the thinner specified for use with that coating. Contamination of the brushes with any other coating, with an improper thinner, or with dirt or sanding residue is not permissible.

d) Brushes used to remove grinding and sanding residue shall have soft bristles and must be cleaned before each use. They must not be contaminated with any foreign material that may be left on the surface to be coated or that may scratch the surface.

Section	Subject
	INTERNAL TANK COATING— APPLICATION OF THIN FILM COATINGS

9.0–SAFETY AND ENVIRONMENTAL

9.1　It is the responsibility of the Contractor and any sub-contractors to perform all work in a manner consistent with all applicable health and safety regulations. The omission of any applicable safety regulation in this specification does not relieve the Contractor or any subcontractors of the responsibility of compliance.

The Contractor must have copies of all applicable regulations governing the work procedures available to all workers and subcontractors at the work site.

9.2　The Contractor must provide safe access to the surfaces to be cleaned, blasted, coated, or inspected. All scaffolding, rigging, ladders, etc. must comply with all applicable regulations. Scaffolding and rigging shall provide easy and safe access to all surfaces for surface preparation, coating application and inspection.

9.3　Abrasive Blasting

9.3.1　All blasting equipment must comply with all applicable regulations. All blast nozzles must be equipped with a "deadman" automatic shutoff device. Blasting hoses, air movers and other equipment must be grounded to dissipate static charges.

9.3.2　Tank must be properly vented during blasting operations to increase visibility and create a safe working environment.

9.3.3　Lighting inside the tank shall provide adequate visibility for the blasting process and safe movement inside the tank. Lighting must meet all applicable safety codes.

9.3.4　All personal protective clothing and equipment must comply with all applicable safety regulations and must function properly during use.

9.3.5　All spent abrasive, empty abrasive bags, etc. shall be disposed of in a manner consistent with all applicable safety regulations. The work area must be kept free of debris to permit safe access.

9.4　Coating Application

9.4.1　All coating application equipment must comply with all applicable safety regulations. Lighting and wiring inside the tank must meet applicable codes and provide adequate visibility for the coating process and for safe movement inside the tank.

9.4.2　All spray equipment must be grounded to prevent accumulation of static charges.

9.4.3　All sources of ignition such as fire, internal combustion engines, welding, and persons smoking shall be kept at a safe distance from the work area during all coating application and drying.

9.4.4 Continuous air movement shall be maintained throughout the tank during coating application, drying, and curing. The ventilation system shall be explosion proof and shall provide sufficient air movement to keep the work atmosphere 20% of the Lower Explosive Limit (LEL) at all times. The air shall be vented in compliance with all applicable safety regulations.

Use air driven fans or venturi type eductors to pull vapors out of the tank. Solvent vapors collect in low areas; design ventilation to move air through such spaces. Position fans to draw contaminated air out of the tank and allow fresh air to flow in to replace it.

9.4.5 All personal protective clothing and equipment must comply with all applicable safety regulations and must function properly during use. Positive pressure helmets or suitable vapor masks must be worn by every person working inside the tank during coating application. Every person entering the tank during coating application or drying shall wear all required masks, respirators, goggles, gloves and protective clothing. Every person entering the tank after drying or curing must wear clean gum soled shoes to prevent slipping.

9.5 Waste Disposal

9.5.1 All unused mixed materials and all waste materials and spillage shall be immediately disposed of in a manner consistent with all applicable safety and waste disposal regulations.

9.5.2 All cans that contained coating materials or thinners, or that were used for mixing materials, must be disposed of properly in accordance with all applicable safety and environmental regulations. In addition, all rags and other items contaminated with coating materials or thinners must be disposed of in a similar manner.

Section	Subject
	INTERNAL TANK COATING— APPLICATION OF THIN FILM COATINGS

APPENDIX A—COATING OF NOZZLES OR FLANGES

The extent of surface preparation and internal coating application for tank nozzles is shown below. Plain, raised face, and ring-joint type flanges are included.)

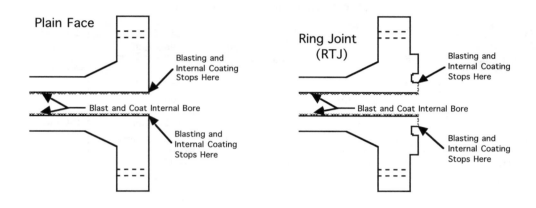

Plain Face

Blasting and Internal Coating Stops Here

Blast and Coat Internal Bore

Blasting and Internal Coating Stops Here

Ring Joint (RTJ)

Blasting and Internal Coating Stops Here

Blast and Coat Internal Bore

Blasting and Internal Coating Stops Here

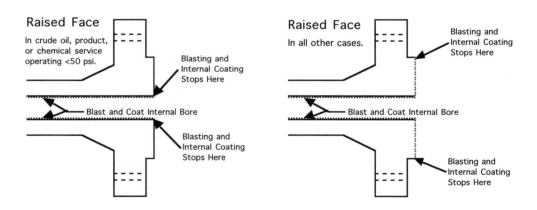

Raised Face

In crude oil, product, or chemical service operating <50 psi.

Blasting and Internal Coating Stops Here

Blast and Coat Internal Bore

Blasting and Internal Coating Stops Here

Raised Face

In all other cases.

Blasting and Internal Coating Stops Here

Blast and Coat Internal Bore

Blasting and Internal Coating Stops Here

Section	Subject INTERNAL TANK COATING— APPLICATION OF THIN FILM COATINGS

APPENDIX B—APPROVED COATING SYSTEMS

The following two tables provide application, drying, and curing requirements for each internal coating system. In each case, the coating product listed is applied direct to metal in at least two coats. Contact OWNER to determine which of the coatings below are acceptable for a specific job.

TABLE 1: Application requirements

Coating Product	Anchor Profile	Dry Film Thickness per Coat	Total Dry Film Thickness	Compatible Caulking Material[1]
Company A (Coal Tar Epoxy)	2–4 mils (51–102 μm)	8–10 mils (203–254 μm)	16–20 mils (406–508 μm)	A-Caulk
Company C (Coal Tar Epoxy)	2–3 mils (51–76 μm)	8–10 mils (203–254 μm)	16–20 mils (406–508 μm)	C-Caulk
Company C (Epoxy-Phenolic)	2–3 mils (51–76 μm)	4–6 mils (102–152 μm)	8–12 mils (406–508 μm)	C-Caulk
Company C (Glass Flake Epoxy Novalac)	2–3 mils (51–76 μm)	8–10 mils (203–254 μm)	16–20 mils (406–508 μm)	C-Caulk
Company D (Epoxy-Phenolic)	2–3 mils (51–76 μm)	5–6 mils (127–152 μm)	10–12 mils (254–305 μm)	D-Caulk
Company I (Coal Tar Epoxy)	2–4 mils (51–102 μm)	8–10 mils (203–254 μm)	16–20 mils (406–508 μm)	I-Caulk
Company S (Epoxy-Phenolic)	2–3 mils (51–76 μm)	5–7 mils (127–178 μm)	10–14 mils (254–356 μm)	N/A
Company P (Epoxy-Phenolic)	2–3 mils (51–76 μm)	5–6 mils (127–152 μm)	10–12 mils (254–305 μm)	P-Caulk

Notes:

1. Caulking material shall only be used when directed by OWNER. The caulking materials listed are high solids epoxy caulks intended for immersion service with little movement. For expansion joints, use Plastic 935 or toehr polysulfide caulk approved by OWNER.

Section	Subject
	INTERNAL TANK COATING—APPLICATION OF THIN FILM COATINGS

TABLE 2: Drying/Curing Requirements

Coating Product	Time Between Coats, (min.)		Final Cure, (min.)
Company A (Coal Tar Epoxy)	*Temp.* 50°F (10°C) 70°F (21°C) 90°F (32°C)	*Min.-Max.* 48–72 hr. or 16–24 hr. or 10–12 hr.	7 days at 70°F (21°C), or 4 days at 90°F (32°C), or 1 day at 120°F (49°C)
Company C (Coal Tar Epoxy)	4 days at 50°F (10°C), or 48 hr. at 60°F (16°C), or 24 hr. at 75°F (24°C), or 12 hr. at 90°F (32°C)		14 days at 50°F (10°C), or 12 days at 60°F (16°C), or 7 days at 75°F (24°C), or 4 days at 90°F (32°C)
Company C (Epoxy-Phenolic)	36 hr. at 60°F, or 24 hr. at 70°F, or 18 hr. at 80°F, or 12 hr. at 90°F		10 days at 70°F, or 5 days at 80°F, or 72 hr. at 90°F, or 8 hr. at 120°F
Company C (Glass Flake Epoxy Novalac)	48 hr. at 50°F, or 32 hr. at 56°F, or 16 hr. at 75°F, or 8 hr. at 90°F		21 days at 50°F, or 14 days at 56°F, or 7 days at 75°F, or 4 days at 90°F
Company D (Epoxy-Phenolic)	36 hr. at 40°F, or 24 hr. at 50°F, or 16 hr. at 60°F, or 10 hr. at 70°F, or 7 hr. at 80°F, or 4 hr. at 90°F, or 3 hr. at 100–120°F		7 days at 40°F, or 6 days at 50°F, or 5 days at 60°F, or 4 days at 70°F, or 60 hr. at 80°F, or 24 hr. at 90°F, or 18 hr. at 100–120°F
Company I (Coal Tar Epoxy)	*Temp.* 50°F (10°C) 75°F (24°C) 90°F (32°C)	*Min.-Max.* 48–72 hr. or 12–16 hr. or 4–6 hr.	7 days at 70°F (21°C), or 4 days at 90°F (32°C), or 1 day at 120°F (49°C)
Company S (Epoxy-Phenolic)	24 hr. at 50°F, or 12 hr. at 68°F, or 6 hr. at 86°F, or 3 hr. at 104°F		24 days at 50°F, or 16 days at 59°F, or 10 days at 68°F, or 7 days at 77°F, or 5 days at 86°F, or 3 days at 95°F, or 2 days at 104°F
Company P (Epoxy-Phenolic)	24 hr. at 60°F, or 16 hr. at 70°F, or 12 hr. at 80°F, or 10 hr. at 90°F		10 days at 70°F, or 7 days at 90°F, or 4 days at 110°F, or 72 hr. at 120°F

Section		Subject **INTERNAL TANK COATING— APPLICATION OF THIN FILM COATINGS**

APPENDIX C—SERVICE CHART

The following service chart will be used by OWNER to select a coating based on the intended service. See notes below.

Coating Product	Maximum Service Conditions for Oil Storage, Water Storage, or Oil & Gas Production Service				Gasoline, Diesel, or MTBE Storage[2]
	Temp.	Press.	PP CO$_2$	PP H$_2$S	
Company A (Coal Tar Epoxy)	140° F (60° C)	100 psi (6.9 bar)	15 psi (1 bar)	0.50 psi (0.03 bar)	Not recommended.
Company C (Coal Tar Epoxy)	120° F (49° C)	100 psi (6.9 bar)	15 psi (1 bar)	0.50 psi (0.03 bar)	Not recommended.
Company C (Epoxy-Phenolic)	180° F (82° C)	600 psi (13.8 bar)	30 psi (2 bar)	1 psi (0.07 bar)	Recommended for Gasoline and Diesel service only at ambient conditions
Company C (Glass Flake Epoxy Novalac)	180 ° F (82° C)	200 psi (13.8 bar)	30 psi (2 bar)	1 psi (0.07 bar)	Recommended at ambient conditions.[1]
Company D (Epoxy-Phenolic)	170° F (77° C)	200 psi	30 psi (2 bar)	0.1 psi (0.007 bar)	Recommended up to 120°F (49°C).
Company I (Coal Tar Epoxy)	140° F (60° C)	100 psi (6.9 bar)	15 psi (1 bar)	0.50 psi (0.03 bar)	Not recommended.
Company S (Epoxy-Phenolic)	180° F (66° C)	200 psi (34.5 bar)	30 psi (2 bar)	0.1 psi (0.007 bar)	Recommended up to 100°F (38°C).
Company P (Epoxy-Phenolic)	180° F (82° C)	200 psi (13.8 bar)	30 psi (2 bar)	1 psi (0.07 bar)	Recommended up to 100°F (38°C).

Notes:

1. Company C (Glass Flake Epoxy Novalac) is a thick film coating with glass flake pigment. It is somewhat more durable than the other solvent resistant coatings on this list.
2. Temperature limits given for solvent resistant coatings are based on existing data. Testing is needed to determine performance at higher temperatures.
3. Installation of anodes is recommended. Contact OWNER for a cathodic protection design if one is not already provided.
4. Service conditions are valid for the coating systems listed above and not the caulk materials listed in Appendix B. Use the caulking materials only if needed to seal an area that is leaking, or to seal off an area that cannot be coated. Caulks may reduce the long-term performance of the coating system. Do not use caulking materials at service temperatures above 120°F (49°C).

Section	Subject **INTERNAL TANK COATING— APPLICATION OF THIN FILM COATINGS**

APPENDIX D—EXAMPLE INSPECTION RECORD FORMS

The attached forms may be used to record inspection results. Other forms are acceptable providing they have been reviewed and approved by OWNER prior to beginning the job.

D1—COATING INSPECTION CHECK LIST

D2—ABRASIVE BLASTING DAILY INSPECTION REPORT

D3—COATING APPLICATION DAILY INSPECTION REPORT

D4—COATING INSPECTION AMBIENT CONDITIONS REPORT

D5—PRE-COATING INSPECTION REPORT

APPENDIX 6C

COATING INSPECTION CHECKLIST			
PROJ. TITLE:	LOCATION:		
AFC or JOB NO.:	PIC*:		
EST. START DATE:	EST. END DATE:		
INSPECTOR:	DATE PREPARED:		

ITEMS DESCRIPTION	YES	NO	N/A
PRE-INSPECTION			
• LOCATE AREAS WHICH ARE HARD TO COAT?			
• VISUAL CONTAMINATES?			
• ROUGH WELDS, WELD FLUX OR SPLATTER?			
• SHARP CORNERS?			
• LAMINATIONS?			
SURFACE PREPARATION			
• CORRECT ABRASIVE?			
• WEATHER SUITABLE FOR BLASTING?			
• SURFACE DEFECTS CORRECTED?			
• SURFACE CLEANLINESS AS CALLED FOR IN SPECIFICATION?			
• ANCHOR PATTERN/PROFILE AS SPECIFIED?			
• ALL DUST REMOVED?			
COATING MATERIALS			
• COATINGS ARE THOSE SPECIFIED?			
• THINNERS/SOLVENTS ARE THOSE SPECIFIED?			
• PRODUCTS PROPERLY LABELED WITH SHELF LIFE?			
• COATINGS ARE CORRECTLY THINNED, MIXED, AND AGITATED?			
• COATINGS HAVE NOT EXCEEDED POT LIFE?			
COATING APPLICATION			
• WEATHER SUITABLE FOR COATING APPLICATION?			
• SURFACE CLEAN FOR APPLICATION?			
• BRUSH COAT WELDS, EDGES, AND ROUGH SPOTS?			
• CORRECT WET FILM THICKNESS (WFT)?			
• CORRECT DRY FILM THICKNESS (DFT)?			
• NO FLAWS? RUNS, DRY SPRAY, HOLIDAYS, BLISTERS, SAGS OR OTHER			
REPORTS			
• TAKE ALL MEASUREMENTS REQUIRED?			
• RECORD AS REQUIRED?			
REMARKS: **			

*PIC - PERSON-IN-CHARGE   **ATTACH EXTRA SHEETS IF NECESSARY

D1—Rev. A, 06/06/96

APPENDIX 6C

ABRASIVE BLASTING DAILY INSPECTION REPORT			
PROJ. TITLE:	LOCATION:		
AFC or JOB NO.:	PIC*:		
INSPECTOR:	WEATHER:		DATE:
NAME OF ABRASIVE MANUFACTURER:			
TYPE AND GRADE OF ABRASIVE:			
ABRASIVE CHECKED FOR: ———— CLEANLINESS ———— SIZE			
AIR SUPPLY CHECKED FOR: ———— CORRECT PRESSURE ————OIL/WATER CONTAMINATION			

ANCHOR PROFILE		HRS. LEFT UNCOATED	REMARKS
MINIMUM	MAXIMUN		

ATTACH BELOW TESTEX PROFILE REPLICA TAPE: **

*PIC - PERSON-IN-CHARGE   **ATTACH EXTRA SHEETS IF NECESSARY

D2—Rev. A, 06/06/96

APPENDIX 6C

COATING APPLICATION DAILY INSPECTION REPORT

PROJECT TITLE:

AFC or JOB NUMBER:

LOCATION:

DATE:

PIC: *

INSPECTOR:

WEATHER:

COATING NUMBER NOTE 1	COATING LAYER NOTE 2	COATING PRODUCT NOTE 3	BATCH NUMBER NOTE 4	APPL'TN METHOD NOTE 5	PREVI- OUS DFT NOTE 6	WFT MEASUREMENTS		DFT MEASUREMENTS		REMARKS
						MIN. NOTE 7	MAX. NOTE 7	MIN. NOTE 8	MAX. NOTE 8	

* PIC - "PERSON-IN-CHARGE" or PROJECT ENGINEER

NOTES:

1. INDICATE COATING NUMBER IN ASCENDING NUMERICAL ORDER
2. INDICATE COATING LAYER AS FOLLOWS:
   P—PRIMER; I—INTERMEDIATE; F—FINISH OR FINAL
3. REFER TO APPENDIX B OF OWNER SPECIFICATION 7301, "INTERNAL COATING—APPLICATION OF THIN FILM COATINGS"
4. OBTAIN NUMBER FROM CONTAINER LABEL.
5. INDICATE APPLICATION METHOD AS FOLLOWS:
   B—BRUSH; CS—CONVENTIONAL AIR SPRAY; AS—AIRLESS SPRAY
6. MEASURE DFT OF COATING PREVIOUSLY APPLIED.
7. MEASURE WFT AS NEEDED AND RECORD.
8. MEASURE DFT.

D3—OWNER 7301 Rev. A, 06/06/96

APPENDIX 6C

COATING INSPECTION AMBIENT CONDITIONS REPORT

PROJECT TITLE:

LOCATION:

AFC or JOB NUMBER:

PIC: *

INSPECTOR:

DATE	TIME	WEATHER	D.B. (°F)	W.B. (°F)	R.H. (%)	S.T. (°F)	D.P. (°F)	REMARKS

D.B. - DRY BULB TEMP. (AIR) W.B. - WET BULB TEMP. (AIR) R.H. - RELATIVE HUMIDITY S.T. - STEEL SURFACE TEMP. D.P. - DEW POINT

*PIC - "PERSON-IN-CHARGE" or PROJECT ENGINEER

NOTES:

1. INDICATE WEATHER AS FOLLOWS:
   S—SUNNY; C—CLOUDY; O—OVERCAST; R—RAINING
2. INDICATE ON REMARKS TYPE OF ACTIVITIES AS FOLLOWS:
   CL—CLEANING; BL—BLASTING; CO—COATING

D4—OWNER 7301 Rev. A, 06/06/96

APPENDIX 6C

PRE-COATING INSPECTION REPORT		
PROJ. TITLE:	LOCATION:	
AFC or JOB NO.:	PIC*:	
INSPECTOR:	WEATHER:	DATE:
PRE-INSPECTION COMMENTS: **		
DEFECTS CORRECTED: **		
PRE-CLEANING METHOD: **		
PRE-CLEANING COMMENTS: **		

*PIC - PERSON-IN-CHARGE   **ATTACH EXTRA SHEETS IF NECESSARY

5

06/23/98   12:45PM   C:\DATA\BOOK97\CHPTR06.M1

APPENDIX 6D

EXCERPTS FROM A COATING SPECIFICATION FOR EXTERNAL COATING FOR OFFSHORE STRUCTURES AND SEVERELY CORROSIVE SERVICE

APPENDIX A—APPROVED COATING SYSTEMS AND APPLICATION NOTES

The following appendix provides a list of approved coating systems and outlines where these systems are to be used. The coating systems are listed in tables by supplier. The Contractor may indicate a preference of supplier, however, Owner reserves the right to make the final selection. Once a supplier has been chosen for a specific project, that supplier will remain the supplier throughout the project. Paint systems of one supplier shall not be mixed with systems or products of another.

Application notes are also included in this appendix. The purpose of these are to provide a more complete description of the system use and clarify some specific application requirements.

Colors of individual coats are specified to provide contrast with the existing surface. Finish coat colors are often project specific. Information on colors must be confirmed by Owner prior to ordering coatings. All coatings must be free of lead and chromates.

TABLE 1: Coating Systems From the xx Company

COATING SYSTEM	SURFACES TO BE COATED	SURFACE PREP. (PROFILE)	PRIME COAT (DFT)	2ND COAT (DFT)	3RD COAT (DFT)	4TH COAT (DFT)	TOTAL DFT
1	Non-insulated structural steel, piping, etc. in offshore splash zone, or other intermittent immersion service such as floating tank roofs. 250°F (120°C) max. continuous, excursions to 300°F (150°C)	SSPC-SP 10 (1.5–2.0 mils) (38–51 μm)	Inorganic Zinc (Green) (2.5–4 mils) (64–102 μm)	Epoxy (White) (4–6 mils) (102–152 μm)	Epoxy (Gray) (4–6 mils) (102–152 μm)	Polyurethane (1.5–2.5 mils) (38–64 μm)	12–18.5 mils (305–470 μm)
2	Non-insulated structural steel, piping, etc., not in splash zone, 250°F (120°C) max. continuous, excursions to 300°F (150°C)	SSPC-SP 10 (1.5–2.0 mils) (38–51 μm)	Inorganic Zinc (Green) (2.5–4 mils) (64–102 μm)	Epoxy (White) (5–7 mils) (127–178 μm)	Polyurethane (1.5–2.5 mils) (38–64 μm)	—	9–13.5 mils (229–343 μm)
3	Deck, metal plate flooring, non-skid surfaces	SSPC-SP 10 (2.5–3.5 mils) (64–89 μm)	(Green) (2–3 mils) (51–76 μm)	Epoxy Non-Skid (15–20 mils) (381–508 μm)	Polyurethane (1.5–2.5 mils) (38–64 μm)	—	18.5–25.5 mils (470–648 μm)
4A	Non-insulated carbon steel or martensitic stainless steel, 250°F–500°F (120°C–260°C)	SSPC-SP 10 (1.5–2.0 mils) (38–51 μm)	Inorganic Zinc (Green) (2.5–4 mils) (64–102 μm)	Modified Silicone Acrylic (Aluminum) (1.5–2 mils) (38–51 μm)	—	—	4–6 mils (102–152 μm)
4B	Non-insulated carbon steel, 500°F–750°F (260°C–400°C)	SSPC-SP 10 (1.5–2.0 mils) (38–51 μm)	Inorganic Zinc (Green) (2.5–4 mils) (64–102 μm)	Modified Silicone (1–2 mils) (25–51 μm)	—	—	3.5–6 mils (89–152 μm)
4C	Non-insulated carbon steel or martensitic stainless steel, 750°F–1000°F (400°C–540°C) or insulated carbon steel, martensitic stainless or high alloy stainless steel, 400°F–1000°F (205°C–540°C)	SSPC-SP 10 (0.5–1.0 mils) (13–25 μm)	Modified Silicone (1–2 mils) (25–51 μm)	Modified Silicone (1–2 mils) (25–51 μm)	—	—	2–4 mils (51–102 μm)
4D	Insulated carbon steel or stainless steel, below ambient up to 425°F (220°C) max. continuous, excursions to 450°F (230°C)	SSPC-SP 10 (2.0–3.0 mils) (51–76 μm)	Epoxy-Phenolic (4–6 mils) (102–152 μm)	Epoxy-Phenolic (4–6 mils) (102–152 μm)	—	—	8–12 mils (203–305 μm)
5	Coating for galvanized surfaces (Total DFT is w/out galvanizing)	SSPC-SP 1	Epoxy Sealer (1–2 mils) (25–51 μm)	Polyurethane (1.5–2.5 mils) (38–64 μm)	—	—	2.5–4.5 mils (64–114 μm)
6	Galvanizing for grating, handrails, etc.	SSPC-SP 8 Pickle	Hot Dip Galvanize per ASTM A123-89, A153-87 and A385-86				By weight
7	Buried and submerged carbon steel, pump casings, piping	SSPC-SP 5 (2.0–3.0 mils) (51–76 μm)	Coal Tar Epoxy (8–10 mils) (203–254 μm)	Coal Tar Epoxy (8–10 mils) (203–254 μm)	—	—	16–20 mils (406–508 μm)
8	Signs: Use System 1 or 2	—	—	—	—	—	—
9	Color coat for previously coated surfaces, or to provide UV protection for PVC or Fiberglass.	Clean Coated Metal w/ Thinner #2. Detergent Wash PVC	Polyurethane (1.5–2.5 mils) (38–64 μm)	—	—	—	—
10	Damaged areas coated with completed System 1 or 2	SSPC-SP 10 or SSPC-SP 3 as required	Epoxy (5–7 mils) (127–178 μm)	Epoxy (5–7 mils) (127–178 μm)	Polyurethane (1.5–2.5 mils) (38–64 μm)	—	11.5–16.5 mils (292–419 μm)
11	OEM coating upgrade for pumps, motors, etc.	SSPC-SP 2 and/or SP 3	Epoxy (5–7 mils) (127–178 μm)	Polyurethane (1.5–2.5 mils) (38–64 μm)	—	—	—
12	Concrete Surfaces requiring coating	Sweep blast	Epoxy sealer (4–8 mils) (102–203 μm) Thinned 30%	Epoxy (4–7 mils) (102–178 μm) or Non-skid Epoxy (15–20 mils) (381–508μm)	Polyurethane (1.5–2.5 mils) (38–64 μm) If needed to add color or UV protection.	—	—
PP	Preconstruction Primer: Use to protect the steel surface during the construction. This can save on costly touch-up painting.	Prepare according to final system requirements.	Weldable Inorganic Zinc (0.75–1.25 mils) (19–32 μm)	—	—	—	—

Notes applicable to the XX Systems.

CHAPTER 7

CATHODIC PROTECTION

INTRODUCTION

Cathodic protection (CP) is defined as a technique to control the corrosion of a metal surface by making that surface the cathode of an electrochemical cell.[1] Since corrosion takes place at the anode of an electrochemical cell, the cathodic surface is protected. In other terms, CP is the use of direct current from an external anode to make the corroding structure cathodic and thus stifle the corrosion. With CP, an electrochemical cell still exists, but the structure no longer corrodes—the structure is the cathode in a cell with an external anode. Of course, the cathode and anode must be in the same electrolyte (water or soil) and electrically connected (with a wire). The direct current may be supplied by a sacrificial (galvanic) anode or from a power source (impressed current). In production operations CP is used to protect the external surfaces of buried and submerged piping, well casings, tank bottoms, offshore structures, and the internal surfaces of water handling tanks and vessels, the free-water sections in separation vessels (such as three phase separators and emulsion treaters), and tank bottoms (with a water layer). This chapter will briefly review the basics of CP, the types of CP, and finish with a discussion of the use of CP in different types of production situations. **Appendix 7A** covers some of the survey and test procedures used in CP.

CATHODIC PROTECTION PRINCIPLES

The proper application of CP changes the flow of current in the electrochemical corrosion cell. Rather than the current flowing between the anodic (corroding) areas and cathodic (noncorroding) areas on the pipe or vessel (structure), CP makes the entire structure cathodic. Direct current impressed on the structure from an external, more powerful, anode overrides the naturally occurring anodic areas. **Figure 7.1** illustrates schematically a basic cathodic protection circuit. Note that the electrochemical corrosion current from anode to cathode ("A") is replaced, or "overridden," by the current from the auxiliary (external) anode ("B").

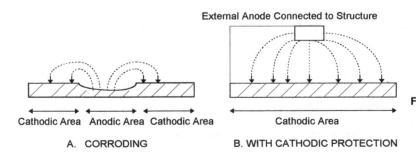

External Anode Connected to Structure

Cathodic Area   Anodic Area   Cathodic Area

A. CORRODING

Cathodic Area

B. WITH CATHODIC PROTECTION

Figure 7.1 Schematic drawing illustrating that CP protects by making the metal structure the cathode in the electrochemical corrosion cell.

CP does not necessarily eliminate the corrosion reaction. It does, however, transfer corrosion from the corroding structure and moves it to an anode or anodes that can be designed for long life and easy replacement.

CP is applicable only to the surface of the metal that is exposed to the same electrolyte as the anode. For example, CP applied to the exterior surface of a salt water tank bottom has no affect on the corrosion on the internal surface of the bottom.

CRITERIA FOR CATHODIC PROTECTION

Over the years, various criteria have been developed to establish the effectiveness of cathodic protection (CP) on various structures. The more common criteria involve measurements of voltage (differences in potential) between the protected structure and the electrolyte.

Probably the most widely used criterion for buried pipes or external tank bottoms involves the use of a copper-copper sulfate electrode as a reference half cell. This electrode consists simply of a copper rod immersed in saturated copper sulfate solution, both being housed in a plastic cylinder with a porous plug on the bottom end (for contact with the electrolyte) and the copper rod extending out the top (for connection to the measuring high-resistance voltmeter or potentiometer). A copper-copper sulfate reference electrode is visible below the technician's left knee in **Figure 7.2**.[2]

Figure 7.2 A technician taking a reading at a CP test station in a pipeline right-of-way. The copper-copper sulfate reference electrode, visible below his left knee, is placed in the soil for the reading. (Photograph courtesy Bass Engineering Co., Longview, TX.[2])

Experience has shown that when a structure-to-electrolyte reading (often referred to as the pipe-to-soil reading) is -0.85V or more negative, relative to a copper-copper sulfate reference electrode, corrosion is essentially stopped on steel structures in natural soils and waters. Overprotection of steel (*i.e.*, generation of potentials substantially more negative than -0.85V) is not normally harmful, but is wasteful and may damage certain coatings on the structure, especially thin film coatings.

An additional criterion for steel is presented in NACE RP0169-96, Control of External Corrosion on Underground or Submerged Piping Systems, Section 6, Criteria and Other Considerations for Cathodic Protection.[3] The alternate is to have: "a minimum of 100 mV of cathodic polarization between the structure surface and a stable electrode contacting the electrolyte." The exact particulars of these criteria and parameters for their determination, as well as CP design details, are covered in NACE RP0169 (latest edition).

Other reference electrodes may be substituted for the copper-copper sulfate reference electrode to meet specific needs. For example, the silver-silver chloride reference electrode is commonly used in seawater since the copper-copper sulfate electrode may be inaccurate if the seawater penetrates the porous plug and contaminates the solution. When other reference electrodes are used, the criteria will be different than -0.85 V. **Table 7.1** lists the equivalents for the commonly used reference electrodes.

TABLE 7.1 Cathodic Protection Reference Electrode Equivalent Voltages
(From NACE RP0675–88, "Control of External Corrosion on Offshore Steel Pipelines,"
Section 5: Criteria for Cathodic Protection.)

REFERENCE ELECTRODES	EQUIVALENT VOLTAGES	REMARKS
Copper-copper sulfate	-0.85 V	—
Saturated KCl calomel	-0.78 V	Often used in laboratory tests
Silver-silver chloride	-0.80 V	In seawater (adjusted for Chloride concentration)
High purity zinc	+0.25 V	—

Of course, direct visual observation of the effectiveness of CP may be possible in many cases (offshore structures, inside tanks), or coupons of the same metal may be installed on the protected structure for periodic checks of the degree of effectiveness of the applied protective current. Finally, where experience has shown that a certain current density has been effective in protecting steel, in a given relatively uniform environment, then this current density, uniformly applied, may be considered an indirect criterion of protection. Current densities of 1 milliampere per square foot (mA/ft^2) $(10.8\ mA/m^2)$ of bare steel pipe will give the desired potential response in most soils. In seawater, some 6 to 8 mA/ft^2 (64.6 to 86.1 mA/m^2) are usually required to protect the corroding areas on steel structures initially. In severe environments (low temperature and/or high flow rates), requirements can be much larger. **Table 7.2** presents some typical design current densities for protection of offshore platforms in different producing areas around the world. Polarization and calcareous deposit buildup tend to reduce the current density required to maintain protective potentials to one-half or even lower than the initial value.

TABLE 7.2 Design Criteria for Cathodic Protection Systems
(From NACE RP0176-94, "Corrosion Control of Steel Fixed Offshore Platforms Associated with Petroleum Production, page 29, Table A1.)

Production Area	Water Resistivity[b] (ohm-cm)	Water Temp. (°C)	Environmental Factors[a] Turbulence Factor (Wave Action)	Lateral Water Flow	Typical Design Current Density[c] mA/m² (mA/ft²) Initial[e]	Mean[f]	Final[g]
Gulf of Mexico	20	22	Moderate	Moderate	110 (10)	55 (5)	75 (7)
West Coast	24	15	Moderate	Moderate	150 (14)	90 (8)	100 (9)
Inlet	50	2	Low	High	430 (40)	380 (35)	380 (35)
North Sea[d]	26-33	0–12	High	Moderate	180 (17)	90 (8)	120 (11)
North Sea[d]	26-33	0–12	High	Moderate	150 (14)	90 (8)	100 (9)
Arabian Gulf	15	30	Moderate	Low	130 (12)	65 (6)	90 (8)
Australia	23-30	12–18	High	Moderate	130 (12)	90 (8)	90 (8)
Brazil	20	15–20	Moderate	High	180 (17)	65 (6)	90 (8)
West Africa	20-30	5–21	—	—	130 (12)	65 (6)	90 (8)
Indonesia	19	24	Moderate	Moderate	110 (10)	55 (5)	75 (7)

(a) Typical values and ratings based on average conditions, remote from river discharge.
(b) Water resistivities are a function of both chlorinity and temperature. In the *Corrosion Handbook* by H. H. Uhlig (New York, NY: John Wiley & Sons, Inc., 1948), the following resistivities are given for chlorinities of 19 and 20 parts per thousand:

	Resistivities (ohm-cm) Temperature (°C)					
Chlorinity (ppt)	0	5	10	15	20	25
19	35.1	30.4	26.7	23.7	21.3	19.2
20	33.5	29.0	25.5	22.7	20.3	18.3

(c) In ordinary seawater, a current density less than the design value suffices to hold the platform at protective potential once polarization has been accomplished and calcareous coatings are built up by the design current density. CAUTION: Depolarization can result from storm action.
(d) Conditions in the North Sea can vary greatly from the northern to the southern area, from winter to summer, and during storm periods.
(e) Initial current densities are calculated using Ohm's Law and a resistance equation such as Dwight's or Crennell's (McCoy's) equation with the original dimensions of the anode.
(f) Mean current densities are used to calculate the total weight of anodes required to maintain the protective current to the platform over the design life.
(g) Final current densities are calculated in a manner similar to the initial current density, except that the depleted anode dimensions are used.

CATHODIC PROTECTION SYSTEMS

There are two approaches or systems for CP based on different ways of supplying the necessary cathodic protection current:

(1) Sacrificial (galvanic) anode systems in which the current is due to a galvanic couple set up between sacrificial anodes and the structure to be protected.

(2) Impressed current systems in which current is supplied (impressed) from an external DC (direct current) power source (commonly a rectifier) via relatively inert anodes.

The selection of the type of system for a particular application, as usual, is another technical/ economic decision. For example, in some instances a higher driving force (voltage) might be required than is available from galvanic anodes and an impressed system would be necessary. In that case, the comparisons would be to select the most profitable type impressed current design. **Table 7.3** lists some "rules of thumb" that may be used for guidance when selecting a CP system.

TABLE 7.3 Sacrificial Anode vs Impressed Current Cathodic Protection Systems

SACRIFICIAL ANODE SYSTEMS ARE USED WHEN:	IMPRESSED CURRENT SYSTEMS ARE USED WHEN:
1. Current requirements are low.	1. Current requirements are high.
2. Soil resistively is low (< 10,000 ohm-cm).	2. Soil resistively is high.
3. Electrical power is not available.	3. Electrical power is readily available.
4. Interference problems are prevalent.	4. Long life protection is required.

SACRIFICIAL ANODE CATHODIC PROTECTION SYSTEMS

Galvanic Anodes. A galvanic anode by definition is: "a metal which, because of its relative position in the galvanic series, provides protection to metal or metals that are more noble in the series, when coupled in an electrolyte."[4] **Table 7.4** shows the galvanic series for metals in seawater.

Galvanic anodes used in oilfield CP are made of special magnesium, aluminum, or zinc alloys, which, when connected to steel, exhibit sufficiently high potentials to develop sufficient current flow through the electrolyte to protect the structure. The principle is the same as that of bimetallic corrosion in Chapter 3.

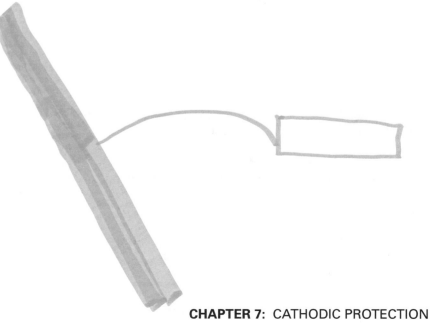

TABLE 7.4 Galvanic Series of Various Metals Exposed to Seawater

ACTIVE END

Magnesium
Magnesium Alloys
Zinc
Galvanized Steel
Aluminum 1100
Aluminum 6053
Alclad
Cadmium
Aluminum 2024 (4.5 Cu, 1.5 Mg, 0.6 Mn)
Mild Steel
Wrought Iron
Cast Iron
13% Chromium Stainless Steel Type 410 (Active)
18-8 Stainless Steel Type 304 (Active)
18-12-3 Stainless Steel Type 316 (Active)
Lead-Tin Solders
Lead
Tin
Muntz Metal
Manganese Bronze
Naval Brass
Nickel (Active)
76Ni-16Cr-7Fe Alloy (Active)
60Ni-30Mo-6Fe-1Mn
Yellow Brass
Admiralty Brass
Aluminum Brass
Red Brass
Copper
Silicon Bronze
70:30 Cupro-Nickel
G-Bronze
M-Bronze
Silver Solder
Nickel (Passive)
76Ni-16Cr-7Fe Alloy (Passive)
67Ni-33Cu Alloy (Monel)
13 % Chromium Stainless Steel Type 410 (Passive)
Titanium
18-8 Stainless Steel Type 304 (Passive)
18-12-3 Stainless Steel Type 316 (Passive)
Silver
Graphite
Gold
Platinum

NOBLE or PASSIVE END

Magnesium anodes are most widely used in soil applications due to their high driving potential. Magnesium is also used in fresh or condensed waters in vessels.

Aluminum anodes are excellent in seawater and brines. Aluminum has the added advantage of an inherently high energy capability per pound of anode. By way of comparison, under ordinary usage, magnesium is consumed at the approximate rate of 17 lbs (7.7 kg) per ampere per year, zinc at a rate of 26 lbs (12.7 kg), and one commercially available aluminum alloy at only 6.8 lbs (3.1 kg).

Zinc anodes are not as common in oilfield systems as magnesium and aluminum. Zinc finds its greatest application in low resistivity soils and some waters. However, zinc has a disadvantage—it has the undesirable habit at elevated temperatures of reversing polarity and become cathodic to steel. Thus, care must be exercised when selecting zinc for cathodic protection application. For example, zinc anodes are not a good choice for fired vessels such as emulsion heaters (heater treaters). The reported reversals occur above 140°F (60°C) to 170°F (76.7°C) depending on the water composition. Even if the zinc anode polarity does not reverse, it may passivate at temperatures above 120°F (49°C).[5]

Design and Installation of Sacrificial Anode Systems. Galvanic anodes are available in many shapes and sizes depending on the application and required life. Anodes for mounting in the water handling sections of vessels and tanks may be in the shape of blocks or slabs or may be spherical. Anodes for burial are usually cylindrical and may be obtained prepackaged, or bare. **Figure 7.3** is a schematic showing typical galvanic anode installations for pipelines—for tank bottoms or other structures in contact with soil, substitute the appropriate word for the word "pipeline."

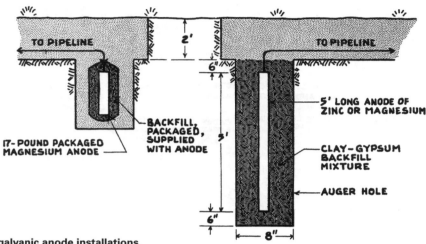

Figure 7.3 Typical galvanic anode installations.

There are basically three components in a galvanic anode installation in soil: the anode, the backfill, and the connection wire. The anode size is determined by the design life of the system and current flow calculations. The purpose of the backfill mixture surrounding the anode is to provide a low resistance contact between the anode and the soil. Smaller anodes may be purchased with the anode and backfill in a permeable package ready to bury. These packaged anodes make it very easy to quickly and economically install anodes for localized ("hot spot") protection. The connection wire is attached to the pipe or structure and must be installed so it will remain mechanically sound and electrically conductive. A common method of attachment is to use a commercial thermite welding technique field kit. Furthermore, buried or submerged connections should be coated with an electrically insulating material that is compatible with the pipe's coating and the wire's insulation.

IMPRESSED CURRENT CATHODIC PROTECTION SYSTEMS

Large quantities of protective current usually require some type of impressed current system. **Figure 7.4** shows a typical rectifier installation on a buried pipeline. With the rectifier alternating current (AC) power is transformed and rectified into direct current (DC), which in turn is impressed on a "groundbed" of graphite anodes. The anode bed is, of course, connected to the positive (+) side of the rectifier, while the pipeline is connected to the negative (−) side, to complete the circuit. Such installations normally generate 10 to 100 amperes or more of protective current at one location.

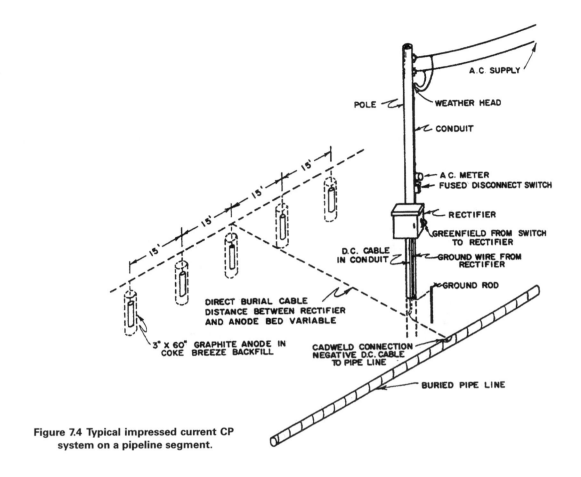

Figure 7.4 Typical impressed current CP system on a pipeline segment.

Impressed Current Anodes. Graphite is not the only material used for impressed current anodes. Other anode materials include high silicon iron, lead-silver alloy, platinum over various substrates such as titanium, mixed metal oxides, lead-platinum or scrap steel such as pipe, abandoned well casing, or railroad rails. The semi-inert anodes of graphite or silicon-iron are used extensively in soils today, but steel ground beds are still being used. The main drawback to steel is its consumption rate (approximately 20 pounds per ampere discharged per year). In salt water, a lead (6% antimony—1% silver alloy) anode has gained wide favor because of its unusually low consumption rate, typically 0.1 pound per ampere per year. Noble metal (or precious metal) electrodes such as platinized titanium are used more and more.

"THINK POSITIVE—And Stay Out of Trouble!"

The watch word for installing impressed current cathodic protection systems is "Think Positive." This refers, of course, to the requirement to connect the groundbed to the positive terminal of the rectifier. Every long-term (and some short-term) pipeliner and cathodic protection specialist can tell horror stories about cases where the rectifier was hooked up backwards.

Hooking the rectifier up backwards reverses the circuit—the pipeline or other supposedly protected structure becomes the anode—the groundbed becomes the cathode and the structure corrodes to protect the groundbed!

Hopefully any mistakes such as this will be caught before commissioning, or at least before severe damage has occurred. Unfortunately, that has not always been true and the first warning of trouble was a corrosion failure.

So Please—Always—THINK POSITIVE!

In all cathodic protection installations for buried structures, it is important that anodes be properly installed so that there is minimum electrical resistance between the anode and the surrounding soil. Where possible, anodes should be placed in areas of low soil resistance such as in old drilling mud pits. A low resistance material is usually packed around the anode to serve as backfill. **Figure 7.5** shows a typical graphite (or silicon-iron) anode installation with coke breeze backfill.

Most impressed current groundbeds are relatively shallow. By definition, a shallow ground bed has one or more anodes installed either vertically or horizontally at a depth of less than 50 ft (15 m). Commonly, there are zones of low resistance soils near the surface, and the ground beds will be much shallower. Often the holes for vertical anodes can be drilled with an auger. Horizontal groundbeds are simply ditched. In certain instances, however, deeper placement is required to reach low resistance stratum or to be able to get the anodes remote from the pipe or structure. Deep groundbeds are defined as those with one or more anodes placed vertically in drilled holes at depths greater than 50 ft (15 m)—often they will be several hundred feet deep. **Figure 7.6** is a schematic of one design for deep groundbeds.

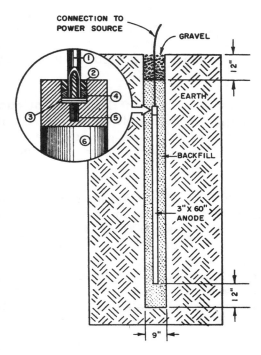

Figure 7.5 Schematic of the installation of a vertical impressed current anode.

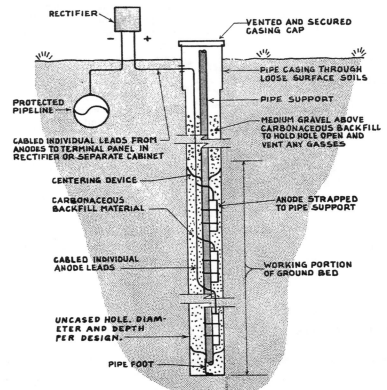

Figure 7.6 Schematic of the installation of a deep well groundbed for an impressed current CP system.

Deep groundbeds are very important to the economic success of many CP systems for pipelines, well casings and surface facilities. NACE RP0572 (latest edition), "Design, Installation, Operation, and Maintenance of Impressed Current Deep Groundbeds"[6] outlines the requirements, considerations and procedures for these groundbeds.

Impressed Current Cathodic Protection Power Sources. Although AC/DC rectifiers are the most common power supply for impressed current cathodic protection, other sources have been and are being used. Where AC power is not available, DC generators can be used for systems with heavy loads. Solar or thermoelectric generators may be used where lesser currents are needed.

Cathodic Protection Interference. One possible problem when using impressed current CP is that of interference on unprotected lines or structure. **Figure 7.7** illustrates the case where interference between a cathodically protected line and an unprotected (foreign) line is aggravating corrosion of the unprotected line. It can be seen that the foreign line receives protection where current enters the pipe, but accelerated corrosion occurs where the current leaves the foreign line. If a proper metallic connection is placed between the protected and unprotected lines, this problem does not occur. Of course, this means both structures are then receiving CP current, and the current required for adequate protection is correspondingly increased.

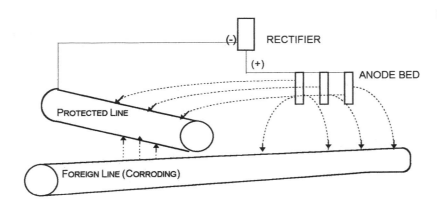

Figure 7.7 A representation of CP interference. Current from the rectifier anode bed is picked up by both the line being protected and the foreign line crossing under it. In order to complete the circuit, the current picked up by the foreign line must leave the line, pass through the soil, be picked up by the protected line, and return to the rectifier. The area where current leaves the foreign line is anodic and the foreign line corrodes.

CP installations should be designed in such a way that interference with other structures will be minimal. Once CP is installed, it is necessary to ascertain whether interference exists and, if so, to take steps to eliminate it. This requires conscientious effort and cooperation among the several parties which may be involved.

Detection and removal of CP installation interference can be a complicated matter, but NACE RP0169 (latest edition)[7] discusses the mechanism of interference, detection of interference currents, and methods for mitigating interference corrosion problems.

SURVEY AND TEST METHODS
IN CATHODIC PROTECTION

Determining the need for and applicability of CP requires special instrumentation and judgment. Because both corrosion and CP are electrochemical in nature, the corrosion-CP survey consists essentially of a well organized and correlated series of electrical measurements. The most important of these are:

- Structure-to-electrolyte potential measurements.

- Current flow (IR drop) measurements, either in the structure itself or in the surrounding electrolyte.

- Electrolyte resistance measurements.

- Current requirement tests.

These measurements in various combinations are used to determine the need for CP, to design CP systems, to commission and evaluate a new system, to monitor a system's performance, and to trouble shoot problems. Discussion of these methods, including generalized procedures and guidelines are included in **Appendix 7A**. More details are available in CP reference books including: Cathodic Protection, 2nd. ed., by H. J. Morgan[8] and Control of Pipeline Corrosion, by A. W. Peabody.[9] Both of these books are so well and widely recognized in the field of corrosion control that they are usually simply referred to as "Morgan's Book" and "Peabody's Book." Both are published by NACE International.

APPLICATION OF CATHODIC PROTECTION TO OIL AND GAS PRODUCTION EQUIPMENT

CP, either by itself or in combination with another control method (such as coatings), is a viable method of corrosion control for most oil field corrosion problems except inside pipes and oil country tubular goods (OCTG). As a generality, CP is not a sound approach inside piping or wells. The spacing is so close that it would be difficult, if not impossible, to get satisfactory current distribution. However, external well casing, buried lines (flow, gathering, distribution, and injection), surface vessels and tanks that set on the ground, as well as the internals of vessels and tanks that handle or store water (including those with water holding sections or water standing in the bottom), are all candidates for CP.

WELL CASINGS

External corrosion of well casing is not a universal problem (*i.e.*, well casings do not fail from corrosion in every well during its producing life). When they do fail, a number of the failures are due to internal not external corrosion. However, enough wells have failed from external corrosion in most operating areas, that control procedures have been developed. The review of oilfield corrosion and its control in Chapter 1 mentioned that cathodic protection is an accepted approach to controlling external casing corrosion. Depending on the circumstances, both sacrificial and impressed current systems are in use. NACE RP0186 (latest edition), "Application of Cathodic Protection for External Surfaces of Steel Well Casings,"[10] covers many of the details of design, operation, and maintenance of both type systems.

Current requirements for well casings, with few exceptions, fall in the range of 1 to 25 amperes. The smaller requirements can frequently be met using galvanic anodes. In many instances, even for such small currents, soil resistance is too high for galvanic anodes and an impressed current system becomes necessary. For economy, one rectifier-groundbed is frequently installed to take care of several well casings, either by running separate negative connections to the wells, or by using the flowlines as current conductors to the wells. In either case, the well casing must be insulated from the flowline. A current controlling resistor can be placed across this insulating fitting to drain a little current from the flowline to the well (to afford some cathodic protection to the flowline, while eliminating possible cathodic interference). Alternately, current can be drained from the well to the flowline where the latter has been used as the current conductor back to the rectifier. Test procedures for design and evaluation of well casing CP are included with the surveys and tests reviewed in **Appendix 7A**.

In many areas, the soil resistivity is such that design of an economical groundbed to produce the desired current at a reasonable voltage becomes a problem, even with rectifiers. Often deeper strata are lower in resistance. In such cases, it becomes economical to use deep groundbeds, as described earlier and illustrated in **Figure 7.6**. These well-type groundbeds have all the anodes placed one above the other in a vertically drilled 6 or 8 in. hole.

The problem of rectifier adjustment arises when a large number of well casings are protected in a field where the surface groundbed resistance to earth may change radically with soil moisture variations. This has led to an increasing usage of "constant current" type rectifiers in well casing cathodic protection installations. These units are designed so that, over a reasonable range of groundbed resistance, the rectifier automatically compensates for increased circuit resistance and tends to maintain the preselected current output of the unit. This feature is not normally required with deep well groundbeds, which are little affected by surface moisture conditions.

A LEAK—REPAIR IT AND PROTECT IT—NOW

Some operators have adopted the practice of installing one or more packaged galvanic anodes at the site of any line leak repair as a part of their repair procedure. The rational is simple:

(1) if the leak was due to external corrosion, the leak has identified a "hot spot" and protection is justified.

(2) if the leak was from internal corrosion or other damage, fluids, particularly brines, will have leaked into the surrounding soil, changing its characteristics, and the odds are a "hot spot" has been created.

Furthermore, if the replacement pipe is bare (uncoated), the new pipe will tend to be anodic to the old pipe in the line and new corrosion cells will be created unless anodes are installed. If the replacement pipe is coated and placed into an otherwise uncoated line, any holidays (voids) or damaged places in the coating will be anodic to the old pipe, and corrosion at the voids could be accelerated due to the anode/cathode area relationship—small anode/large cathode = accelerated corrosion.

When the installation of packaged anodes is a part of the "normal" repair procedure, the cost of adding protection is quite economical. (A typical installation is shown in **Figure 7.8**.[11]) The repair crew has the needed anodes and installation kits as a part of their repair supplies and equipment at the job site—no special trips, no special clearances, no delays deciding what to do—it is automatic.

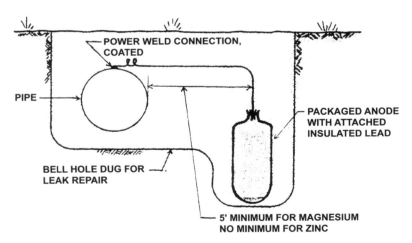

Figure 7.8 Installation of packaged anode during repair of a line leak.[10]

Interference with well casings by nearby CP installations is a greater problem than that with pipelines because both detection and alleviation are difficult. Surface measurements, backed up by a casing potential profile when in doubt, must be used in any case of suspected interference with a neighboring well casing. Fortunately, the trend to field wide application of CP to well casings, together with balancing of individual well potentials, has minimized interference problems from well to well. However, there has been a somewhat greater problem with interference by pipeline cathodic protection systems on well casings.

FLOWLINES, GATHERING LINES, DISTRIBUTION LINES, INJECTION LINES, AND PIPELINES

All of the buried field piping made of steel, whether it is used for flow, gathering, distribution, or injection lines may be subject to external corrosion. Coatings or cathodic protection or both have been the usual methods of corrosion control in recent years. Older lines are often bare steel that is repaired or replaced when failures occur.

If the line is well coated and not very long, the current requirements will usually fall in the range where installation of galvanic anodes, singly or in groups, is the most practical means for achieving CP. **Figure 7.3** shows typical magnesium anode installations.

Bare field lines may not justify CP except under very corrosive conditions. They may be reconditioned, coated, and placed under complete CP, as mentioned above, or they may be surveyed by the surface potential profile (two electrode) technique and subsequently placed under "hot spot" protection with galvanic anodes. Known leak areas, or "hot spots," may be satisfactorily protected by a limited number of galvanic anodes.

Critical trunk lines and transmission lines are normally surveyed, spot protected if bare, or placed under complete CP if coated. Most newly installed lines of any importance will be well coated, making the task of complete CP very economical and relatively simple.

Lines under cathodic protection should be electrically isolated (using insulating unions, flanges, couplings, or nipples) from unprotected structures so that the CP current will be confined to the structure for which it was intended. Even one metallic contact (*e.g.*, to a well casing not under CP) can cause substantial loss of protection on the pipeline. This is because the bare well casing adds a large amount of steel surface to the CP circuit; probably much more surface than was used in the system design. Therefore, an inspection and maintenance program for insulating fittings is important to assure continuing isolation. Insulating fittings have other uses besides isolating CP systems. They are used to break up corrosion currents between pieces of equipment and to isolate different metals from one another. Electrical isolation and insulating fittings are discussed in greater detail in Chapter 9.

SURFACE EQUIPMENT AND VESSELS

Equipment such as production and salt water disposal tanks, heater-treaters, accumulators, separators, and filters are prone to corrosion from produced brines. Elevated temperatures, coupled with the presence of sulfate-reducing bacteria (SRB) in many instances, leads to short service life unless CP is applied. This is particularly true, as might be expected, for the fire tube, emulsion and free-water sections in heater-treaters. In one South Texas field, corrosion failures of the fire tubes occurred in about three months without protection. **Figure 7.9** shows a cathodically protected heater-treater in service for 7 years. The photograph shows five through-wall anodes in different water containing sections of the treater. Note that the lead wires go up the wall in electrical conduit.

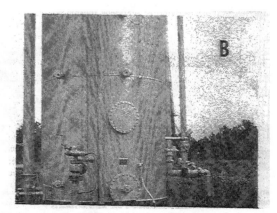

Figure 7.9 CP anodes installed in various sections of a heater treater (emulsion treater). Note that the grooved fitting heads of five through-wall impressed current CP anodes are visible.

Multiple anodes are required because baffles separate the sections of the treater and the close confines limit how much steel surface each anode can "see." For example, to protect the entire surface of the fire tube requires at least one anode on each side of the tube. Furthermore, in the short distances within any vessel, the coverage of any one anode is limited. An old adage states that an anode can protect only what it can "see"—it cannot see around corners into the next compartment. **Figure 7.10** compares the coverage of an anode in a vessel compartment to that of a light bulb in a similar situation.

Current density requirements can range from 5 to 40 ma/sq. ft (50 to 400 ma/sq. m) of bare water-immersed steel.[12] In the absence of specific data, 10 ma/sq. ft (100 ma/sq. m) is commonly used for design estimates. The choice of a current source is primarily a matter of the availability of AC power.

Where AC power is available, rectifiers may be used to protect one or more vessels,

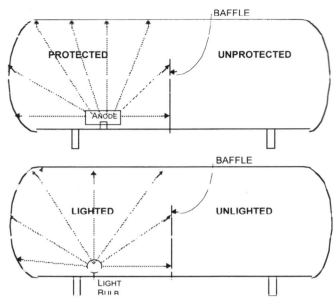

Figure 7.10 This sketch illustrates that in a confined space (such as in a water-packed vessel), CP provides protection to the areas in the line of sight of the anode. Thus, to protect the compartment to the right of the baffle, an anode will be required on that side of the baffle as well.

using graphite or other anode material installed in special through-wall mounts. Some of the newer anodes are very small and may be conveniently lubricated in and out of the mount while the vessel remains in operation. While graphite anodes can suffer some reduction in output from production chemicals in produced fluids, the anodes large surface area allows development of adequate current flow in all but very rare situations. Chlorine-resistant high-silicon cast iron anodes may be used where graphite is stifled by oil saturation.

Where AC power is not present, adequate protective current can be generated by either magnesium or aluminum anodes mounted through the wall in the same fashion as the graphite anodes. **Figure 7.11** shows two such anodes. In this case, the galvanic anode circuit is completed externally by a jumper wire to the vessel wall **(Figure 7.12)**. The use of jumper wires allows current flow to be measured and adjusted for each individual anode at its point of mounting. Because magnesium is very active, its current output to the vessel must be highly restricted to avoid wasteful overprotection. However, this results in greatly reduced anode efficiency since the anode will continue to corrode at almost the same rate and only a fraction of its corrosion current is being utilized to protect the vessel.

Figure 7.11 Galvanic anodes for insertion through a vessel wall. (Figure 7.12) The dark area at the top is the nonmetallic insulator, and the mounting head with the lead wires.

Figure 7.12 Galvanic anode in place, inserted through a vessel wall. The lead wire is connected to the vessel shell at the manway.

The aluminum anode offers much lower, but still adequate, output in oilfield brines, while maintaining current efficiencies on the order of 60% to 70%.

Zinc anodes should not be used in produced water above ambient temperature unless tests in the water under service conditions indicate that they are satisfactory. Zinc will reverse polarity with steel in many electrolytes at elevated temperatures and cause corrosion of steel rather than protect against it.

Brine storage tanks are usually protected from internal corrosion by CP or a combination of a coating and CP. Where coatings are used, care must be exercised to restrict the potential across the coating film, too high a potential can result in blistering and severe coating damage. This is particularly easy to do with improper adjustment of a rectifier system, but even magnesium anodes can develop injurious potentials unless current output is properly restricted. Once again, aluminum with its lower potential offers a safe and more than adequate source of protective current for coated vessels.

Impressed current and galvanic anodes are often suspended from the tank deck via special deck mounts. Anodes can be inspected and replaced conveniently with such an arrangement. Some vessel aluminum and magnesium anodes are designed to mount on a threaded stud welded to the vessel shell. **Figure 7.13** is a sketch of such an anode. **Figure 7.14** is a photograph of a similar anode mounted on the shell in the free-water section of an internally coated vessel. These shell mount anodes are available in several sizes and shapes, and a number may be stacked for increased life. Vessel entry is required to inspect and replace this type anode.

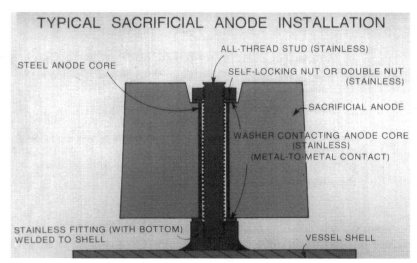

TYPICAL SACRIFICIAL ANODE INSTALLATION

ALL-THREAD STUD (STAINLESS)

STEEL ANODE CORE

SELF-LOCKING NUT OR DOUBLE NUT (STAINLESS)

SACRIFICIAL ANODE

WASHER CONTACTING ANODE CORE (STAINLESS) (METAL-TO-METAL CONTACT)

STAINLESS FITTING (WITH BOTTOM) WELDED TO SHELL

VESSEL SHELL

Figure 7.13 Drawing of a shell mounted galvanic anode.

Figure 7.14 A galvanic anode mounted on the shell of an internally coated vessel to provide protection at holidays or damaged places in the coating. (This is a similar installation to the one sketched in Figure 7.13). Note that the anode is mounted in a plastic box. The objective was to avoid too much current flow in the vicinity of the anode. Experience indicated that boxes were not necessary in this application, and they were omitted on replacement anodes.

Like oil storage tanks, discussed later in this chapter, the external bottoms of water tanks are in contact with soils that, even if not normally corrosive, frequently become so due to seepage or spillage. Thus, the same consideration should be given to CP of the external bottom of water tanks as described for oil tanks.

While "fresh" waters may not be as corrosive as brines, equipment handling surface waters for water flood projects must be protected from corrosion. Once again, a combination of coatings and CP can approach 100% protection against corrosion of the submerged surfaces of such equipment. Unless the water is quite conductive, magnesium anode or an impressed current system will be required to provide sufficient protective current. Care must be exercised in locating the anodes to give good current distribution to all submerged equipment surfaces, especially in vessels containing internal compartments or baffles.

OIL STORAGE TANKS

Present environmental concerns and regulations have focused attention on leaking, above-ground storage tanks (ASTs). Emphasis has been placed on avoiding leaks, detecting leaks, and secondary containment should a leak occur. Inspection and verification of tank soundness is very important. Generally speaking, oil production lease storage tanks have had a good history of mini-mizing leaks. Construction practices and installation designs to allow water to drain from beneath the bottoms has helped to minimize the effects of corrosion. Goals of "zero tolerance" for leaks have resulted in a continuing evolution of inspection and corrosion control approaches and procedures.

Internal Protection. Because the layer of conducting basic sediment and water (BS&W) is usually quite shallow, CP of an internal tank bottom is much more difficult than if the tank was partially filled with water. For this reason, internal CP of oilfield lease tanks is not frequently used. Internal coating of the bottom and 18 in. (46 cm) up the side have been more common than CP. However, on larger tanks in centralized production facilities, in terminals and in refineries, galvanic anodes distributed over the bottom on insulating pads or blocks have been utilized to give good results. Since the anodes will not operate properly if covered with oil, it is necessary to maintain a water level higher than the anodes. Anodes of magnesium, zinc, and aluminum have been used for this purpose, with aluminum again offering the advantage of longer life.

External Protection. With the emphasis on eliminating tank leakage mentioned above, external tank bottom protection techniques are continuing to be developed. CP designs are rapidly changing to match the changing requirements. For example, with containment designs that place an impermeable membrane in the tank's sand or gravel foundation, there may be only inches of room between the membrane and the tank bottom. This places quite a restriction on past methods of anode positions to get current properly distributed under the tank. The tight spaces have lead to numerous designs utilizing anodes made as "mats" or spiraled wire anodes. When installing new tanks, the corrosion control design must be worked out to match the containment and other environmental concerns.

Existing tanks can be retrofitted with CP where and when required. Smaller tanks, or groups of tanks, can be successfully protected with galvanic anodes. Impressed current systems may have large rectifier units with distributed beds of graphite or silicon iron anodes. A centrally located deep well groundbed may be used to distribute the current needed for protection of large areas of steel tank bottoms. A current density of 1 mA/ft^2 (10.76 mA/m^2) will usually prove adequate, if the current is well distributed.

A problem occurs in measuring the effectiveness of the applied CP because the tank potential at the periphery will usually not represent the true potential at the center of the tank. For this reason, some operators carry a potential 0.05 to 0.10 V higher (more negative) than the minimum -0.85 V at the rim, to be reasonably assured that the center area will be at or near -0.85 V.

Where new tankage is being constructed, a "permanent" reference half cell can be placed below the tank bottom near the center. Both silver/silver chloride and high purity zinc encapsulated in an appropriate backfill are used as permanent reference electrodes. As shown in **Table 7.1** the equivalent voltages to the copper/copper sulfate electrode's (–)0.85 V are (–)0.80 V and (+)0.25 V, respectively. A lead wire is brought out to a test box at the tank rim, where tank-to-reference cell potentials can be measured once CP is applied. Techniques have been developed for placing reference electrodes under existing tanks.

NACE RP0193 (latest edition), "External Cathodic Protection of On-Grade Metallic Storage Tank Bottoms,"[13] presents guidelines for the design, installation, and maintenance of such CP systems.

OFFSHORE DRILLING AND PRODUCTION STRUCTURES

The oil industry has a tremendous investment in offshore drilling and production structures, both fixed and floating (movable), including marine terminals of various types. Corrosion of these structures has been an expensive problem and a great deal has been learned about corrosion rates, structure design to minimize corrosion damage, and methods of combating corrosion.

NACE RP0176 (latest edition), Corrosion Control of Steel Fixed Offshore Platforms Associated with Petroleum Production,[14] presents the various corrosion control approaches. **Figure 1.6** in Chapter 1 illustrates the corrosion zones, relative corrosion rates, and corrosion control approaches for each zone. Also listed in Chapter 1 is NACE RP0176-94's definitions of the three corrosion zones: atmospheric, splash, and submerged. The submerged zone is the underwater portion of the platform below the splash zone including the portion below the mud line. It's also the zone where CP is applicable and the preferred approach to corrosion control. When properly designed, installed, and conscientiously maintained, CP can be essentially 100% effective in combating corrosion in the submerged zone. CP systems for marine structures may be impressed current or sacrificial, depending upon platform design, AC power availability, and economics (including a consideration of the relative ease of maintenance between the two systems).

Platform Design. The design of the jacket and the shape, size and configuration of the structural elements impacts the effectiveness of the CP system. NACE RP0176-94 discusses design features to simplify the application of CP, such as the need to use tubular members for the submerged structure, the need to avoid skip and tack welding (all welded joints should be continuous), and the need to avoid having underwater lines positioned in a way that they shield the structure from CP.

Criteria for Protection. The basic criteria for CP, using a silver/silver-chloride seawater reference electrode for the potential measurements, is a negative voltage of at least -0.80 V between the reference and the structure. The most common method for measuring potentials involves suspending the electrode from the deck to various water depths. This approach gives the general condition of the CP, but it does not usually define problem areas. A more precise approach is for the reference electrode to be handled by a diver or a remotely operated vehicle (ROV). Such a survey can result in a much more detailed and more meaningful survey. Visual inspection, including ROV videos, can reveal the actual condition of the structure, such as, any pitting or cracks as well as the presence of calcareous coating **(Figure 7.15)** from CP.

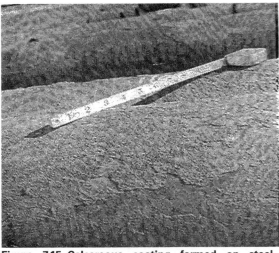

Figure 7.15 Calcareous coating formed on steel cathodically protected while submerged in water.

Calcareous coatings will slowly develop on cathodically protected structures in seawater. While these are extremely poor coatings in the conventional sense, they can ultimately reduce current requirements by 50% or more, and they are very helpful in extending current spread along a cathodically protected bare pipeline or well casing.

Galvanic Anodes. Like anodes for other applications, anodes for offshore platforms may be alloys of magnesium, zinc, or aluminum. These alloys are available in a variety of shapes and sizes. Thus, they can be selected to provide protective current to specific offshore platforms with optimum current distribution for the design life of the structure. Different methods may be used to attach the anodes to the structure depending on their type and application, but most importantly, a low resistance electrical contact must be maintained throughout the operating life of the anodes. The performance of galvanic anodes in seawater depends upon the alloy's composition (particularly true for zinc and aluminum). Most sacrificial anode CP systems installed on new structures utilize aluminum alloy anodes. The aluminum anode galvanic system is the most common CP method for offshore structures. The complexity of the structure makes the design and control of current density much more difficult with impressed current systems than with galvanic systems.

Anodes are selected to provide a specific life, often a 20- or 25-year life. Fixed structures will have the anodes attached in the fabrication yard. **Figure 7.16** shows a typical 20-year (725 lb.) anode installed on a platform. It is important that the total weight of all anodes be included in the structural design calculations for the platform. Cases have been reported where an impressed current system was selected for an offshore platform because the required total weight of galvanic anodes exceeded the design loading for the platform.

Galvanic anodes suspended from the deck find an application where the platform is in relatively shallow water, where supplemental protection is needed, or as a retrofit. Because of

Figure 7.16 A 725-lb aluminum anode in place on a structural member of an offshore platform. Note several other anodes on members in the background.

well recompletions and secondary recovery projects, the active life of many platforms have been extended beyond the design life of the cathodic protection system. Consequently, considerable work has been done developing economical techniques for effectively retrofitting anodes on platforms.[15]

Impressed Current Systems. Typically impressed current systems employ rectifiers with large current output ratings to minimize the number and space occupied by such units. **Figure 7.17** shows a rectifier on an offshore facility. A widely used anode material has been lead-6% antimony-1% silver alloy. Other anode materials that have been used with some success are lead-platinum, graphite, and a silicon-iron-chromium alloy. The lead-antimony-silver anodes may either be suspended or placed in special holders for rigid attachment to the underwater platform members. Suspended systems are somewhat more susceptible to mechanical damage, but they are simple to install and relatively easy to maintain. Impressed current anodes also may be mounted on concrete sleds that lay on the bottom with the cables installed through "J" tubes. The sleds may be placed under the platform, or set at a remote distance, or both as required for current distribution.

Impressed current systems are capable of long-term protection but are less tolerant of design, installation, and maintenance shortcomings than sacrificial anode systems. Good service can be expected if proper attention is paid to mechanical strength, connections, cable protection, choice of anode type, and integrity of power source. Routine comprehensive system monitoring should be provided.

Figure 7.17 A CP rectifier on an offshore facility.

Subsea Structures. Subsea completion well heads, flowlines, and oil storage units are being more widely used as oil production moves into deeper water offshore and into shipping lanes. The concerns, problems, and solutions are essentially the same as for offshore platforms. Coatings supplemented with CP is the usual approach to corrosion control. However, corrosion-resistant metals are seeing widespread use in some offshore areas (*e.g.*, the North Sea). External CP may be the impressed current or galvanic anode type, depending on the particular circumstances.

ROLE OF PROTECTIVE COATINGS

As discussed in the previous chapter, protective coating systems are one of the basic approaches to corrosion control. However, since no approach is 100% effective, 100% of the time, many critical situations use the combination of coatings and cathodic protection. In fact, when it comes to buried structures, the combination is often the most economical approach.

For example, pipeline coatings supplemented with CP can be a more economical approach to control corrosion on a pipeline than either technique would be by itself. Not only can the combination provide near 100% protection, but it can allow the use of a lower cost coating system and a much simpler CP system. In many cases, an uncoated line would require an impressed current system for adequate corrosion control, yet corrosion on the same line could be completely controlled with coating supplemented with a sacrificial anode system to protect holidays (voids) and damaged places in the coating.

The importance of the combination is highlighted by NACE RP0169[16], "Corrosion Control of Underground or Submerged Piping" and NACE RP0675[17], Control of External Corrosion of Offshore Pipelines," both cover coatings and CP.

The use of sacrificial anode systems to supplement internal vessel and tank coatings is an accepted technique for controlling corrosion in water handling vessels and water sections of multiphase vessels.

Coatings have only been used in limited cases on the exterior of well casings. However, as mentioned elsewhere, some operators cement-to-surface to provide a cement sheath on the casing. Even though the cement sheath is not complete, the bare surface area is drastically reduced, and again the demands on the CP system are decreased.

About the only place where coatings have not been economically justified as a means of reducing the cost of corrosion control by CP is the submerged areas of steel offshore platforms.

REFERENCES

1. NACE Standard RP0169-96, "Control of External Corrosion on Underground or Submerged Metallic Piping Systems" Section 2, Definitions (Houston, TX: NACE, 1996), p.1.

2. Private communication, Bass Engineering Co., 1996.

3. NACE Standard RP0169-96, Section 6, Criteria and Other Considerations for Cathodic Protection (Houston, TX: NACE, 1996), p. 13.

4. NACE Standard RP0169-96, Ibid., Section 2, p.2.

5. NACE Standard RP0193-93, "External Cathodic Protection of On-Grade Metallic Storage Tank Bottoms" Section 7 (Houston, TX: NACE, 1993), p. 7.

6. NACE Standard RP0572 (latest edition), "Design, Installation, Operation, and Maintenance of Impressed Current Deep Groundbeds" (Houston, TX: NACE).

7. NACE Standard RP0169 (latest edition) Ibid.

8. H. J. Morgan, Cathodic Protection, 2nd ed. (Houston, TX: NACE, 1987).

9. A. W. Peabody, Control of Pipeline Corrosion, (Houston, TX: NACE, 1967).

10. NACE Standard RP0186 (latest edition), "Application of Cathodic Protection for External Surfaces of Steel Well Casings" (Houston, TX: NACE).

11. A. W. Peabody, Ibid., p.123.

12. NACE Standard RP0575-95, "Internal Cathodic Protection Systems in Oil-Treating Vessels" Section 4, Criteria (Houston, TX: NACE), p. 3.

13. NACE Standard RP0193 (latest edition), "External Cathodic Protection of On-Grade Metallic Storage Tank Bottoms" (Houston, TX: NACE).

14. NACE Standard RP0176 (latest edition), "Corrosion Control of Steel Fixed Offshore Platforms Associated with Petroleum Production" (Houston, TX: NACE).

15. M. W. Mateer, K. J. Kennelly, "Designing Anode Retrofits for Offshore Platforms," MP 33, 1, (1994): p. 32.

16. NACE Standard RP0169 (latest edition).

17. NACE Standard RP0675 (latest edition), "Control of External Corrosion on Offshore Steel Pipelines" (Houston, TX: NACE).

APPENDIX REFERENCES

7A-1. A. W. Peabody, Control of Pipeline Corrosion (Houston, TX: NACE, 1967), p. 35.

7A-2. NACE Standard RP0186 (latest edition), "Application of Cathodic Protection for External Surfaces of Steel Well Casings" (Houston, TX: NACE).

7A-3. A. 1W. Peabody, Ibid., Chapter 6, Survey Methods and Techniques, p. 38–50.

APPENDIX 7A

SURVEY AND TEST METHODS IN CATHODIC PROTECTION

POTENTIAL MEASUREMENTS

Potential readings are customarily given in millivolts or volts. Because a voltage is really a difference in two potentials, the "potential" as reported is a voltage reading between the structure being investigated and a convenient reference electrode (most frequently a copper-copper sulfate half cell) placed in the electrolyte near the structure. Typical potential values for different metals in neutral soil or water, measured with respect to a copper-copper sulfate reference electrode, are presented in **Table 7A.1**.

TABLE 7A.1 Practical Galvanic Series

METAL	VOLTS[1]
Commercially pure magnesium	-1.75
Magnesium alloy (6% Al, 3% Zn, 0.15% Mn)	-1.6
Zinc	-1.1
Aluminum alloy (5% zinc)	-1.05
Commercially pure aluminum	-0.8
Mild steel (clean and shiny)	-0.5 to -0.8
Mild steel (rusted)	-0.2 to -0.5
Cast iron (not graphitized)	-0.5
Lead	-0.5
Mild steel in concrete	-0.2
Copper, brass, bronze	-0.2
High silicon cast iron	-0.2
Mill scale on steel	-0.2
Carbon, graphite, coke	+0.3

[1] Typical potential normally observed in neutral soils and water, measured with respect to copper sulfate reference electrode.

"Structures" can, of course, be anything immersed in or in contact with soils and waters, or containing waters.

Pipelines

It is easier, for purposes of this particular section, to select for discussion one type of structure, a buried steel pipeline, with the understanding that the discussion is applicable to any structure in its particular environment.

The potentials encountered usually range from a few millivolts to several volts, and in order to obtain accurate potential measurements against a copper-copper sulfate or other reference electrode, an instrument of high sensitivity is required. If a high resistance millivolt meter or voltmeter is used, it should have a sensitivity rating of at least 50,000 ohms/V. Ordinary multi-test meters cannot be used satisfactorily for cathodic protection (CP) survey work. These precise readings require a direct reading electronic type voltmeters, a potentiometer-voltmeter, or a straight potentiometer.

The meter, plus two reference electrodes (usually copper-copper sulfate), and necessary test leads and contact devices, are the minimum equipment required for a potential survey.

In making the survey, the structure is contacted at risers, through valve boxes, test stations, or by use of a device such as a contact bar. It is extremely important that a good, low-resistance electrical contact be established with the buried structure. The negative post of the voltmeter is connected through suitable leads to the pipeline contact, and the positive post is connected to the reference electrode. If a copper-copper sulfate electrode is used, the pipe will exhibit a negative polarity. This is shown schematically in **Figure 7A.1a**. The potential of the structure is taken with the electrode firmly embedded in the earth directly over the structure. The structure-to-earth potential (P/S) is recorded. This procedure is repeated at suitable intervals throughout the entire system under study. Areas of more negative potential indicate anodic or corroding areas **(Figure 7A.1b)**. For Example, "Prior to the application of CP, readings taken from point to point above a bare pipeline, subject to soil corrosion, could range only from a low in the order or -0.1 to -0.3 V (in the most cathodic areas) to a high approaching -0.8 V (in the most anodic areas)." [7A-1]

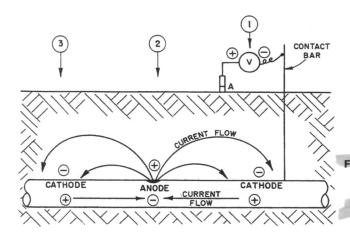

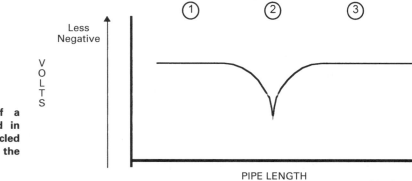

Figure 7A.1a: Diagram showing measurement of pipe-to-soil potentials, using a contact bar. Note polarity in soil and pipe. Pipe-to-soil potential obtained at "1" and "3" will be more cathodic (less negative) than that obtained at anodic (corroding) area at "2."

Figure 7A.1b Re-presentation of a graph of the data collected in Figure 7A.1a. The circled numbers correspond to the positions in 7A.1a.

Casing Potential Profile Tool

The casing potential profile tool (**Figure 7A.2**) plays an important part in casing corrosion control work. Although the name of the tool is "casing potential profile," the measurement is actually a potential difference, and the plotted data represent a casing potential difference profile. This tool consists of two sets of spring-loaded contacts spaced 10 to 26ft (3 to 8m) apart. These sets of contacts are electrically insulated from each other and from the body of the tool. Leads from the contacts are connected to a microvoltmeter at the surface. Run in a well with the tubing removed and the hole filled with oil, the tool is placed at the desired depth, the contacts are set to make good electrical contact with the wall of the casing, and a reading is taken of the voltage between the knives. This voltage is the IR drop in the length of casing due to currents traveling either up or down, and the amount of IR drop (since the resistance, [R], of the casing wall is assumed to be constant in a string containing all the same grade and size casing) is proportional to the amount of current flowing. The polarity of the voltage measured at the surface indicates whether current is flowing up or down.

By taking a series of readings at intervals, and connecting the points, a curve or log is obtained that can be interpreted to provide a variety of information. The left hand curve in **Figure 7A.3** is an example of a log that might be obtained in a casing under so-called "native state" conditions (*i.e.*, with no external CP current applied). The right hand curve represents a log with CP current applied.

In evaluating the results of such logs, a positive slope of the plotted voltage (IR) drop vs depth indicates an increase in the amount of current being picked up by the casing. Likewise, a negative slope normally indicates a discharge of current from the casing and since current leaving indicates an anodic area, it would also indicate a corroding area. There are other things that can cause a change in slope. For example, a change of resistance due to a change in casing wall thickness or change of pipe grade could cause changes in slope. The spacing of the contacts on the tool will influence the possibility of finding small local corrosion cells, indicating only those anodic areas extending over a much longer interval of pipe. However, the casing voltage profile log does give a very important general picture of what is happening on the outside of the casing.

A more detailed description of the casing potential profile test method and interpretation is given in NACE RP0186 (latest edition), "Application of Cathodic Protection for External Surfaces of Steel Well Casings."[7A-2]

Figure 7A.2 Casing potential profile tool.

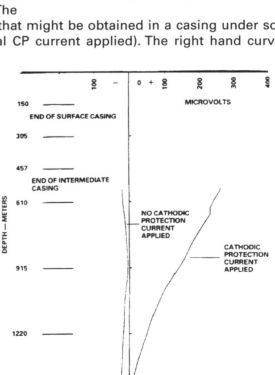

Figure 7A.3 Typical casing potential profile plot.

CURRENT FLOW (IR DROP)

Procedure 1. The direction of direct current flow in the structure (pipeline) can be determined using a direct reading millivolt meter or potentiometer. The area or location where current flows from the structure to the earth is where corrosion is occurring. This is detectable by noting direction and magnitude of current flow in the pipe. The point at which it reaches a maximum value and reverses its direction of flow is the point at which corrosion is occurring. The magnitude of current flow, which can be calculated or estimated from the millivolt readings and the pipe resistance between contact points, provides a rough approximation of metal loss per year which is occurring.

Corrosion may still be occurring in the absence of measurable current flow in the structure due to local cell action between the contact points. For this reason, the IR drop measurement of current in the structure is useful only to locate gross anodic areas.

The method is illustrated in **Figure 7A.4**. Because accurate readings as low as one millivolt may be required, the resistance of the test leads and contacts to the structure must be low, on the order of 1%, compared to the internal resistance of the voltmeter.

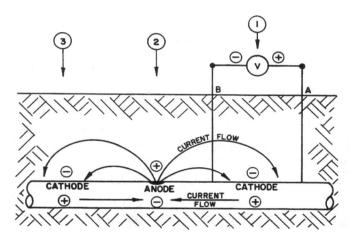

Figure 7A.4 Diagram showing measurement of IR drop to determine direction and of current flow. Note the potential difference is measured between contact bars A and B by a low resistance voltmeter. Current flow in the pipe is from (+) to (-); thus, anodes will be at the most negative points on the pipe.

Knowing the resistance of the pipe, current flow can be calculated from Ohm's Law:

$$I = E/R \qquad\qquad (1)$$

where I is the current in amperes, E is the potential in volts, and R is the pipe resistance in ohms (between contact points).

If the resistance of the pipe under investigation is not known, it may be estimated from published tables for various sizes of steel pipes, or calibrated on the spot by impressing a known current through a test section of the pipe and noting the IR drop produced.

Procedure 2. Because the same current flowing in the pipe must also be flowing in the adjacent soil, where the much greater soil resistance produces millivolt readings of much larger magnitude than in the pipe, a modification of the technique is widely used on buried bare pipe. It is called the "surface potential" or "two-electrode" survey.

The surface potential survey requires a high resistance millivolt meter, or potentiometer-voltmeter with polarity reversal switch, two copper-copper sulfate electrodes, and suitable test leads. A survey crew also will need a pipe locator and a soil resistivity meter, because it is essential to stay immediately over the pipe and to know the soil resistivity at anodic areas.

The two copper-copper sulfate electrodes, which should be kept in good condition so as to read within 2 millivolts of each other, are placed over the pipe at a suitable distance apart, usually 20ft (6m), and the potential difference (in millivolts) and electrode polarity is read on the meter and recorded. The electrodes are then moved down the line 20ft (6m), maintaining the set spacing. In this manner, millivolt readings and electrode polarity are recorded over the full length of the line being surveyed. **Figure 7A.5** illustrates the method. It should be noted that pipe-to-soil potentials are not necessary, although they can be readily obtained at any point where they may be considered desirable, by contacting the pipe.

Anodic and cathodic areas are identified as points of potential reversal. Because the anodic areas are of greatest significance, these are identified during the course of the survey. Soil resistivity measurements, usually coupled with "side drain" millivolt readings, also are obtained at that time. These measurements will be needed later to properly interpret the severity of the anodic areas and to select the number and size of anodes needed in the "hot spots."

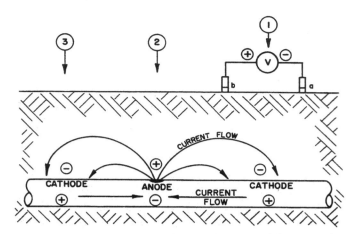

Figure 7A.5 Surface potential method for determining corrosion. This involves electrodes (a) and (b) connected through a voltmeter (V). Potential is measured between the two electrodes. When the two electrodes are moved to position (2), the reading will be more positive, indicating an anodic or corroding area. When the electrodes are moved to position (3), the readings will be more negative, thus helping to locate the anodic area.

These and other tests are covered in more detail in Peabody's chapter on survey methods.[7A-3]

SOIL (OR WATER) RESISTIVITY MEASUREMENTS

Since current flow to and from the pipe will generally occur at the areas of lowest earth resistivity, it is logical to assume that low resistivity areas could be anodic. This method then determines only the opportunity for corrosion as related to earth resistivity and the location where such corrosion would be expected. It does not indicate whether or not corrosion is actually occurring, or how fast.

This technique is one of determining the resistivity of the earth, expressed most correctly as ohm-centimeters, at preselected areas along the pipeline. The resistivity may be determined by the use of a four-pole instrument or single-point probes. Actual resistance values alone usually have little meaning; greater significance of the survey data lies in the differences in soil resistivity values along the line. Some companies have selected 2,000 ohm-cm as the suspect value, *i.e.*, at a resistance below this value, serious corrosion is expected. It should be pointed out, however, that serious corrosion can also occur on bare pipe where a sharp change in soil resistance occurs (*e.g.*, from 5,000 to 50,000 ohm-cm).

The results of the survey may be used to select areas for installation of protective measures such as coatings and CP.

CURRENT REQUIREMENT SURVEYS

The actual amount of current required for CP of a given structure can be calculated in several ways. In this section, CP is meant to imply complete corrosion control (as evidenced by compliance with some selected criterion such as -0.85 V potential to a copper-copper sulfate electrode), rather than "hot spot" protection. The latter has a very definite place in the economic scheme of things for existing bare pipe, which rarely justifies 100% CP.

Pipeline

If a bare pipeline, or other structure, lies in soil or water of known general characteristics, the CP system may be designed based on applying a selected current density (milliamperes/sq. ft) to the structure, provided the current is properly distributed.

On large bare structures, it is seldom practical to temporarily apply the amount of current needed to achieve protective potentials; therefore, CP design is usually approached on the current density basis described earlier. In areas where previous experience may be lacking (*e.g.*, produced waters, polluted rivers, or estuaries, etc.), the use of test coupons with a range of applied current densities over a period of several weeks or months has been helpful in arriving at the proper current density on which to base the full-scale design.

With coated structures, taking again a pipeline as an example, it is possible to set up a temporary CP drain point and determine how much current will be needed to protect either the entire line, if it is relatively short and is insulated from other structures, or to protect a given portion of the line. On long lines, several such tests may be necessary, especially if substantial differences in coating condition and/or soil resistivity is anticipated in different areas. Temporary test currents of up to about 10 amperes can be applied by a storage battery, and as much as 100 amperes can be applied by a welding generator. The temporary "groundbed" used to discharge the test current into the soil may be any existing noncritical structure not electrically connected to the pipeline under test, such as an abandoned section of line or well casing. In many cases, a suitable temporary groundbed for test purposes must be constructed of driven steel rods, aluminum foil, or actual anodes that can be left in place for a later permanent installation or installed in such a manner as to be removable for reuse. It is desirable to locate the test beds, at least for the larger current drains, at a distance from the pipeline similar to that which might be expected for the later, permanent groundbed installation.

Well Casing

Surveys of well casings for the application of cathodic protection (CP) may include several of the above described techniques.

Casing potential profile tool is used to first locate gross anodic and cathodic areas and then to ascertain the effect of temporary CP currents applied at the well head.

The right hand curve of **Figure 7A.3** represents a log which might be obtained while current is being applied to the casing from a temporary source. In this log, the entire curve has been shifted to the right, and the formerly anodic portion is now cathodic, indicating that the test current is entering the casing at all points from top to bottom. As stated earlier, these examples are somewhat idealized. In many cases, several different values of test current may have to be applied before the correct amount is chosen. To conserve logging time (as well as downtime for the oil or gas well being logged), estimates of predicted current are oftentimes made, and there are a variety of techniques used to make these estimates. Some operators use, as a rule of thumb, a certain amount of current per unit area [1 mA/ft^2 (10.76 mA/m^2)] is a typical amount] to arrive at an estimate for confirmation by the voltage profile log. Others use the "E log I" technique described in the following paragraph to make their estimates.

E log I surveys are another technique for determining the current requirements for CP of well casings. **Figure 7A.6** shows a schematic of the equipment set-up for the test. Essentially, this method consists of applying increasing increments of current to the well casing for fixed intervals of time, typically two or three minutes. After each time interval, the current is turned off and an instant open-circuit potential of the casing to a judiciously placed reference electrode on the surface is obtained. These data, when plotted on semi-log paper, give a curve similar to that shown in **Figure 7A.7**. From theoretical considerations, the current given by the intercept of the two straight-line portions of this curve **(Point A** in **Figure 7A.7)** would indicate the current adequate to polarize (protect) the casing. Due to other considerations, and because of generally better correlation with the effect of applied currents on the casing potential profile, it has been a common practice to use the current value of the first point to fall on the second straight-line portion of the curve **(Point B)** in the design of cathodic protection systems for well casings.

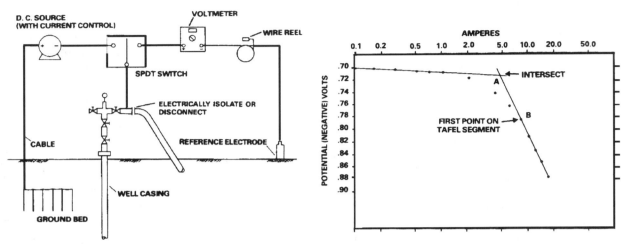

Figure 7A.6 Equipment set-up for E log I test.   **Figure 7A.7 Sample E log I plot.**

Most corrosion engineers accept the fact that establishment of the true current requirement for protection of well casings is not anything like an exact science. However, many thousands of wells have had CP applied to them on the basis of such data, generally with excellent results.

CHAPTER 8

CHEMICAL TREATMENT

INTRODUCTION

The words "chemical treatment" cover many activities in oilfield operations—from the use of chemicals to clean out a well or stimulate the formation, to the use of what's often referred to as "oilfield chemicals"—depending on where and who is using the term. This chapter will deal with the chemicals that are used directly or indirectly in the control of corrosion. Some materials, such as those used to scavenge oxygen or control microbiological activity will be discussed in Chapter 9.

FUNDAMENTALS OF CORROSION INHIBITORS

A successful inhibitor program involves selection of the proper inhibitor, application with a technique that assures that the inhibitor gets a chance to film, and monitoring and periodic review to confirm control and "flag" changes in conditions that require treatment modification. Therefore, inhibitor programs must be designed for specific wells or systems, their mechanical features, and operating procedures.

Corrosion inhibition is accomplished by one or more of several mechanisms. Some inhibitors retard corrosion by adsorption to form an invisibly thin film (monomolecular film); others form visible bulky precipitates that coat the metal and protect it from attack. Another common mechanism consists of causing the metal to corrode in such a way that a combination of adsorption and corrosion product forms a passive layer. Included in the definition are those substances that, when added to an environment, retard corrosion but do not interact directly with the metal surface. This type of inhibitor causes conditions in the environment to be more favorable for the formation of protective precipitates, or it neutralizes an acidic component in the system.

Most inhibitors form some type of film on the protected metal surface. The first layer formed may be strongly bonded, perhaps by an electrical charge exchange analogous to a chemical reaction. Such strong bonding is called "chemisorption." Weaker physical bonding forces are also involved, especially during deposition of subsequent layers of the film.

There are many types of corrosion inhibitors for various applications. Generally they can be grouped into two broad categories: inorganic and organic **(Table 8.1)**. The inorganic inhibitors are most commonly used in cooling waters, heat mediums, and sweetening processes (*e.g.*, closed loop or recirculating systems). The organic film formers are used in oil, gas, and water systems and are the most common inhibitors in oilfield applications.

TABLE 8.1 Corrosion Inhibitor Classification/Use

INORGANIC CORROSION INHIBITORS	ORGANIC CORROSION INHIBITORS
• Cooling tower water	• Oil, gas, & water wells
• Heat/cooling mediums	• Flowlines
• Dehydration glycol	• Gas systems
• Sweetening system amine solutions	• Water systems

INORGANIC CORROSION INHIBITORS

The inorganic corrosion inhibitors are usually metal salts, which will passivate the surface of a metal that normally would not be passivated in the environment. These are water soluble chemicals that react with the metal surface to produce a layer that has protective qualities. A constant (or fixed) concentration is required; therefore, close control is necessary. Care must be taken with some materials because too high or too low concentration can cause accelerated corrosion. Furthermore, they are usually pH sensitive (that is, the pH must be maintained within certain limits to assure passivation). Another reason they are not used in production streams is that the inorganic inhibitors usually will not work if chlorides are present and most of the waters in production operations contain chlorides. The inorganic inhibitors fall into two classes: anodic and cathodic.

ANODIC INHIBITORS

As the name indicates, the anodic inhibitors react mainly at the anodic areas—this is where corrosion is taking place—and the film formed is a reaction product that is essentially a corrosion product. The net effect is to slow down or stop the corrosion reaction by eliminating the anodic areas. Anodic inhibitors can be divided into two categories: passivators and nonpassivators.

The passivators inhibit in the absence of oxygen. Examples of anodic passivators include the chromates and the nitrites. At one time, the chromates were the inhibitors of choice in the open cooling water systems in plants; however, because of their toxicity, environmental regulations have almost eliminated their use.

The nonpassivators, conversely, require oxygen to be present for their reaction. A common example would be the polyphosphates.

Some sources refer to the anodic inhibitors as "dangerous inhibitors." Insufficient dosage will result in incomplete coverage of the anodic areas. These small bare anodic sites will be coupled to the large cathodic areas. The large cathode/small anode relationship, of course, can lead to greatly accelerated pitting at the anodic sites.

CATHODIC INORGANIC INHIBITORS

On the other hand, the cathodic inhibitors are active at the cathodic sites and thus reduce the cathode/anode relationship and slow down the corrosion reaction. Examples of the cathodic inhibitors are calcium salts, magnesium salts, and zinc salts. While these may be effective inhibitors in fresh water, most oilfield brines contain dissolved salts or gases that would react and cause the inhibitors to precipitate. For example, zinc salt inhibitors will precipitate as zinc sulfide with hydrogen sulfide, or calcium can be precipitated as calcium sulfate scale by dissolved sulfates.

ORGANIC CORROSION INHIBITORS

The most common corrosion inhibitors in use in oilfield systems are the so-called "organic film forming inhibitors." Therefore, unless stated otherwise, the remainder of this chapter will be dealing with the organic inhibitors. These are polar organic materials consisting of molecules that have a charge on each end. The polar molecule is often depicted as if it were a tadpole, with a head and a tail (Figure 8.1A). Because of the charges, these polar organics are surface active and are attracted to and tend to cling to solids (Figure 8.1B). Thus, they can form a protective barrier (film) on a metal surface. The long chain hydrocarbon tail on the inhibitor molecule is oleophilic (i.e., it has an affinity for oil). The net result in oil systems (or produced water system with traces of oil carryover) is an inhibitor/oil film on the metal surface. In effect, an oil-wet condition has been reestablished on the metal surfaces (Figure 8.1C). As discussed in a previous chapter, oil wet surfaces repel water and thus break up the corrosion cell by effectively placing a barrier between the electrolyte and the metal surface.

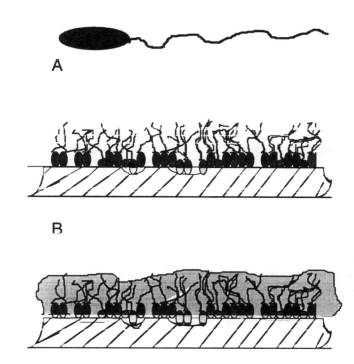

Figure 8.1 Stylized polar organic corrosion inhibitor.
A. Inhibitor molecule.
B. Inhibitor film (monomolecular).
C. Inhibitor/oil film.

The inhibitor film is not permanent and must be repaired or reestablished from time to time. The ability of an inhibitor to maintain a film in a given system, or to repair holidays (breaks or voids) in the film, is known as "film persistency." Film persistency is a measure of how long an inhibitor film will remain intact (*i.e.,* how long will it take to wear away or break down the inhibitor film to the point where it's not fully protective?) Generally, the inhibitors used in oil and gas well systems have good film persistency and re-treatments can be infrequent. Some gas systems that are dry of liquid hydrocarbons may require the continuos injection of an inhibited oil.

Another inhibitor characteristic is its filming efficiency—a measure of the completeness of the film and the protection it provides. Usually called "percent protection," it is determined by measuring the metal loss with and without the inhibitor in laboratory and/or field test procedures.

An important inhibitor characteristic that is often overlooked and very seldom measured is the time it takes for an inhibitor film to form. It is common to assume that all that is necessary is to expose a metal surface to an inhibitor solution and instantly the inhibitor molecules will adsorb onto the metal forming the protective barrier. In reality, the adsorption takes a finite amount of time. As would be expected, the filming time is a function of concentration, solubility, temperature, and other variables of the specific inhibitor and system being treated. The filming time is very important in most of the batch treatments discussed later in this chapter.

CORROSION INHIBITOR FORMULATIONS

Most inhibitors used in oilfield applications are liquids. Their density will vary from 7 to 12 lbs/gal (0.8 to 1.4 kg/L) depending on the chemical nature of the inhibitor, its solvent system, and the application.

It is quite common to talk about inhibitors as if the drum contained 100% of the molecules that form the film, and that is not correct. The drummed inhibitor is a mixture of materials compounded to give certain properties (both physical and chemical) to the formulation.

The drum we buy, contains a material we call inhibitor, that is a mixture of inhibitor base (the "tadpoles") and additives in a diluent (sometimes called the carrier or the solvent) **(Figure 8.2)**.

The inhibitor bases are compounded of various chemicals that will form films and have specific properties. Most of the bases are organic amines and/or amine salts. They may be fairly long chain molecules (with 16 or 18 carbon atoms) or ring compounds. Generically, they may be classified as diamines, quaternary ammonium chlorides, poly-amido-amines, or imidazolines. Often the base materials are amine salts, which means that they have been reacted with other organic materials such as organic acids (*e.g.*, dimer-trimer acids, acetic acid, etc.). Several different base

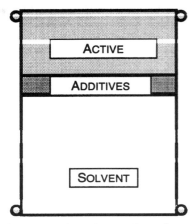

Figure 8.2 Components in a drum of corrosion inhibitor.

chemicals are used (although not as many as one might think). The same base material may be in many different formulations designed to give various specific properties of solubility, dispersability, and film persistence for specific applications.

The additives are used to help these properties, to stabilize the mixture, and to prevent emulsion formations.

The solvent may be a number of materials (from diesel oil to heavy aromatic hydrocarbons or water and alcohol). The solvents are important from several standpoints. Many inhibitor bases are solids or too viscous to handle at 100% active and many need to be diluted before they will be soluble or dispersible in the crude or water system. Of course, some suppliers have been known to go overboard on the amount of diluent used (solvents are the cheapest material in the drum), and cut rate or "competitive" inhibitors are often very low in active inhibitor components. This is why we should not be extremely concerned about the price per gallon. It is the "use" cost that is the most important.

CORROSION INHIBITOR PROPERTIES

Selection of a specific inhibitor formulation for a specific program requires matching the inhibitor properties with the system's fluids, its environment, and application technique to provide optimum economical corrosion control, while at the same time avoiding introducing other operating problems. For example, the ideal inhibitor should be soluble enough in a system's fluids to have the mobility to get to the metal surface, yet insoluble enough to have good film persistency, but it must not form "gunk" that plugs injection wells or surface equipment. It must have sufficient surface active properties to clean the surface and work its way through and under deposits, but it cannot form unbreakable emulsions of the well fluids.

The need for different properties is the reason each oilfield chemical supplier has so many different formulations available. The properties needed for treater truck inhibition of a rod pumping well are not exactly the same as those for a gas-lift well; in fact, the properties required by all rod pump wells are not the same. An inhibitor to be used in a gas well flowline will have different properties than the inhibitor used downhole in the same well. **Table 8.2** lists some of the properties and characteristics that should be considered when selecting a corrosion inhibitor.

TABLE 8.2 Important Considerations for Corrosion Inhibitor Selection

Inhibits corrosion in the system
Solubility/Dispersability
In diluent
In carrier
In produced fluids
Oil
Water
Gas
Partitioning (between oil & water)
Compatibility with other chemicals
Emulsification properties
Pour point (viscosity)
Freeze point
Freeze-thaw stability
Thermal stability
Corrosiveness
Mobility of individual components
Foaming properites
Compatibility with downstream process
Environmental concerns

Inhibits corrosion in the well or system. This may sound like an unnecessary concern; however, all corrosion inhibitors do not effectively inhibit corrosion in all systems.

Solubility/Dispersability is one of the most important properties of corrosion inhibitors and is also another way of classifying inhibitors. All corrosion inhibitors can be classified as to their water and oil solubility and dispersability characteristics. Generally, the manufacturer's product data sheets give solubility in oil, fresh water, and brine. Inhibitors may be described as "oil soluble-water dispersible," "water soluble-oil dispersible," "oil soluble-water insoluble," "water soluble-oil insoluble," or some other descriptor that indicates their solubility/dispersability characteristics. These characteristics are important for several reasons.

Since the inhibitor must get to the metal surface if it is to form the film, its solubility/dispersability in the produced fluids must be considered. The equipment being inhibited and/or the treating method also enter into the selection process. For example, when treating a flowline where water collects and flows along the bottom, the water solubility of the inhibitor may control the selection of the inhibitor even if the majority of the fluids are hydrocarbons. Yet, in a gas well being treated by tubing displacement, the most cost effective inhibitor will most likely be a heavy-film-former that is basically water insoluble and would simply float over the water in the corroding zone. Since the solubility/dispersability at system temperatures can be quite different than at room temperature, the use temperature property becomes an important consideration. It's often thought that as temperatures are increased materials become more soluble. This is not necessarily true. Some inhibitors that are water soluble at room temperature will float out at well temperature. While that might be an advantage inside the tubing string (there might not be as much tendency for the inhibitor to desorb), it would be a disadvantage for the inhibitor to float to the top if the inhibitor was in the packer brine in the casing/tubing annulus.

Many treating techniques call for diluting the inhibitor in a proper solvent (diluent) before application. Depending on the inhibitor formulation, water, methanol, glycol, field crude, diesel, or kerosene may be selected. The diluent and the inhibitor's solvent system must be compatible to avoid problems. For example, an inhibitor formulated in an aromatic solvent may require an aromatic diluent. Such an inhibitor could come out of solution if the diluent is not an aromatic oil. The inhibitor supplier should be consulted for the proper choice of a diluent. An inhibitor is generally considered soluble in a diluent if the inhibitor-diluent mixture remains clear. An inhibitor is considered dispersible if it can be evenly dispersed in the diluent by moderate hand shaking. The quantity of diluent is almost always equal to or greater than the quantity of inhibitor. The dispersion of the inhibitor in the diluent may break rapidly (*i.e.*, in less than a minute). This is a temporary dispersion. An inhibitor that remains uniformly dispersed in the diluent is considered a "dispersible inhibitor."

Partitioning between oil and water is an indication of the proportion of the inhibitor that will be in the oil phase and the water phase. This can be important in some applications. For instance, will the inhibitor used to treat a rod pumping well also perform satisfactorily in the flowline where the free-water runs along the bottom of the line? Also, will enough inhibitor be in the water leaving the heater treater to provide inhibition in the water disposal system?

Compatibility of corrosion inhibitors with other chemicals is ordinarily no problem when the inhibitor and other chemicals are present in use dosages (concentrations of a few ppm). However, in some cases, two or more chemicals will react with each other, nullifying their effectiveness. In addition, in the concentrated form (as they are supplied) many oilfield chemicals are not compatible with corrosion inhibitors (or each other) because of variations in solvent system, type of chemical (cationic vs anionic), etc. Actually, many corrosion inhibitors are not compatible with each other. Therefore, chemicals should not be mixed before injection, nor should they be injected at the same point in a line or vessel. Each chemical should be injected with its own tank, pump, line, and injection fitting. Furthermore, the separate injection points should be far enough apart so that the chemicals are well diluted before they meet.

Emulsification properties of a corrosion inhibitor can be a concern because their surface active nature can cause emulsions in water-oil systems. Some of these emulsions break quite readily, while others are extremely stable and practically impossible to break. The inclusion of an emulsion breaker in a corrosion inhibitor is no guarantee against formation of stable emulsions. Produced fluids should be tested to have reasonable assurance that no stable emulsion will be formed by a specific corrosion inhibitor.

Pour point is the temperature where the inhibitor will no longer pour. The pour point, freeze point, and freeze-thaw stability are very important properties in cold climates.

Freeze point is, of course, the temperature where the inhibitor freezes. A very important value in northern (cold) climates, particularly when the inhibitor drums (or other containers) are stored outdoors.

Freeze-thaw stability, or freeze-thaw stable, means that after a frozen inhibitor is thawed, it will continue to be (or return to) a homogenous material with the same properties as before freezing.

Thermal stability indicates that the inhibitor will retain its characteristics at an elevated temperature, usually bottomhole temperature. The stability is very important in high-temperature wells, and can be important in certain well applications, which would hold the inhibitor at a temperature for extended periods (*e.g.*, techniques using chemical injection valves where the inhibitor or inhibitor mixture is "stored" in the casing/tubing annulus). Since many inhibitor bases are made at reaction temperatures above 400°F (204°C), degradation of the molecule is not as much of a concern as changes in inhibitor properties, for instance, solubility or separation of the components. However, degradation can occur in the 400°F to 500°F (204°C to 260°C) high-pressure gas wells.

Corrosiveness as a property of a corrosion inhibitor may sound ridiculous, but some inhibitors in their "as delivered condition" may be quite corrosive, even though they inhibit corrosion at use concentration in the system. This is why some formulations are delivered in lined drums. Information on the corrosion characteristics of a specific corrosion inhibitor is important when selecting materials for chemical injection facilities. Because they might be changing formulations during a project's life, some operators install all chemical injection facilities with corrosion-resistant components (often type 316 [UNS S31600] stainless steel is the material of choice).

Mobility of the corrosion inhibitor base, when the solvents are removed, is critical in situations where the inhibitor is injected into dry gas (such as gas-lift gas). An inhibitor should be fluid enough to flow down the casing even if all the solvent has flashed off into the gas.

Foaming properties of an inhibitor usually are not a concern at the normal low use dosages. However, in some batch treating situations where high concentrations can enter separation facilities or plants, foaming of the produced fluids could create operating problems. Thus, the foaming tendencies of the inhibitor in the specific field fluids should be determined. Many water system corrosion inhibitors are "heavy foamers" and an overdose (such as a runaway pump) can upset a water plant. Reports of water plants "filled with soap suds" are not uncommon.

Compatibility with downstream processes is important to avoid the situation where the inhibitor would upset or foul a process or operation. For example, inhibitors could cause foaming and glycol loss in glycol dehydration units, upset gas sweetening processes, foul drybed units, or upset refinery catalysts.

Environmental concerns include not only the implications of an inhibitor spill, but also, in normal operation, where does the inhibitor ultimately end up? Is that a problem?

Many of the above properties and information can be found on the inhibitor supplier's product data sheets. Other product information may be found on the Material Safety Data Sheet (MSDS) that must be supplied for each chemical delivered to a users location. (See the sidebar, "MSDS—It's the Law.") Together these two sources supply a lot of information on production chemicals.

"MSDS—It's the Law"

The Material Safety Data Sheet (MSDS) is just what the name implies—a form that supplies information on a material for use in an emergency or accident.

In the United States each chemical manufacturer or vendor is required to furnish an MSDS for any material supplied to a location (this includes samples for testing). The user is required to have the MSDS available to company and emergency personnel. These regulations were designed to minimize risks at the time of spills, fires, or other accidents.

MSDS forms have 16 sections, covering a variety of topics, including such items as: product identification, composition or information on ingredients, and hazards identification, first aid, fire fighting, and accidental release measures, handling and storage requirements, and exposure control/personnel protection are covered. Typical physical and chemical properties, and stability and reactivity data are given. Toxicological, ecological, disposal, transportation and regulatory information is listed. The final section is for information that may be required by a specific state or local authority.

The amount of detail and thoroughness of the information may vary depending on the chemical, it's hazard level, and the supplier; but the MSDS does have a lot of information. Depending on the chemical, the composition may only be very generic, but it gives a clue to the chemistry and to the solvent system used. With the exception of biocides and other materials that must be registered (labeled) the exact formula (percentage composition) is not required. The physical and chemical properties section is another that gives very helpful information. It's well worth the effort to get familiar with the sheets for chemicals you may be using. The information is available. After all it's the law.

SELECTION OF THE INHIBITOR

The first step in inhibitor selection is to review the system, its physical layout, mechanical considerations, and fluids being handled (locating any special or unique factors).

The second step is to select the applications method(s) that assure the chemical gets to where it is needed when it is needed. Sometimes there is only one choice, other times several techniques could be used. As usual the final decision is based on both technical and economic factors.

The third step is to review the properties that will be required for the application technique (other than that it must be a corrosion inhibitor).

Finally, after the system is reviewed, application methods selected, and the property requirements outlined, an inhibitor may be selected. Oftentimes the specific inhibitor is picked based on past experiences in similar situations and a field trial is started. In other cases, particularly for large programs, or when unique properties are required, screening tests are performed to compare several inhibitors. The most effective is then selected as the one to go to field trial. In such cases, important physical characteristics must be compared as well as performance tests.

INHIBITOR APPLICATION

No matter what the chemical formulation or how good an inhibitor is, it will not do the job unless it is properly applied. Therefore, inhibitor application is quite important. The inhibitor must get to the metal surface, if it is going to lay down its film. Many so-called "inhibitor failures" were actually "application failures." There are a number of methods of introducing the inhibitor into a well or surface system. Some of the methods involve periodic treatments, and others require continuous injection.

INHIBITION OF PRODUCING WELLS

There are many approaches to inhibitor applications when it comes to producing wells. **Table 8.3** lists a number of methods for both wells with packers and those with open annuli. As noted in the table, several of these methods have very limited application; however, they were included since they may be used for special cases. Some of the more common or more widely used applications are briefly reviewed in the following paragraphs. The details of the various methods are presented in **Appendix 8A**. The description of each application technique includes the type of well(s) where it is used, basic approach and mechanism, treating procedure, treating frequency, monitoring, and comments (pros and cons).

TABLE 8.3 Corrosion Inhibitor Application Methods for Well Treatment

THE METHODS FOR INHIBITOR TREATMENT OF WELLS

With packered annuli include:

    Formation Squeeze

    Tubing Displacement

    Nitrogen Squeeze or Nitrogen Displacement

    Partial Tubing Displacement and Yo-Yo

    Treating Strings

    Limited Application

      Weighted liquids

      Dump bailers

      Wash bailers

      Inhibitor sticks

      Chemical injector valves

    Gas Lift Gas Addition

With open annuli include:

    (Usually sucker rod pumped and other artificial lift wells):

    Annular Batch—Operator applied or by treater truck.

    Continuous—With a chemical injection pump.

Formation Squeeze Treatment. As the name implies, for the formation squeeze the inhibitor is actually squeezed (pumped) back into the formation by displacing it with liquid (*e.g.*, crude, diesel, condensate, or other appropriate fluid). Often the inhibitor selected is a heavy film former that has superior film persistency. The inhibitor is deposited on the tubing as it is pumped into the well and it is adsorbed on (films on) the formation rock. The bulk of the squeezed fluid will be produced back when the well is put back on production. Thus, more inhibitor is filmed onto the tubing as it is produced. The theory for the long life is based on the inhibitor being desorbed from the formation rock over a period of time, thus providing inhibitor molecules to repair the film on the walls of the tubing. Depending on the specific application, treatment may provide inhibition for 3 months to 1 year. Thus, retreatments are very infrequent.

The main concerns with using formation squeezes have to do with the cost of individual treatments and the possibility of "formation damage." The higher cost of individual treatments are usually offset by the long time between treatments. Formation damage is a possibility in some reservoirs (those where the formation is natively water wet) because the inhibitor will form its inhibitor/oil film and will, in effect, oil-wet the reservoir rock. Relative permeability characteristics will change because of the reversal in wetability, which could result in lower well productivity. Depending on the formation characteristics and the actual production rate vs the maximum production rate, the oil-wet film theoretically could restrict flow. The formation squeeze was originally developed as a method for inhibiting the entire tubing string on gas-lift wells. An inhibitor injected with the gas will provide protection only from the working valve up to the surface.

Tubing Displacement Treatment. It was discovered that the treatment life was about as long for treatments where the inhibitor was not pumped into the formation, as it was when inhibitor was pumped into the formation. Thus, the tubing displacement approach was developed. Basically, the procedures are the same, except the inhibitor or inhibitor mix is only displaced to the end of the tubing. A theory to explain this long life is that the multimolecular film provided by the heavy film forming inhibitors is in effect self-repairing. That is, as inhibitor molecules desorb from the thick film, they are available to (and do) replace molecules that have desorbed further up hole.

At the present time the tubing displacement or partial tubing displacement treatments are the most common for packered oil and gas wells.

Nitrogen Squeeze and **Nitrogen Displacement Treatments.** As the names imply, these treatments are variations where the squeeze or displacement fluid is nitrogen rather than a liquid hydrocarbon. They have been used where the bottomhole pressure is insufficient to unload the column of liquid.

Partial Tubing Displacement and **Yo-Yo Treatments.** These treatments are also variations of displacement treatments for wells with low bottomhole pressure. In both cases, a volume of inhibitor mix and displacement fluid less than the volume of the tubing (often 1/3 or 1/2) is pumped into the tubing, the well is shut-in long enough for the liquids to drain to the bottom, and then the well is brought back on. In the case of the yo-yo treatment, when the liquid reaches the well head, the well is shut-in and the fluids allowed to fall to bottom once more. The sequence of liquid to surface—shut-in to fall may be repeated several times. Thus the name yo-yo, since the inhibitor is "yo-yoed" up and down, providing multiple passes to allow more opportunity for film formation.

Treating Strings. The treating string approach is an offshoot of the earlier practice of running a dual string of tubing—one the producing string, the other the "kill string"—in higher pressure gas wells. The kill string was to provide a way to pump drilling fluid to kill the well if problems developed. Both parallel and concentric configurations were used. When these wells needed corrosion inhibitor treatment the kill string became the treating string. Although the kill string approach has generally been abandoned, treating string use has become more widespread with the advent of 3/8 and 1/2 in. stainless steel tubing. The treating string approach is the most versatile method for inhibitor application in many situations where other methods have not been successful or are extremely costly. For example, the deep hot high-pressure gas wells, which require continuous treatment, and in situations where packered gas or oil wells cannot be economically shut-in for treatment, are candidates for treating strings. There is also a potential application for some of the new small diameter (3/8 in. or less) strings in gas-lift wells that have a serious corrosion problem.

Gas-Lift Wells. The lift gas is often used as a carrier for the inhibitor in wells produced by gas lift. The main drawbacks to this approach are two fold: (1) the interior of the tubing will only "see" inhibitor from the working valve up, and (2) an inhibitor designed for lift gas service may not be the most effective inhibitor for the well's fluids.

For successful inhibition with lift gas, the inhibitor must be injected into each individual well's lift gas stream. Inhibitor injection at a central point in a trunk-and-lateral lift gas system looks very cost effective on paper. However, this approach has not been successful, even with attempts to atomize the inhibitor so it will be carried with the lift gas. Tests to determine inhibitor carry through have shown that the inhibitor droplets fall from the gas in a relatively short distance (even with the short distances on an offshore platform). The liquid stream running along the bottom of the line is not properly distributed to the wells. Apparently the technology to provide the molecular sized particles that would stay in the gas is just too expensive for oil field operations. Even if the technology were economical, the central injection might not work since, in many cases, the correct amount would not necessarily be delivered to each well. The well that needs the highest lift gas volumes may not be the one that needs the most inhibitor and vice versa.

When inhibitor is introduced with the lift gas, it enters the tubing at the working valve and thus, there is no treatment below that valve. Furthermore, inhibitor effectiveness may be reduced due to compromises that must be made in inhibitor selection. The solvents tend to flash out of the inhibitor formulation when it is injected into the dry lift gas, so selection is limited to those materials that remain as very mobile liquids even without the solvent.

To date, a common solution has been to run coated tubing and use the lift gas-introduced inhibitor to protect the damaged areas in the coating above the working valve. After all, that is where the most wireline damage should be. In some cases corrosion-resistant alloy (CRA) tubing is run below the working valve.

Another solution mentioned earlier has been to perform tubing displacements or formation squeeze treatments on gas-lift wells.

Hydraulic Pump Wells. Power fluid is often used as a carrier for the inhibitor in wells produced by subsurface hydraulic pumps. The appropriate inhibitor can be continuously injected into the power fluid (power oil or power water). The dosage is based on total production (power fluid plus formation fluid) just as if it were a rod pumped well. Care must be taken to select an inhibitor that will not foul the power cylinder. When power water is used, the power water tank should be gas blanketed to maintain air (oxygen)-free conditions (just as if it were a water flood facility to avoid oxygen entry into the well). (Air-free operation is reviewed in Chapter 9.) If the power oil has been de-gassed so that no formation gas is evolving in the power oil tank, it may be desirable to gas blanket that tank also. Since the inhibitor is in the power fluid, the well only will be treated from the pump's engine-end up to the surface. Other means of corrosion control may be necessary below that point.

Treatments Down the Casing-Tubing Annulus. Batch treatment down the casing annulus is the usual method to treat wells without packers. Most sucker rod pumping wells are treated by some version of this approach.

Batch-and-flush treatment is the term used for the most common version. A few gallons of inhibitor are lubricated or pumped down the annulus followed by several barrels of fluid to flush it to the fluid level. The most common treatments are those done with treater trucks (also called "shot" trucks). A truck equipped with tanks, meters, pumps, and quick connect hoses hooks up to a well, injects the prescribed amount of chemical followed by several barrels of flush fluid (oil or water), disconnects, and drives to the next location. There are, however, still a number of wells treated manually by the pumper or operator who will fill a "chemical pot" on the casing wing valve and divert a portion of the well stream down the annulus for a few minutes to flush down the well. Typical treating volumes and dosages are presented in **Appendix 8A**.

Other variations of treatment down the annulus of nonpackered wells include: the batch-and-circulate treatment, automated (semi-batch) treatment, and continuous treatment with bypass flush.

Batch-and-circulate treatment is an approach generally reserved for treating problem wells when the batch-and-flush treatments are not effective. The procedure is the same except rather than a simple flush, the well's production may be diverted to the annulus for a period of time so that the inhibitor/fluid in the annulus is circulated around one or more times.

Extended batch treatment (sometimes referred to as "circulate and park") is another variation of the standard batch treatment developed for wells with high pumping fluid levels in the annulus. A large amount of inhibitor (as much as one drum) is placed in the annulus of the well. The well is put on complete circulation and circulated until the inhibitor goes down the annulus, up the tubing, and back into the annulus. The well is then put back into production leaving the inhibitor in the annulus. As the annular fluid level fluctuates, small amounts of inhibitor are carried in the oil into the tubing, thus periodically treating the tubing and pump for weeks or months after the chemical was added. A variation on this type of treatment recirculates the well every month or so, each time leaving the bulk of the inhibitor in the annulus. It must be remembered that this technique depends on very careful calculation or measurement of the circulated volumes to assure that the inhibitor is stored in the annular fluids. If volumes are missed and the inhibitor slug is produced to the battery, treatment will cease without the operator's knowledge.

Automated (semi batch) treatment uses treating equipment designed for automatic injection of inhibitor followed by produced fluid flush or circulation. Times can be set to vary the amount of inhibitor, flush, and frequency.

Continuous treatment with bypass flush involves a chemical feed pump to continuously inject inhibitor into a small stream of produced fluids bypassed into the annulus. Various types of chemical pumps may be used including mechanical pumps operated by a push rod from the walking beam or small gas powered pneumatic pumps. The volume of the bypass produced fluids is not critical, as long as a positive flow is maintained down the annulus.[1]

NACE RP0195-95. Although by title this recommended practice is for "Corrosion Control of Sucker Rods by Chemical Treatment,"[2] it covers many of these procedures for down-hole corrosion inhibition as they apply to sucker rod pumped oil wells. In addition, it contains recommendations for the protection of rods during transportation and storage, well servicing, and inhibitor program evaluation. This same information is presented in API RP 11BR, "Recommended Practice for Care and Handling of Sucker Rods," Section 2.[3] [This is an excellent example of cooperation between societies. NACE RP0195 and API RP11BR, Section 2 were balloted simultaneously in 1994 in their respective organizations. Thus, the final documents present a consistent story to the production industry.]

INHIBITION OF SURFACE FACILITIES

The various surface systems often require different corrosion inhibitor formulations than those used in producing wells to match the various application schemes.

For this chapter, surface facilities include: flowlines, gathering lines, injection lines, separation equipment, piping, heat exchangers and coolers, vessels and tanks, gas handling facilities, glycol dehydration equipment, sweetening equipment, heating/cooling media, water injection facilities, and gasoline plant facilities.

In other words, everything in the oil field except the wells themselves.

Flowlines and Gathering Systems. Oftentimes, the downhole inhibitor will provide protection for the flowline. That's the usual case with artificial lift well lines. However, many corrosive gas well streams will require additional inhibition for flowlines and gathering systems.

When flowline inhibition is required, it is injected continuously at the wellhead. A water soluble or highly water dispersible inhibitor is used. Thus, the inhibitor will be carried in the water along the bottom and in low places in the line. The dosage usually is based on water production.

Some of the larger diameter gathering lines may require additional inhibition. If the upper part of the line is cooled (such as on a subsea line), water may condense along the top of the line. If the flow rates and liquid volumes are high enough to have mist flow or slug flow, then the top of the line will "see" inhibitor. On the other hand, if the rates are low, the inhibitor will only be in the liquids along the bottom, and another approach will be needed (*e.g.*, frequent pigging or modification of piping to increase the velocity).

If the line is equipped for pigging, an inhibitor slug can be periodically pushed through the line between two pigs. By using two pigs, the inhibitor will be wiped on all the internal surfaces. In such cases, a heavy film forming inhibitor (such as those often used for tubing displacement treatments) is used. The heavy film formers have a highly persistent film and relatively infrequent treatments are required. Thus, the line would only need to be retreated when it is pigged for liquids removal, at a minimum of once a month (12 times per year).

If there are no pigging facilities, then an inhibitor formulation containing both a vapor phase and a filming inhibitor could be used. Since it is difficult to determine the dosage requirements for this application, and since vapor phase inhibitors often are not effective, the inhibition with pigs is the surest and the preferred approach.

Some flowing oil well lines on wells that aren't being treated will also require inhibition. In that case, the wells usually aren't making much water, so the downhole tubing is oil-wet—but as the water separates out and flows along the bottom of the line, after a while the bottom of the line becomes water wet. After all, as far as the bottom of the line is concerned, it's "seeing" 100% water.

Production and Plant Facilities. When it comes to production facilities and plants, the use of corrosion inhibitors is a viable method of corrosion control. However, inhibitors do have their limitations. For example: do not depend on inhibitors for corrosion control in valves, pumps, compressors, or similar equipment where velocities and turbulence may be high. Use corrosion-resistant metals where corrosion control is needed.

Vessels and tanks are not good candidates for inhibitor treatment. Do not depend on inhibitors for corrosion control in separation vessels and tanks. Proper distribution of the inhibitor throughout the vessel is the main problem. Although inhibitors may work in some vessels, the use of internal coatings and corrosion-resistant materials—supplemented with cathodic protection in free-water sections—is usually a better approach.

As a generality, the entire shell should be coated. Even if the inhibitor added upstream of the vessel would provide protection in the liquid portions of the vessel, the gas space will not see any inhibitor and will be subject to corrosion. The inhibitor will be in the oil and/or water phase.

Piping systems corrosion, on the other hand, often can be controlled with chemical treatment. Inhibitors do have applications in liquid piping and many auxiliary systems.

However, manifolds can present problems—distribution of the inhibitor is the difficulty. If areas of the manifold do not "see" the inhibited fluids, the inhibitor film will not be formed or maintained. When the manifold corrosion is to be controlled with inhibitors, the manifold needs to be designed and operated for good inhibitor distribution. This may require making certain that the entire header is active. That is, there should be flow throughout the header. To accomplish this, will require some planning in the design and in the day-to-day operation.

Other important design considerations are out-of-service branch connections and other nonflow piping areas ("dead legs") in manifolds. To minimize the dead area, the valves should be as closely coupled to the header as possible. In some cases dead legs in headers can be minimized by having block valves in the header itself. This technique can be useful when some of the header is designated "for future use." Extra valves do add to the cost of the job, but they can be the most economical approach when corrosive fluids are being handled. The purchase of an extra valve or two may be more economical than building the manifold from corrosion-resistant materials—particularly if the fluids contain inhibitor to protect other piping.

If for some reason it is impossible or impractical to have the entire manifold active on a routine basis, then it may be necessary to periodically flow through normally "dead" areas.

Dead leg problems and solutions are further reviewed in Chapter 9.

Gas Handling Systems and Plants. Corrosion inhibitors have several applications in gas handling systems.

In many systems, the first piece of equipment the produced gas, condensate and water will see is a flowline heater. The flowline inhibitor should provide satisfactory failure control in the heater tubes (unless the velocity through the tubes is extremely high and erosion is the cause of failures—inhibitors cannot be expected to control erosion—inhibition has been very successful in controlling corrosion/erosion).

After the gas stream is heated and choked, it usually goes to a separator—either at the well site or at a central facility. As mentioned earlier, the inhibitor will be carried with the liquids; thus, the flowline inhibitor can provide inhibition to the condensate and water streams off the separator—depending how it partitions. In some cases, it may be necessary to add inhibitor to the water to provide sufficient control in the water system.

The gas from the separator will be wet, and thus may be corrosive wherever any water condenses on the pipe wall. In some systems, inhibitor may be added to the wet gas piping, while in others, resistant materials may present the most economical approach, and still in others, monitoring, inspection, and planned replacement may be best. If inhibitor is used, it will need to be the vapor phase neutralizing type. The dosage will have to be worked out for the specific case. Of course, there is no way that sufficient neutralizing inhibitor will be added to neutralize all the acid gas in the gas stream—that's not the intent. The inhibitor is required only to control the pH of any condensed water. Care must be exercised if the gas is going to a glycol dehydrator. Excessive inhibitor can cause foaming of the glycol and excessive glycol losses.

As discussed in the Chapter 9, dehydration is the best method for controlling corrosion in corrosive gas streams, and as such, is the preferred method of control in gas pipelines, distribution, and injection systems. Chapter 9 also discusses corrosion control for the glycol system itself.

Gas coolers, particularly wet gas coolers, present a challenge for inhibition. This is true whether they're fin fans, or shell and tube. Proper distribution of inhibitor into each tube or throughout the shell interior and on all the tube surfaces can be a problem. When it's known at the design stage that a cooler will be handling a corrosive gas, the wet gas will normally be on the tube side, and the tubes will be made of a corrosion-resistant alloy. On the other hand, many coolers are installed with carbon steel tubes. Later, if it's discovered that the stream is corrosive, the decision must be made to retube with alloy or to try to control the corrosion with inhibitor.

If inhibitor is the choice, a vapor phase neutralizing amine is required. The usual liquid film former cannot be depended upon to enter all the tubes. The vapor phase neutralizing inhibitors are carried in the gas stream and dissolve in the water when and where it condenses. They are usually formulated from low molecular weight amines—the lightest and cheapest is ammonia. However, ammonia is the most difficult to use (small variations in dosage can create large swings in pH).

The main problem with the use of the vapor phase neutralizing materials is determining the proper dosage. Since they neutralize the acid gases, monitoring the pH of draw off water is the best way to make sure that the dosage is in the right range. A mentioned earlier, the objective of the use of the neutralizing amines is not to neutralize all the acid gas in the gas stream, only the amount that dissolves in any condensed water. Corrosion coupons or other corrosion monitoring devices are used to verify that corrosion is being controlled. Maintaining the proper pH is important, since too low a pH will not control the corrosion and too high a pH is a waste. Extreme overdoses of inhibitor could cause other problems (*e.g.*, incompatibilities with downstream processes, for instance, glycol dehydration). By the way, do not use the vapor phase amines (particularly ammonia) if copper alloys (*e.g.*, brasses or bronzes) or aluminum alloys are present in the system.

In spite of all these restrictions, there are instances where inhibitor can be used to control corrosion in gas coolers.

Amine sweetening systems are one area in a gas processing facility where inhibitors are used with success. Basically, corrosion in these systems is controlled by maintaining the proper solution strength and the proper acid gas loading, supplemented with inhibitor.

Normally, the inhibitor package for the amine solution is an inorganic inhibitor, such as a vanadate, provided by the amine vendor. The main operating duty with such inhibitors is to maintain the proper dosage.

Cooling water systems come in two basic types: the once-through systems and the recycle systems (which involve cooling towers).

Many of the once-through systems operated in the production industry use seawater and are located offshore or on the coast. Since the water is dumped back into the ocean, chemical treatment is frowned on by the regulatory agencies. Corrosion is controlled by using alloys and other corrosion-resistant materials.

On the other hand, corrosion control with chemicals is the "norm" for the recirculating systems. Depending on the needs of a particular system, corrosion inhibitors, chemicals for pH control, scale control, and microorganism (*e.g.*, algae) control may be used. Each system is unique (the makeup waters) as well as the problems; therefore, they need to be handled on a case-by-case basis. In most cases, cooling water treatment to control corrosion, scale, and biofouling is handled as a package by a cooling water treating vendor. Many of the chemicals used in cooling water systems are subject to rather strict environmental regulations, and these are continually evolving.

Heating/cooling media used in the closed system recirculating heating and cooling systems usually are glycol/water solutions. Oftentimes, these are proprietary fluids that contain an inhibitor package supplied by the manufacturer. As a generality, these inhibition packages work quite well, so long as they are maintained according to the manufacturers instructions. Care must be taken to assure that the makeup water has a low-mineral content. Most vendors specify a maximum chloride content of 100 ppm. If there is calcium in the water, part of the inhibitor formulation may precipitate out and cause scaling on exchanger tubes. Scaling can be a particular problem in heating systems. As would be expected, corrosion is more of a problem in heating systems than in cooling systems. These systems will have fewer problems when operated air-free, and with gas blankets on the tanks.

WATER INJECTION SYSTEMS

Water injection systems include both produced water disposal and water floods where source water and produced water are injected. It was mentioned previously that the major cause of corrosion in water is oxygen, and that in most water systems air-free operation is all that's required to control corrosion. However, some produced water and some subsurface source waters are corrosive even air-free (and they'll be even more corrosive if air is allowed to enter).

If inhibitor is required, air-free conditions must still be maintained. These inhibitors will not control oxygen corrosion. The types of inhibitors that will control oxygen corrosion in fresh waters will not work in brines. Inhibitor selection often is based on the inhibitors solubility in a particular water at the various temperatures in the system.

In most cases, the inhibitor will be injected continuously at dosages of 10 to 15 ppmv (parts per million by volume). Depending on the system, the inhibitor may be injected at one central location, or injection may be necessary at each water source point.

OTHER TYPES OF INHIBITORS

Well Acidizing Inhibitors

Well stimulation acid is used to increase production from wells by reacting with acid soluble portions of the formation rock, thus increasing the permeability of the formation. They are also used to remove acid soluble scales and deposits from the tubing and the face of the formation. Various acid solutions are used. The most common acid is 15% hydrochloric acid (HCl). Hydrofluoric acid (HF), HF-HCl mixtures, and organic acids may be used. These acids are extremely corrosive to carbon steel and can cause corrosion of corrosion-resistant alloys (CRA). Therefore, special inhibitors (commonly referred to as "acid inhibitors") are used. The acid inhibitors are generally proprietary materials provided as a package by the acidizing firm. The inhibitor package is designed to match the conditions of a specific well. Well temperature, acid volume, time of exposure of the tubing to the acid, presence of hydrogen sulfide (H_2S), and tubing metallurgy are important considerations. NACE RP0273–95, "Handling and Proper Usage of Inhibited Oilfield Acids,"[4] has guidelines for the use of acid inhibitors and operating considerations for minimizing acid corrosion.

For years, inorganic passivating inhibitors were used successfully. Arsenate compounds were the most widely used; however, they fell out of favor. First, problems of "poisoning" refinery catalysts restricted their use. Currently, health, safety, and environmental concerns, for all practical purposes, have eliminated arsenates from oilfield application.

Today's stimulation acid inhibitors are organic compounds; however, by and large, they have different structures than the organics used in the typical oil/gas/water inhibitors discussed in most of this chapter. Most acid inhibitor formulations combine several different organic materials that act synergistically to provide the desired protection. Coal tar based quaternary compounds, various acetylenic alcohols, formic acid generators, and similar materials make up the acid inhibitor.[5]

When an acid job is to be performed, an inhibitor and dosage are selected based on the expected inhole temperature. Dosages vary from a range of ½ to 1 percent by volume (%v) at lower well temperatures (below 150°F [66°C]), to the range of 2 to 3%v at the higher well temperatures (above 300°F [149°C]). For high temperature applications, cooling down the well is recommended in NACE RP0273–95.[6]

A major corrosion concern involves the spent acid that returns when the well is brought back onto production. In most cases the acid will be only partially spent, with a pH of 4 or less (still on the acid side), and the corrosion inhibitor will have been left in the formation. Thus, the spent acid will be corrosive and should be removed from the well as quickly as possible.[7]

When the use of CRA increased, it was discovered that the acid inhibitors that worked quite well with carbon steel tubulars did not adequately protect the CRA. However, special inhibitors were developed. Since the mid-1980s quite a bit has been published worldwide on the investigations of acid corrosion of CRA's and the effects of inhibitors. (Several articles on acid inhibition and CRA are listed in the bibliography at the end of this chapter. The books listed cover many facets of inhibition, including discussions on acid inhibitors.)

Volatile Corrosion Inhibitors

Another class of corrosion inhibitors that are different than the oil/gas/water system inhibitors discussed in the bulk of this chapter are called volatile corrosion inhibitors (VCI). These are also vapor phase corrosion inhibitors, and are sometimes listed as "vapor phase inhibitors (VPI)." However, the chemistry as well as the usage is quite different than the vapor phase neutralizing amines that were discussed earlier in this chapter in the section on gas handling.

VCI are used in contained spaces, often under atmospheric conditions with moisture and oxygen. In other words, VCI are primarily inhibitors for metals in storage or transit. Wrapping papers, plastic film, envelopes, and bags impregnated with VCI are used for protection of parts and apparatus until they are needed. Various powder or liquid formulations may be placed inside vessels, piping, engines, heat exchangers, and similar equipment for protection during mothballing (lay-up) of off-line facilities. One important exception to that relatively temporary protection is their use in instrument, electronic device, and electrical enclosures to prevent corrosion or tarnishing of switches and contacts.

VCI protect by the emission of vapors from a solid or liquid formulation. Vapors fill the confined space to reach the various surfaces to be protected. Their big advantage is probably that the inhibitive materials can reach inaccessible crevices and gaps in equipment or part.[8]

The amount of VCI required is a function of the volume, and the length of time protection will be required. In instances where the VCI protected area is opened periodically for service, or operation, the VCI will have to be replaced periodically.

SUMMARY OF CORROSION INHIBITION

Corrosion inhibition can be summarized as follows:

- There is a wide variety of corrosion inhibitor formulations available for use in the various environments we encounter. They can be selected to handle most of the environments in oil and gas production systems, except where oxygen is present (oxygen exclusion is required).

- The application technique used must match the system's mechanical and process considerations to assure that the inhibitor reaches the metal surface when and where it is needed.

- The choice of the specific program is a combination of technical and economic considerations.

- Inhibition programs should be monitored and periodically reviewed, because process systems are continuously changing.

- The programs need to be modified or adjusted periodically to optimize the program for cost effectiveness.

REFERENCES

1. NACE Standard RP0195-95, "Corrosion Control of Sucker Rods by Chemical Treatment" (Houston, TX: NACE, 1995), p.3.
2. NACE Standard RP0195 (latest edition) Ibid.
3. API RP 11BR, "Recommended Practice for Care and Handling of Sucker Rods, Section 2" (Washington, D.C.: American Petroleum Institute).
4. NACE Standard RP0273-95, "Handling and Proper Usage of Inhibited Oilfield Acids" (Houston, TX: NACE: 1995).
5. M. Walker, private communication, November, 1997.
6. NACE Standard RP0273-95, Ibid., Section 2.4, p. 2.
7. NACE Standard RP0273-95, Ibid., Section 2.5, p. 2.
8. C. Fiaud, "Theory and Practice of Vapour Phase Inhibitors" in A Working Party Report on Corrosion Inhibitors, European Federation of Corrosion Publications Number 11 (London, England: The Institute of Materials, 1994), p.1.

BIBLIOGRAPHY

Books—Collections

European Federation of Corrosion. *A Working Party Report on Corrosion Inhibitors.* European Federation of Corrosion Publications Number 11. London, England: The Institute of Materials, 1994.

Hausler, R. H., ed. *Corrosion Inhibition—Proceedings of the International Conference on Corrosion Inhibitors,* held May 16-20, 1983. International Corrosion Conference Series, NACE-7. Houston, TX: NACE, 1988.

Nathan, C. C., ed. *Corrosion Inhibitors.* Houston, TX: NACE, 1973.

Papers—Articles

Cizek, A. "A Review of Corrosion Inhibitors used in Acidizing." CORROSION/93, paper no. 92. Houston, TX: NACE 1993. Also published as "Corrosion Inhibitors used in Acidizing." MP 33, 1(1994): p.56–61.

Kane, R. D., and S. M. Wilhelm. "Compatibility of Stainless and Nickel-Based Alloys in Acidizing Environments." CORROSION/89, paper no. 481. Houston, TX: NACE, 1989.

Walker, M. L., and T. H. McCoy. "Effect and Inhibition of Stimulation Acids on Corrosion-Resistant Alloys." CORROSION/86, paper no. 154. Houston, TX: NACE, 1986.

Walker, M. L., J. M. Cassidy, K. R. Lancaster, and T.H. McCoy. "Acid Inhibition of CRA: A Review." CORROSION/94, paper no. 19. Houston, TX: NACE, 1994.

APPENDIX 8A

DOWNHOLE CORROSION INHIBITOR APPLICATION TECHNIQUES FOR OIL AND GAS WELLS

This appendix outlines examples of corrosion inhibitor treatments utilizing various application techniques that could be used for downhole corrosion control in oil and/or gas producing wells. These examples may be used for estimation of well, equipment, and manpower requirements and costs for comparison with other corrosion control approaches. However, they are not "final" designs. Details of specific treatments would need to be developed for actual treatment of specific wells.

Application techniques outlined include the following: formation squeeze, tubing displacement, nitrogen squeeze or displacement, partial tubing displacement (and yo-yo), treating string, weighted liquids, dump bailer, wash bailer, inhibitor sticks, chemical injection valve, gas lift gas, and batch and flush/circulate treatment down the annulus.

FORMATION SQUEEZE

Type Well

Usually gas wells, but have been used in gas-lift and flowing oil wells.

Basic Approach and Mechanism

1. Corrosion inhibitor is pumped into the tubing, displaced into the formation with an overflush of fluid, the well is shut-in for a period, and then slowly returned to production. The inhibitor may be preceded by a slug of fluid to precondition the surface for the inhibitor film.

2. The inhibitor film is laid down on the tubing during pump-in and "reinforced" by the high concentration of inhibitor, which returns when the well is first returned to production.

3. A portion of the inhibitor remains in the formation and feeds back at low concentration over several weeks time, thus providing inhibitor molecules to repair the film.

Treating Procedure

1. Surface conditioning (for water removal and to prepare the surface for the inhibitor film): pump methanol or a diesel/surfactant mix into the tubing. The selection and exact formula for the pretreatment slug is determined for each well.

2. Inhibition: pump in corrosion inhibitor "neat" (without dilution). Both oil soluble and heavy film former types of inhibitor are used. The volume will vary for the well. Two to 40 drums (110 to 2,200 gal [416 to 8,327 L]) have been used.

3. Displacement: follow inhibitor with lease condensate, crude, or diesel and displace into formation with sizable overflush (50 to 200 bbls). The size of the overflush will depend on the formation volume and how far the inhibitor is to be displaced. The inhibitor is placed into the formation away from the wellbore.

4. Pumping rates: as slow as practical. Maximum 4 to 6 bbls/min (0.6 to 0.95 m^3/min) (the slower the pump-in, the more exposure of inhibitor to the tubing).

5. Shut-in: 8 to 12 hours to allow inhibitor dispersion and filming in the reservoir.

6. Production: return well to production slowly for the first 2 to 4 hours. This will allow additional filming by the returning inhibitor and reduce the possibility of treater upsets.

Treating Frequency

Typically, retreatments are required every 2 to 6 months. Actual schedule would be worked out from monitoring results. Usually retreatments have a longer life than the first treatment on a well.

Monitoring

In addition to corrosion rate monitoring, the inhibitor slug return and residual chemical should be monitored (at least for early treatment). Coupons are to be changed during each treatment so that coupons will be exposed to the inhibitor.

Comments

1. Applicable for use with existing completions.
2. Provides positive placement of inhibitor to bottom of well.
3. Good chemical distribution to tubing surfaces.
4. Allows preparation of metal surfaces for filming.
5. Does not provide control of inhibitor available to "repair" film; dependent on rate of return from formation.
6. Downtime is required for pump-in and shut-in periods.
7. Relatively large volumes of fluids are displaced into formation: produced fluid from wellbore, methanol or surfactant slug, inhibitor, and diesel.
8. Relatively infrequent retreatments required.
9. Large volume of fluid must be handled for each treatment.
10. Surface equipment requirements are high-volume, high-pressure pumps, displacement fluid tanks or trucks.
11. Odds of achieving good corrosion inhibition (*e.g.*, chemical placement, film formation, film maintenance, etc.) when treating schedule followed—excellent.
12. From the standpoint of corrosion inhibition alone, this is a "preferred" method of inhibitor application for gas wells and packered oil wells.

TUBING DISPLACEMENT

Type Well

Usually gas wells, but may be used for gas-lift and flowing oil wells.

Basic Approaches and Mechanism

1. Corrosion inhibitor mix is pumped into the tubing, pumped to the bottom with a flush fluid, the well is shut-in for a period, and then slowly returned to production. The inhibitor may be preceded by a slug of fluid to precondition the surface for the inhibitor film.

2. The inhibitor film is formed on the tubing during pump-in, distributed and strengthened during shut-in, and refilmed when the well is slowly returned to production.

3. The inhibitor used is a so-called "heavy film former" or "macro film former," which provides a multimolecular film. Extended film life is obtained since this type film tends to repair itself with molecules from the multi-molecular layer.

Treating Procedure

1. Surface conditioning (for water removal and to prepare the surface for the inhibitor film): pump methanol or a diesel/surfactant mix into the tubing. The selection and exact formula for pretreatment slug is determined for each well.

2. Inhibitor: pump in inhibitor mix, 1 to 2 drums (55 to 110 gal [208 to 416 L]) inhibitor concentrate diluted in 5 to 10 bbls (795 to 1,590 L) of condensate or diesel. Use a macrofilm forming type inhibitor, which has limited oil and water dispersability.

3. Displacement: follow inhibitor mix with sufficient diesel, lease condensate, or crude to displace mix to bottom of well.

4. Pumping rate: $1/2$ to 1 bbl/min (90 to 160 L/min) (if higher pumping speeds are required, use larger amounts of inhibitor mix).

5. Shut-in: 4 hours.

6. Production: return well to production slowly for the first 2 to 4 hours. This will allow additional filming as the inhibitor is brought to the surface.

Treating Frequency

Typically, retreatment is required every 2 to 6 months (approximately every 3 months). Schedules will vary, depending on well production rates and fluid characteristics. Actual schedule would be worked out from monitoring results. Usually retreatments have a longer life than initial treatments. Therefore, second treatments are normally scheduled 1 month after initial treatment.

Monitoring

In addition to corrosion rate monitoring, the inhibitor slug return may be monitored on early treatments. Coupons should be changed during the treatment so that the coupons will be exposed to the inhibitor slug.

Comments

1. Applicable for use with existing completions.

2. Positive placement of inhibitor to bottom of well.

3. Good chemical distribution.

4. Allows preparation of metal surfaces for filming.

5. Inhibitor film repair based on "macrofilm."

6. Downtime required for pumping in and for shut-in period (less downtime than for formation squeeze).

7. Tubing volume of produced fluids displaced into formation.

8. Relatively infrequent retreatments required.

9. Relatively large volumes of fluid required (one tubing volume).

10. Relatively low volume of chemical required on yearly basis.

11. Surface equipment requirements are high-pressure pumps, chemical mix tanks or trucks, and flush fluid tanks or trucks.

12. Less likelihood of emulsion by slugs of macrofilm inhibitor than with more oil soluble/ dispersible compounds.

13. Odds of achieving good corrosion inhibition (*e.g.*, chemical placement, film formation, etc.) when treating schedule followed—excellent.

14. From just the standpoint of corrosion inhibition alone, this is a "preferred" method of inhibitor application for gas wells and packered oil wells.

NITROGEN FORMATION SQUEEZE OR TUBING DISPLACEMENT

Type Well

Gas wells with bottomhole pressure insufficient to unload a full column of liquid.

Basic Approaches and Mechanisms

Same as formation squeeze or tubing displacement, except nitrogen is used to displace fluids to the bottom of the well.

Treating Procedure

Same as formation squeeze or tubing displacement, except for nitrogen displacement.

Treating Frequency

Should be same as formation squeeze or tubing displacement for a given well.

Monitoring

Similar to formation squeeze or tubing displacement.

Comments

1. The use of nitrogen reduces the relative permeability affect, which would be expected with liquid flushes.

2. See formation squeeze and tubing displacement.

3. Requires nitrogen service.

4. Allows positive placement of inhibitor in low-pressure wells.

5. Odds of achieving good corrosion inhibition (*e.g.*, chemical placement, film formation, film maintenance, etc.) when treating schedule followed—very good.

PARTIAL TUBING DISPLACEMENT AND YO-YO TREATMENT

Type Well

Gas wells with bottomhole pressure insufficient to unload full column of liquid.

Basic Approaches and Mechanism

1. Corrosion inhibitor mix is pumped into the tubing, followed by a partial tubing volume of flush fluid, the well is shut-in to allow the liquid to fall to bottom, and then slowly returned to production. The inhibitor may be preceded by a slug of fluid to precondition the surface.

2. For "yo-yo" treatment, the well is shut-in for a second time as soon as liquid reaches the tree.

3. The inhibitor film is formed on the tubing during pump-in and falls to the bottom, and refilmed when the well is slowly returned to production. Two additional "passes" of the inhibitor are provided with each "yo-yo."

4. The inhibitor used is a so-called "heavy film former" or "macrofilm former," which provides a multi-molecular film.

Treating Procedures

1. Surface conditioning (for water removal and to prepare the surface for the inhibitor film): pump methanol or a surfactant diesel mix into tubing.

2. Inhibitor: pump in inhibitor mix, 1 to 2 drums (55 to 110 gal [208 to 416 L]) inhibitor diluted with 5 to 10 bbls (795 to 1,590 L) of lease condensate or diesel. Use a macrofilm forming type inhibitor which has limited oil and water solubility.

3. Displacement: follow inhibitor mix with partial tubing volume (usually $1/3$ to $1/2$) of lease condensate or diesel.

4. Pumping rate: $1/2$ to 1 bbl/min (90 to 160 L/min).

5. Shut-in: a minimum of 8 hours (or until "normal" shut-in wellhead pressure is achieved) to allow mix to reach bottom.

6. Production: return well to production slowly for first 2 to 4 hours. This will allow filming as the inhibitor is brought to the surface.

7. For "yo-yo" treatment: when liquid hits the tree, shut-in the well again (repeat steps 5 and 6).

Treating Frequency

Typically, retreatments will be required each 1 to 3 months. Schedule will depend on well production rates and fluid characteristics. Actual schedule would be worked out from monitoring results.

Monitoring

Coupons should be changed during the treatment so that they are exposed to the inhibitor return.

Comments

1. Applicable for use when BHP is too low for full tubing displacement.

2. More positive placement of inhibitor than by simply pumping in inhibitor mix and shutting in.

3. Successful treatment depends on sufficient shut-in to get inhibitor to bottom.

4. Good chemical distribution as long as inhibitor reaches bottom.

5. Yo-yo treatment assures good film formation.

6. Allows preparation of metal surfaces for filming.

7. Inhibitor film repair based on "macrofilm."

8. Downtime required for pumping in and for shut-in period. Well may be down for a day.

9. Relatively infrequent retreatments required.

10. Relatively large volumes of liquid required ($1/3$ to $1/2$ tubing volume).

11. Relatively low volume of chemical required on yearly basis.

12. Surface equipment requirements are high-pressure pumps, chemical mix tanks or trucks, and flush fluid tanks or trucks.

13. Less likelihood of emulsions by slugs of macrofilm forming inhibitor than with more soluble/dispersible compounds.

14. Odds of achieving good corrosion inhibition (*e.g.*, chemical placement, film formation, film maintenance, etc.) when treating schedule followed—good.

15. From just the standpoint of corrosion inhibition alone, this is a "preferred" method of inhibitor application for low BHP gas wells.

TREATING STRING

Type Well

Any gas or oil well with packer.

Basic Approach and Mechanisms

A parallel or concentric treating string is run to the bottom of the well, preferably to below the packer. Thus corrosion inhibitor may be introduced at the bottom of the hole by pumping down the treating string. Either batch or continuous treatment may be used.

Treating Procedure

1. Inhibitor: any type of corrosion inhibitor can be used and injected neat or mixed with carrier oil, depending on well requirements.

2. Treatment: can be batch or continuous, as required. Treater truck use is possible.

Treating Frequency

Would depend on individual well's need.

Monitoring

Corrosion rate and inhibitor carry through.

Comments

1. Requires well workover to run treating string to existing wells. String should be run to bottom (*i.e.*, through the packer).

2. Positive placement of inhibitor to bottom of well if string is run below packer. Otherwise, inhibitor is introduced just above packer through a chemical injection valve.

3. Good chemical distribution.

4. Could inject pretreatment solution to prepare surfaces before initial treatment.

5. Inhibitor film maintained by optimizing dosage and treating frequency.

6. No downtime required for treatment.

7. No fluids displaced into formation during treatment.

8. Fairly frequent retreatments may be required; however, schedule can be optimized by matching treatment and chemical.

9. Relatively small volumes of fluids required for flush or diluent.

10. Low to medium volumes of chemical required on a yearly basis.

11. Surface equipment requirements depend on treating approach. Could require chemical injection pump and tank at each well or could use treater truck for batch treatments.

12. Odds of achieving good corrosion inhibition (*e.g.*, chemical placement, film formation, film maintenance, etc.) when treating schedule followed—excellent.

13. From the standpoint of corrosion inhibition alone, this would be the most versatile method of inhibitor application and for some operators is the preferred method for packered oil and gas wells (including high-pressure, high-temperature, acid gas wells).

WEIGHTED LIQUIDS

Type Well

Low-pressure gas and oil wells.

Basic Approach and Mechanisms

1. Corrosion inhibitor base is formulated in a high density liquid to make a weighted liquid corrosion inhibitor (9+ lb/gal [1.1+ kg/L]).

2. The required amount of inhibitor is batched into the tubing and the well is shut-in long enough to allow the inhibitor to fall to bottom.

3. The inhibitor film is formed where the liquid contacts the tubing wall and when the well is brought back on production.

Treating Procedure

1. Inhibitor: use a weighted liquid corrosion inhibitor. If H_2S is present, the inhibitor must be formulated for use where H_2S is present. Weighted inhibitors up to 12 lb/gal (1.4 kg/L) are available for use where there is no H_2S.

2. Pump or lubricate chemical into well:

   A. Initial treatment: use a sufficient amount of chemical to displace rat-hole volume with chemical (for example, if rat hole holds 4 bbls (168 gal [635 L]), use 4 bbls of inhibitor for initial treatment).

   B. Routine treatment: use $1/2$ to 1 drum of inhibitor.

3. Shut-in: allow chemical to fall to bottom. Rule of thumb for gas wells: allow 1 hour for each 1,000 ft (305 m) of depth. For oil wells, time will vary depending on weight of inhibitor. To be on the safe side, it is best to shut-in at least overnight.

4. Production: return well to production slowly to allow filming from produced fluids and to reduce possibilities of treater upsets.

Treating Frequency

Varies. Could be as often as weekly or could be monthly. Actually, schedules would be determined from monitoring results.

Monitoring

Corrosion rate and inhibitor return.

Comments

1. Does not require inhole equipment change.

2. Inhibitor placement to bottom of well will depend on accuracy of estimate of shut-in time requirements (and wells being shut-in for required time).

3. Chemical distribution should be relatively good if chemical gets to bottom. Chemical should run along bottom of deviated portion of tubing.

4. Provides no surface preparation for filming. Thus, filming is dependent on inhibitor's surfactant and filming ability.

5. Inhibitor film repaired by frequent retreatment.

6. Long downtime required.

7. Little, if any, fluids displaced into formation.

8. Frequent treatments may be required.

9. No flush or diluent required.

10. Relatively high volume of chemical required on a yearly basis.

11. Surface equipment requirements are lubricator or high-pressure pump. Could equip well for "truck treating."

12. Inhibitor will be very viscous at cold temperatures.

13. Inhibitor selection limited by number of available weighting agents that may be used.

14. Odds of achieving good corrosion inhibition (*e.g.*, chemical placement, film formation, film maintenance, etc.) when treating schedule followed—fair.

DUMP BAILER

Type Well

Low-pressure gas or oil wells.

Basic Approach and Mechanism

1. The corrosion inhibitor is placed at the bottom of the tubing string with a wireline dump bailer. Sufficient runs are made to place the required dosage.

2. The tubing is exposed to the inhibitor as the well is brought back on production. Thus, contact time will be relatively short and insufficient to give long film life.

Treating Procedure

1. Inhibitor: use an oil soluble/water dispersible type of inhibitor that exhibits properties for quick filming.

2. Dump inhibitor at bottom of well with dump bailer. Make as many runs with bailer as required to achieve dosage:

    A. Initial treatment: 10 to 20 gal (38 to 76 L).
    b. Routine treatment: 5 to 10 gal (19 to 38 L).

3. Production: return well to production at lowest practical flow rate to give maximum contact time for film formation.

Treating Frequency

Once per week. Actual treating frequency and dosages will be determined by monitoring results.

Monitoring

Corrosion rate and inhibitor return.

Comments

1. Can be used with existing completions.

2. Positive placement of inhibitor at bottom of tubing.

3. Chemical distribution—fair to good, depending on ability to return well to production very slowly.

4. Provides no surface preparation for filming. Thus, initial filming dependent on inhibitor's surfactant and filming ability.

5. Film maintenance depends on frequent retreatments before "old" film is destroyed.

6. Downtime required depends on wireline time requirements.

7. Little, if any, fluids displaced into formations.

8. Relatively frequent retreatments required.

9. No flush or diluent fluids required.

10. Medium amount of chemical required on yearly basis.

11. Surface equipment requirements are wireline unit with associated equipment, dump bailer, and pump for transferring inhibitors from drums to bailer.

12. Odds of achieving good corrosion inhibition (*e.g.*, chemical placement, film formation, film maintenance, chemical selection, etc.) when treating schedule followed—fair.

WASH BAILER

Type Well

Low-pressure gas or oil wells.

Basic Approach and Mechanism

1. A "wash" or "spray" type hydraulic bailer is used to place corrosion inhibitor throughout the tubing string. Multiple runs are required to provide complete coverage.

2. The tubing is thus exposed to a high concentration of inhibitor as it is "sprayed" from the bailer, while the well is shut-in for the bailer runs, and as the well is brought back on production.

Treating Procedure

1. Inhibitor: use a macrofilm forming-type inhibitor that has limited oil and water dispersability.

2. Bailer: run bailer to bottom, trip and unload inhibitor as bailer is pulled out of hole. Repeat, tripping bailer at higher level each run (overlap previous run to assure coverage). Coverage and, thus, number of runs will depend upon capacity and design of bailer.

3. Production: return well to production at slow rate until tubing volume unloaded. This allows more filming time.

Treating Frequency

Estimate retreatments required each 1 to 3 months. This will vary depending on well production rates and fluid characteristics. Actual schedules will be based on monitoring results.

Monitoring

Corrosion rate. Coupons should be changed during treatment so that coupons will be exposed to inhibitor as well is brought back on.

Comment

1. Applicable for use with existing inhole equipment.

2. Reasonably positive chemical placement throughout tubing string.

3. Chemical distribution should be good if bailer operates properly.

4. Provides no surface preparation for filming; thus, film life may be shorter than with tubing displacement when using same macrofilming chemical.

5. Inhibitor film repair based on macrofilm properties.

6. Downtime required depends on wireline time requirements.

7. Little, if any, fluids displaced into formation.

8. Relatively infrequent retreatment required.

9. No flush or diluent required.

10. Relatively low volumes of chemical required on a yearly basis.

11. Surface equipment requirements are wireline unit with associated equipment, wash bailer, and pump to transfer inhibitor from drum to bailer.

12. Odds of achieving good corrosion inhibition (*e.g.*, chemical placement, film formation, film maintenance, etc.) when treating schedule followed—very good.

13. From a standpoint of corrosion inhibition alone, this would be a "preferred" method of inhibitor application.

INHIBITOR STICKS

Type Well

Low-pressure gas.

Basic Approach and Mechanisms

1. Corrosion inhibitor base is combined with a wax and cast into solid sticks, 1½ in. (38 mm) diameter, 18 in. (0.46 m) long. One stick is equivalent to approximately one quart of field strength liquid inhibitor.

2. The required number of sticks are lubricated into the tubing and the well is shut-in sufficiently long to allow the sticks to fall to bottom.

3. The sticks are designed to melt at bottom-hole temperature, thus releasing the inhibitor to the produced fluids.

Treating Procedure

1. Inhibitor: corrosion inhibitor sticks. Dosage usually based on 1 stick/MMCF production.

2. Lubricate: lubricate sticks into tubing.

3. Shut-in: allow sticks to fall. (Rule of thumb: shut-in 1 hour per 1,000 ft (305 m) of depth in straight hole; fall rate in deviated hole would have to be determined.)

4. Production: return well to production slowly to allow filming from produced fluids.

Treating Frequency

Weekly.

Monitoring

Corrosion rate monitoring and inhibitor residual.

Comments

1. Would not require inhole equipment changes.

2. Wax in sticks could create emulsion and/or foaming problems.

3. Odds are poor that sticks will fall to bottom; they may hang up at subsurface safety valve (SSSV) or in deviated holes, or could "bridge."

4. Sticks must reach bottom to melt and release inhibitor. If they are not exposed to near bottom-hole temperature, they will soften at best and could be produced back to plug SSSV or wellhead equipment.

5. Odds of achieving good corrosion inhibition (*e.g.*, chemical placement, film formation, film maintenance, etc.)—very poor.

6. Odds of achieving satisfactory corrosion control by this method—very low.

7. Odds of operational problem resulting from sticks not melting—high.

8. This method is not normally recommended.

CHEMICAL INJECTOR VALVE

Type Well

Packered oil or gas well.

Basic Approach and Mechanism

1. A chemical injection valve is run in the tubing string just above the packer and the casing/tubing annulus is filled with corrosion inhibitor/diesel mix.

2. Additional inhibitor/diesel mix is pumped into the annulus to open the valve and inject inhibitor into the stream. Treatment may be by batch or continuous.

Treating Procedure

1. Inhibitor: load annulus with inhibitor/diesel mix:

   A. Use an oil soluble/water dispersible inhibitor with excellent long-term solubility in diesel.

   B. Mix should be 10% to 20% inhibitor. The exact mixture will be based on the rate at which chemical can be pumped through the chemical injection valve, as well as producing volumes and expected treating requirements.

2. Inject inhibitor mix by pumping additional mix into the annulus. Volumes and pumping times should be developed based on treatment results:

   A. Batch treatmens: inject inhibitor mix at a rate to achieve a dosage of approximately 300 parts per million for at least 1 hour. For example: a 3,000 barrels fluid per day (BFPD) (477 m^3/day) would require 16 gallons (60.6 liters) of a 10% mix injected for one hour for each treatment.

   B. Continuous treatment: if only very low rates can be injected through the chemical injection valve, continuous treatment could be required. For oil wells, a dosage of 12 to 25 ppm would probably be necessary. This would be $^1/_2$ to 1 gal (1.9 to 3.8 L) of inhibitor (5 to 10 gal [19 to 38 L] of a 10% mix) per 1,000 bbls (159 m^3) of fluid treated. For gas wells, assume one quart (0.95 L) of inhibitor (2.5 gal [9.5 L] of a 10% mix) per MMCF (28,300 m^3) gas.

3. Initial Treatment:

   A. It is assumed that the tubing will be exposed to the inhibitor mix when that fluid is placed in the annulus. If the routine treatment is started within a week, no other "initial" treatment should be required.

   B. If routine treatment does not start immediately, an "initial" treatment to establish the film will be necessary. Details of such a treatment will have to be worked out. Such a treatment might involve pumping inhibitor mix at a relatively high rate for several hours with the well flowing at a low rate.

Treating Frequency

The optimum batch treating schedule would have to be developed based on well needs—for estimation purposes, assume that a 1 hour batch treatment would be required:

- Once/week for low volume wells.
- Twice/week for mid volume wells.
- Daily for high volume wells.

Monitoring

Corrosion rate and inhibitor residual monitoring could be used.

Comments

1. Requires workover to install chemical injection valve, cleaning of annulus of mud and solids, and placement of inhibitor diesel mix in annulus of existing well.

2. Provides placement of chemical at chemical injection valve location. Tubing below valve would be unprotected.

3. Chemical distribution should be good.

4. Depends on initial filming procedure for surface preparation.

5. Allows varying of dosage and treating frequency to optimize film maintenance.

6. No downtime required for routine treatment.

7. Fluids displaced into formation only if workover requires killing well. No fluids displaced to formation during treatment.

8. High volume wells could require daily treatment.

9. Relatively large volume of inhibitor and diesel required (annular volume; plus routine treatment).

10. Surface equipment requirements are chemical injection pump and chemical injection tank at each well. Could use "treater truck" for batch treatments.

11. Provides quite a bit of flexibility for dosages and treating frequency.

12. Difficult to change inhibitor formulation.

13. Odds of mechanical problem with chemical injection valve (plugging or cutting out)—high. Also, problems with the chemical valves could lead to dumping the annular inhibitor mix while changing out valve.

14. Odds of achieving good corrosion inhibition (*e.g.*, chemical placement, film formation, film maintenance, etc.) when everything is working, and treating schedule followed—good.

15. Due to mechanical problems, the chemical injection valve is not normally recommended.

GAS LIFT GAS

Basic Approach and Mechanisms

Inhibitor is introduced into the tubing through the working gas-lift valve to provide inhibition from that valve to the surface. Inhibitor may be injected continuously into the lift gas at the wellhead or batched in periodically. The inhibitor formulation must be designed for injection into dry gas (to prevent "gunking" out of the inhibitor).

Treating Procedure

1. Inhibitor: an inhibitor formulated for introduction into dry gas (*i.e.*, no evaporation of solvent or the active ingredient is a liquid after solvent evaporation) would be injected into the gas at each wellhead. Usually an oil soluble/water dispersible inhibitor would be used.

2. Initial treatment: a batch in 20 gal (76 L) inhibitor mixed with 80 gal (304 L) diesel.

3. Treatment could be batch or continuous with the volume and injection rate based on treatment results:

    A. Batch treatment: inject an inhibitor diesel mixture of up to 10 gal (39 L) inhibitor and 40 gal (151 L) diesel.

    B. Continuous treatment: base dosage on 12 to 25 ppmv (parts per million by volume) inhibitor in produced fluids ($1/2$ to 1 gal inhibitor/1,000 BFPD)(1.9 to 3.8 L inhibitor/ 159 m^3 per day).

Treating Frequency

Batch treatment would vary with well production—typically once/week.

Monitoring

Corrosion rate and inhibitor carry through.

Comments

1. Applicable for use when wells are being gas lifted.

2. Treatment effective only from working gas-lift valve to surface.

3. Chemical distribution should be good above working valve.

4. Surface preparation by initial dosage.

5. Film maintained by frequent treatment.

6. No downtime required for treatment.

7. No fluids displaced into formation.

8. Relatively frequent retreatment.

9. A medium amount of diesel required as diluent.

10. Low to medium yearly volume of chemical required.

11. Surface equipment requirements are chemical injection pump and supply tanks required at each well. Batch treatment could be performed with treater truck.

12. Chemical selection somewhat limited by properties required for injection into dry gas.

13. No inhibition provided below the working gas-lift valve.

14. Odds of achieving good corrosion inhibition (*e.g.*, chemical placement, film formation, film maintenance, etc.) from the working valve up, when treating schedule followed—very good.

15. Most likely use of this application is to supplement coated tubing by providing protection in the wireline damaged areas.

BATCH AND FLUSH/CIRCULATE TREATMENT DOWN ANNULUS

Type Well

Rod-pumped oil wells and other unpackered wells.

Basic Approach and Mechanism

1. Inhibitor with a suitable volume of flush is added to the annulus of an unpackered rod-pumped oil well after the annulus has been prewet with flush fluids. The flush fluid may be well fluids, or deaerated water from a treater truck. In some cases the treater truck may use lease crude for flush. Some wells may require circulation to achieve satisfactory treatment. In those instances, after the inhibitor is added to the well, the production of the well is then redirected down the annulus to circulate the inhibitor throughout the tubing and annulus.

2. The frequency of the treatment along with the type and amount of inhibitor and flush are process variables.

3. The treatment can be administrated by either production personnel or by truck treatment.

Treating Procedure

1. Prewet: in order to wet the annular space so the inhibitor will run down the casing to the fluid level, produced fluids are flushed down the annulus for several minutes. If treatment is by treater truck, typically one barrel (0.16 m^3) of flush fluid is used for pre-wet. The prewet is particularly important in some wells to prevent a build up of inhibitor at the top of the annulus.

2. Inhibitor: typical inhibitor for this use is an oil soluble/dispersible material with little or no water solubility/dispersability. The volume of flush is typically $1/2$ barrel for every 1,000 ft of well depth.

3. Inject: volume of inhibitor followed by flush into well annulus. Oil should be used as flush in wells with high carbon dioxide (CO_2) contents. Water is acceptable in other cases though not preferred. For circulation treatments, after the annulus is treated with the inhibitor/flush, redirect the production from the tubing down the annulus to circulate the well. Circulation should continue long enough to distribute the inhibitor throughout the tubing and annulus.

4. The initial treatment: done with 5 to 25 gal (19 to 95 L) of inhibitor to lay down a good film. This should be done each time the well is pulled. Thereafter the regular treatment should be performed.

Treating Frequency

Recommended treating frequency is based on total fluid production as follows:

WELL PROD. RATE	TREATING FREQUENCY	INHIBITOR VOLUME
<25 BPD	Monthly	1 gal (3.785 L)
25 to 50 BPD	Bi-monthly	1 gal
50 to 100 BPD	Weekly	1 gal
100 to 500 BPD	Weekly	1 gal/100 BPD (3.785 L/16 m^3/day)
500 to 1,000 BPD	Weekly	5 gal (19 L)
>1,000 BPD	2 to 3 times weekly	2 to 3 gal (7.6 to 11.4 L)

Monitoring

Corrosion rates and failure records can be used.

Comments

1. The well must not have a packer.

2. No special equipment is needed except a chemical pot and flush piping for operator treating and connections for a hose and recirculation piping for treater truck applications.

3. Chemical distribution should be excellent.

4. Adequate circulation of fluid greatly improves the effectiveness.

5. Odds of achieving good corrosion inhibition (*e.g.*, chemical placement, film formation, etc.) when treatment schedule is followed—very good.

6. This is the preferred method of treating unpackered rod-pumped oil wells.

CHAPTER 9

CONTROL OF THE CORROSIVE ENVIRONMENT

Since it's not possible to control the external environment, this chapter will cover items that allow control of the internal environment (or at least modify it to reduce corrosion problems).

Subjects such as system design to minimize or eliminate corrosion, oxygen exclusion, oxygen removal, dehydration, control of deposits, and microbiological problems and their control are the main topics for discussion. While some of these involve the original planning, design, and installation (or retrofit), most are operational and maintenance considerations.

DESIGNING TO AVOID CORROSION AND DESIGNING FOR CORROSION CONTROL

The watch word is: "design corrosion out—don't design corrosion in." The design of any well, pipeline, piping system, facility, or plant can affect the severity of corrosion at that facility and/or affect the practicality or costs of corrosion control efforts.

The first step is to determine where and when in the project corrosion problems are likely to occur. Wells, lines, facility piping, vessels, and auxiliary equipment are all candidates for corrosion either from start up or sometime later in the project's life. As mentioned in earlier chapters, gas wells and gas handling facilities are most likely to present corrosion problems from start-up. Oil well projects, on the other hand, usually will not require corrosion control until later in their life—when water production increases. Of course, in sour oil production where hydrogen sulfide (H_2S) is present, sulfide stress cracking (SSC)-resistant materials will be needed from the beginning. The production from water floods using seawater as the injection water has traditionally experienced reservoir souring. So if seawater injection is planned, SSC-resistant materials should be considered on the producing side. Water injection systems themselves require corrosion control planning and design (oxygen removal from waters and its exclusion from all systems are covered later in this chapter).

When designing a facility, it is very important to consider operating and maintenance requirements, not just maintenance of the corrosion control system, but general facility maintenance. Many corrosion problems can be avoided with proper preventative maintenance programs. As we'll discuss in a moment, many of the steps to maintain an oxygen-free system are based on operating and maintenance procedures. Equipment should be selected that not only does the job intended, but is relatively simple to repair (replace seals, packing, etc.).

PROCESS LAYOUT

Location or position of equipment in a process can influence corrosion control requirements. For example, the farther upstream a corrosive gas is dehydrated, the less corrosion control will be required in the remainder of the system. With sufficient dehydration, bare carbon steel is all that is required for most downstream facilities. (The term "sufficient dehydration" is also discussed later in this chapter.)

DESIGN FOR COATING

Vessel and tank internal coatings are discussed in Chapter 6. The need for a vessel "designed for internal coating" cannot be overemphasized. The features of removable internals (piping, baffles, etc.), properly designed and executed welds, nozzle sizes, etc. must be included in the design specifications.

DESIGN FOR INSPECTION

As discussed in the next chapter, inspection is a very important part of any corrosion control program. Yet many oilfield facilities are not designed for inspection.

Vessels and tanks often do not have manways (or sufficient manways) to enter and properly clean or inspect their condition. Many that do have adequate manways often do not have all the necessary valves so they can be blocked out of the system for purging or inspection. Often, even when the valves were installed, they have not been maintained and they will not seal bubble tight. In those cases the entire facility must be shut in—a costly procedure in many facilities. To minimize the effect of valve problems, some operators use "double-block-and-bleed" valve arrangements. (For those not familiar with the term, the "double-block-and-bleed" approach is the use of two valves connected in tandem with a bleed valve in between. After the valves are closed the pressure between is bled-off.) The theory is that even if one of the valves is leaking, the other will hold and the vessel may be safely depressured and purged for entry.

DESIGN FOR MONITORING

Various types of monitoring techniques besides inspection are discussed in Chapter 10. In the early life of some facilities, corrosion will not be much of a problem so monitoring efforts will be minimal. Later on, however, control efforts, such as inhibition, may justify extensive monitoring. When coupon mounting locations, sample connections and the like are included in the initial construction, they are relatively inexpensive, certainly when compared to retrofitting costs (and downtime).

DESIGN FOR CHEMICAL TREATMENT

The cost of chemical treatment can be minimized by providing valving for chemical injection in the construction of new facilities, even if the treatment is not needed immediately (*e.g.*, a new oil well system where initial water production is low). History has proved that some forms of chemical treatment—corrosion inhibitor, scale control, biocide, etc.—will be needed later in the field's life. The most likely points for future injection can be selected during the design stage and small (1/4 to 1/2 in. [6.35 to 12.7 mm]) valves installed at minimum cost during construction. When system downtime is factored into the cost, the addition of chemical injection points, at a later date, when they are needed, will be more expensive than installation on initial construction.

DESIGN FOR PIGGING

While most cross county pipelines have pig launchers and receivers, most flowlines, gathering systems, and water or gas injection systems do not. Nevertheless, the ability to pig such lines can play an important role in controlling their corrosion. Pigs can be used to "wipe" heavy film corrosion inhibitors on the inside surface of wet-gas lines, clean deposits and debris from lines, apply biocide while removing biofilm, or inspect the line for corrosion and damage (smart pigs). All of these duties are in addition to the more common use of pigging to remove water and condensate from gas lines or waxes and solids from crude oil lines.

Designing pigging facilities into piping systems is particularly important for corrosive gas systems and water systems where surface waters are the supply water, or two or more waters are mixed. The ability to pig field and interplatform lines offshore is also very important because of the higher costs of operating a facility offshore. Even if the pigging facilities are not installed at the start, if the piping system is designed for pigging, the actual launchers and receivers can be added at a later date much more economically than rebuilding the system.

WATER MIXING

When dealing with source water, it is not good practice to mix source and produced waters. Not only are there potential compatibility problems from the standpoint of scale and deposits, but there are some little understood corrosion problems that can occur.

The industry has examples of water floods where two waters (produced and source waters) are essentially noncorrosive when air-free and kept separate. However, if they are mixed, the result is severe corrosion problems.

Ideally, therefore, the two water systems should be kept completely separate—going to separate pump and separate injection wells. Manifolds can be designed that will let wells be switched from source water to produced water as the produced water volumes increase.

When this is not practical or possible, waters have been injected in tandem. That is—pump one water for a while, then switch to the other—back and forth. This can be fairly easily accomplished by using sequencing divert valves. The one thing to watch out for with such a system is leaking divert valves. Valve maintenance is extremely important to assure no mixing.

PIPING DESIGN

In the design of piping systems three conditions can lead to corrosion problems: water traps, dead legs, and high velocities.

Water Traps. Water traps are low sections of lines that allow water to collect (and thus water wet the pipe) even when very little water is present.

Probably the most common water traps in plant installations are created when piping is brought down to ground level for a control loop. These will collect water and are candidates for pipe repair when they blow out due to corrosion. Another common water trap occurs in plants and in field flowlines where lines drop down to go under other lines or roads.

It is virtually impossible to avoid all water traps in piping. However, they should be kept to a minimum. Where practical, drain valves should be installed in the trap and periodically drained. Certainly, water traps should be some of the first areas to inspect when an inspection program is initiated. **Figure 9.1** shows a photograph of a common sight in plants and large production facilities. Almost every line drops to "working level" before rising up for the next vessel.

Figure 9.1 Typical plant piping. Note the control valve piping forming water traps.

Dead Legs. Dead legs also are common in most piping systems. Dead legs are branch lines or the ends of piping that have no flow and the fluid is stagnant. They may be dead all the time (ends of piping systems or extensions for future expansion), they may be dead during part of the project (sections of manifolds), or they may be "no-flow" lines that are used intermittently (relief lines, drain lines, recirculation lines, etc.).

These can be particularly troublesome in water injection system piping. Not only does corrosion occur in dead legs, but they can serve as breeding grounds for bacteria. They are out of the mainstream and miss any chemical treatment and they serve as a source of re-infecting the system after treatment.

Again, it is virtually impossible to eliminate all dead legs in piping, but they can be minimized in the piping design by such things as:

- Eliminating dead ends in manifolds.

- Placement of valves to have the shortest practical dead legs.

- Providing drains so the dead areas can be periodically flushed.

- Using ells rather than tees.

- Having branch lines come off the top rather than the side or bottom.

Each piping system is unique, but when the piping designer is conscious of the need to minimize dead legs, then it is surprising sometimes how "clean" the design can be.

Velocity Effects. The opposite of dead legs can also create problems, that is, areas of high velocity. Chapter 3 discussed erosion/corrosion where solids in liquid streams or liquid droplets in gas streams can remove corrosion products exposing the clean metal to more corrosion.

Up to now, about the only guideline available to determine erosional velocities (sometimes referred to as critical velocities) is the formula in API RP-14E[1]:

$$V_e = \frac{C}{\sqrt{pm}} \tag{1}$$

Where: V_e is the fluid erosional velocity (feet/second), C is the empirical constant (commonly 100 to 125), and pm is the gas/liquid mixture density at flowing pressure and temperature (pounds/cubic foot).

There are indications that this formula for erosional velocity is too conservative and that higher velocities are tolerable in many situations. This subject continues to evolve as several long-range research programs on velocity and erosional effects are ongoing at various universities. Several articles on erosional velocity are listed in the bibliography at the end of the chapter.

The safest thing to do at the moment is to periodically inspect piping that is operating at a high velocity so you won't be caught by surprise.

ELECTRICAL ISOLATION

The term "electrical isolation" (sometimes called "insulation") is a corrosion control method that truly breaks up the electrochemical cell. The objective of the installation of an isolation fitting is to break the metallic path, or at least to increase the resistance in the corroding circuit as much as possible.

Electrical isolation is used in the following cases:

- Breakup the external corrosion circuit in buried facilities, such as the circuit between well casings and flowlines, or well casings and tank bottoms.

- Breakup bimetallic couples (galvanic couples) to prevent dissimilar metal corrosion, such as stainless steel piping connected to the nozzle of a coated vessel or stainless steel internals in an internally coated vessel.

- Isolate cathodically protected structures, such as isolating a cathodically protected well from its flowline or a cathodically protected line from a tank battery.

In the first two uses the electrical isolation is the corrosion control method in the latter, it augments the primary method, cathodic protection (CP).

There are several types of fittings for electrical isolation. Probably the most common is the insulated flange. **Figure 9.2** is a drawing of an insulating flange and its components.[2] A flange insulation kit contains insulating sleeves for the studs or bolts, the insulating washers for each end of each bolt, and the insulating gasket. Kits are available to match various sizes, pressure ratings, and types of flanges. **Figure 9.2** shows a flat face flange. Insulating gaskets are also available for ring-groove flanges.

Insulating flanges are not the only type of isolation. Insulating unions, both hex nut and hammer unions, are available. Insulating couplings, made like standard pipe coupling, but with nonmetallic threaded inserts, are manufactured for low-pressure service. Some operators use short, 1 to 2ft (0.3 to 0.6m) long, fiberglass nipples in flowlines at the wellhead to provide well-to-flowline isolation. Sketches of these and other

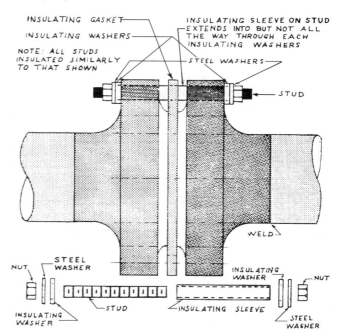

Figure 9.2 Insulated flange assembly.

isolation fittings, as well as detailed discussions on electrical isolation, are available in NACE Recommended Practice RP0286-86, "The Electrical Isolation of Cathodically Protected Pipelines."[3]

Figure 9.3 Insulated flange in the field. Note the bolt insulation and insulating washers. Anything wrong with this picture?

When installing electrical isolation, it's very important that the isolation not be bypassed or shorted by another connection. **Figure 9.3** is a photo of just such an installation where the control line bypasses the insulated flange.

Earlier chapters discussed galvanic attack, corrosion due to the coupling of metals that are far apart in the galvanic series. It's at the design stage where these couples can be minimized or avoided. The design needs to include electrical isolation if different metals are required due to other corrosion control considerations. For example, when stainless steel piping is used with a coated carbon steel vessel, the stainless steel must be isolated to avoid accelerating corrosion at holidays in the coated vessel nozzle. This is due to the large stainless steel cathode and small carbon steel anode.

If the line is handling low resistance produced water, the flange insulation alone may not be satisfactory. A longer current path could be necessary. In such cases, the first few feet of the stainless steel should be internally coated. This will give a longer current path through the water. Furthermore, if there are holidays in the coating in the stainless steel spool, the galvanic couple (carbon steel to stainless steel) will be small anode and small cathode. When the vessel and piping are mounted on a metal floor (such as on an offshore platform or in a building), the insulated flange can be bypassed (shorted) through the vessel supports, the floor, and the pipe supports. In that case two insulated fittings will be required—one at each end of the internally coated stainless steel spool. The pipe supports should be outside the spool.

Actually the use of electrical isolation is not complicated. It just requires a simple review of the system, keeping in mind the objective of breaking up possible current paths.

Figure 9.4 illustrates another use of insulation to avoid a direct bimetallic couple. The stainless steel instrument flange is electrically isolated from the carbon steel nozzle.

Regardless of the purpose for installing the insulation, it is very important to periodically test the flange to verify that it is still providing isolation. The wellhead-flowline insulation should always be tested whenever it is been removed for well work. NACE RP0286-86 lists several tests including: checking the pipe-to-soil potential each side of the flange in a pipeline with one side under CP, audio frequency pipe locators, radio frequency meters, and a magnetometer system.[3]

Figure 9.4 Flange insulation isolating stainless steel instrument from carbon steel piping.

OXYGEN EXCLUSION

As stated several times, oxygen is the greatest accelerator of corrosion. Therefore, oxygen exclusion is the primary method of corrosion control in all systems.

Since oxygen is not native to producing formations, the only oxygen in a system will be that let in due to the design or the operating and maintenance practices.

In many systems, oxygen exclusion is the only method of corrosion control needed (keep oxygen out, no significant corrosion; let oxygen enter, severe corrosion problems.)

When there are other corrosive agents, such as CO_2 and H_2S, the corrosion will be much more severe if oxygen enters the fluids. In most cases, the methods used to control corrosion (*e.g.*, inhibitors) will not satisfactorily control oxygen corrosion.

PRODUCING WELLS

Since most flowing oil and gas wells operate with a positive pressure, oxygen seldom creates a problem. However, artificial lift wells may have low enough pressure to have oxygen enter under many conditions. For example, pumping wells that are produced on a cycle or that are shut-in periodically can draw in air as the annular fluid level is drawn down from the shut-in level to the pumping level.

Rod-pumping/well-stuffing boxes can also be oxygen entry points. When pumping wells are having corrosion problems in the pumping tee and the first few feet of flowline, oxygen may well be the problem. Oxygen can be drawn in on the downstroke (even if oil and water do not leak out on the upstroke). The oxygen will corrode the steel in the pumping tee and maybe 10 ft of flowline before it is all used up. From that point on, the system is oxygen-free.

WATER SYSTEMS

Most oxygen problems exist in surface facilities, particularly water injection systems. The paper on oxygen and water mentioned in Chapter 1 goes into quite a bit of detail on some of the problems of oxygen in water injection and disposal systems.[4]

It is really not difficult to design and operate a water system oxygen-free as long as a few simple steps are followed and the personnel involved understand what they are trying to accomplish (and why).

The most common method of maintaining oxygen-free conditions is through the use of gas blankets on supply wells and tanks, and to have vessels (*e.g.*, filters) fluid packed. Maintenance of all seals and packing is, of course, important. Conditions that allow drawing a vacuum on wellheads, trees, or lines should be avoided. Most of the maintenance items are "common sense" and can become second nature to properly trained, experienced personnel.

Gas Blankets. The design of gas blankets is not complicated.[4] The details of a blanketing system will vary to fit the needs of each installation.

Just keep in mind that the objective of the gas blanket is to maintain a positive pressure on the gas space at all times so that air cannot enter. Some thoughts along this line include:

- High blanket pressures are not required. "Ounces" (or "inches") of pressure are sufficient on most tanks. Gauges should be installed so that the pressure can be routinely checked and adjusted when required.

- The regulators and gas lines should be sized to admit gas at a rate high enough to maintain the pressure when the fluid level drops. Some installations where tank drawdown rates vary tremendously have parallel regulators to assure a sufficient gas supply under any conditions. The small volume regulator opens first, and usually this is adequate to handle normal pressure fluctuations. If the drawdown is too rapid for that regulator to keep the blanket pressure up, the second (larger) regulator opens.

- Regulators should be located as close to the gas entrance point as practical, and should be installed so that condensation will not block off the gas flow. (**Figure 9.5**) Drain valves should be installed on the blanket gas lines to allow removal of trapped water or hydrocarbons. This is particularly important in areas where the regulator is housed in a building to avoid freezing, and the low pressure gas is piped to the top of the tank. Unless it is periodically drained from the line to the tank, the condensed liquids will build up and shut off the gas flow.

Figure 9.5 Gas blanket pressure regulator mounted on top of a water tank. The short horizontal pipe on the tank side of the regulator effectively eliminates the possibility of condensation blocking off the gas flow.

- When "field gas" is used, regulators should be installed for easy removal for cleaning.
- The gas source should be oxygen-free. That may sound unnecessary to mention, but there has been at least one instance where gas off a deaeration tower was used to blanket the tank of deaerated water. In another case residue gas containing 2% to 3% oxygen was used for blanket gas.

There are several ways to minimize the amount of gas required to maintain a gas blanket. The simplest method is to design the system for minimum fluid level fluctuations by sizing supply well pumps to closely match injection requirements. When the wells do not have to cycle often, their fluid levels remain constant, and gas is not pumped in and out. In many cases, minimum cycling has other advantages, such as longer pump life, less sand production, etc. Minimum cycling of supply wells also lets the supply tank operate with minimum fluctuations of water level. The tank gas blanket requirements are also held to a minimum.

The ideal way to check a gas blanket to make certain that is it is truly a "gas" blanket is with an oxygen meter. However, in most cases in the field, a blanket is checked merely by opening the thief hatch to see if there is a "blow." This is quite satisfactory if the regulator can be heard dumping gas to the tank when the hatch is opened, and if the tank is being pumped down or has a constant fluid level and is not "filling."

Some underground waters are quite "gassy" and under certain conditions may provide "self blanketing." Be very careful when depending upon self blanketing. Make certain that sufficient gas is evolved in the supply well annulus to replace the void when the well "kicks on." If the annular pressure drops to zero or below as the fluid level drops, supplementary gas will be required. The same holds true in supply water tanks.

By the way, if "self blanketing" is used, blankets should be periodically checked to make certain that conditions have not changed as the supply zone is depleted.

Do not depend upon self blankets on produced water tanks! Experience has shown that they do not work.

In the early days, oil blankets were sometimes used on supply wells and tanks rather than gas blankets. **(Figure 9.6)** However, oil blankets will not keep a system oxygen free. Oxygen is soluble in oil. In fact, it may be 5 to 25 times as soluble in hydrocarbons as in oilfield waters. At their best, oil blankets may "slow down" oxygen entry. At their worst, they oil coat solid particles in the water and create well-plugging problems, or the dump valve fails to close and the oil blanket is pumped to the injection wells.

Figure 9.6 As illustrated by this photograph of an open water tank, early in the history of water injection some operators felt that an oil blanket would keep oxygen out of the water. Later it was realized that oxygen was more soluble in oil than in water and tanks were closed and gas blanketed.

OXYGEN ENTRY

As mentioned earlier, proper maintenance is important in maintaining oxygen-free conditions.

Pumps. An often overlooked source of oxygen entry is the centrifugal pump. If the seals start leaking, air (oxygen) is sucked into the pump.

Figure 9.7 is a reproduction of a chart from a recording oxygen meter located downstream of a centrifugal transfer pump.[4] Water from a deaeration tower was being pumped through filters. Water from the tower contained less than 20 parts per billion (ppb) dissolved oxygen. The dissolved oxygen levels downstream of the pump varied as high as 800 ppb (left portion of the chart). The seals in the pump were leaking. When the pump's seals were replaced, the oxygen dropped to the tower outlet level. The same phenomena has been noted on centrifugal charge pumps for positive displacement injection pumps. Plumber pumps themselves can leak oxygen when not properly packed.

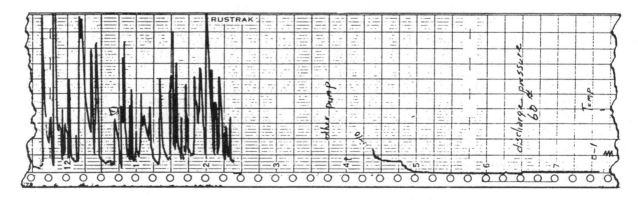

CENTRIFUGAL PUMP No. I
Packing leaking___ Oxygen entering

CENTRIFUGAL PUMP No. 2
New packing ___ No oxygen leakage

Figure 9.7 Oxygen meter recorder chart. Note the oxygen meter was calibrated in % oxygen saturation equals 0% to 10% full scale (equivalent to 0=0.79 mg/L dissolved oxygen in this specific water).[4]

Supply Wells. Other sources of oxygen entry in water systems include the supply wells themselves. The annulus should be gas blanketed unless there is sufficient gas for a self blanket. The supply wells most likely to cause problems are those that operate cyclically. If there is insufficient blanket, air is drawn into the annulus each time the well "kicks on" and the fluid level drops.

A similar problem occurs when the foot valve at the pump and/or a check valve fails when the pump shuts in. In this case, the water drains back out of the tubing and/or out of the supply line. A vacuum is created, and air is drawn into the line. When the well comes on, a tubing full (or line full) of air is pumped to the water supply tank. In some instances it will take several hours to work off the effects of such "slugs" of air.

For these reasons, it is good operating practice in systems with several supply wells for most wells to run continuously with only one well used as a "swing" well. This is another reason why it is important to size supply well pumps close to the water requirements so that cycling can be kept at a minimum. Foot valve and check valve operation should be checked periodically to make certain they are holding and the water does not "drain back."

Injection Wells. Many injection systems have wells that take the required amount of water on a vacuum (particularly in the early life of a flood before "fill up"). Wellhead fittings will often leak air under a vacuum, even though they hold pressure without leaking. Thus, it is good practice to maintain a positive pressure on all fittings and take the pressure drop at the last valve before the water goes underground. Pinching back on such a valve and holding a positive pressure of 15 to 25 psig on all well site fittings has been a very effective method for controlling corrosion in injection well tubing in several floods.

Appendix 9A is a checklist for troubleshooting oxygen-free-water injection systems.

GAS PLANTS

Oxygen problems are not exclusively the privilege of oil fields and water injection systems—plants have many oxygen problems.

Gasoline plants with vacuum gathering systems are especially subject to accelerated corrosion due to the oxygen that's brought in from leaks in the incoming lines. The challenge of oxygen exclusion becomes one of first removing the oxygen.

But you do not have to have a vacuum gathering system to have problems—any location where the pressure gets below atmospheric is a potential oxygen entry point.

Corrosion itself isn't the only problem from air entry in a plant. At least one plant had to replace a major portion of the plant inlet piping. Not only was the oxygen corroding their system, but the nitrogen that was left from the air was diluting the gas so much they could not meet the British Thermal Unit (BTU) requirement of their gas sales contract.

A plant reported that it was having corrosion and solids problems in their amine sweetening system. It turned out that much of their problem was due to oxygen. They did not have a vacuum gathering system, but the incoming gas carried some solids, and they were regularly having to change the elements in the inlet filter separators. It seems there were no provisions to purge the air from the filter separators after each filter change, and the air was carried right into the amine tower. Apparently, the oxygen not only contributed to corrosion, but it oxidized dissolved iron which in turn became insoluble iron sulfide and precipitated in the system.

Another plant solved some of their amine system problems by deoxygenating their make-up water for the amine system.

OXYGEN REMOVAL

Surface waters (*e.g.*, river, lake, or seawater) used in some water floods as source water are aerated, and the oxygen must be removed to minimize corrosion problems. The most common methods of removing oxygen from aerated waters are mechanical deaeration (utilizing counter current gas stripping towers or vacuum towers) and chemical scavenging.

The choice of the removal method depends largely on the economics of the project. As a generality, stripping towers are used when large quantities of dissolved oxygen are to be removed and/or large volumes of water are to be handled. Chemical scavengers are used to remove small amounts of oxygen, and sometimes for removing the residual after tower deaeration. The final decision is an economic-technical one.

GAS STRIPPING TOWERS

Gas stripping towers are the most frequent type used in oilfield operations (commonly, they will be tray-type towers [**Figure 9.8**]). Natural gas is the most common stripping gas. However, nitrogen has been used when the natural gas was not available or the available gas supply was unsatisfactory, for instance, high in H_2S.

Gas stripping towers are (usually) properly designed if the manufacturer is supplied with sufficient information regarding the project. However, there are several practical considerations to remember when planning, installing, and operating towers:

- Meters should be installed on both the water and gas streams. These are needed to evaluate tower performance, select the optimum gas-water ratio for the specific installation, and to allow varying the gas feed with changing water and oxygen conditions. The latter is important because in practice, towers are seldom operated under design conditions, certainly not throughout the life of the project.

- The gas source should be sweet gas. Although sour gas will perform the stripping function, the H_2S and oxygen will chemically react to form free-sulfur in the system. Under severe conditions, the free-sulfur will be deposited on

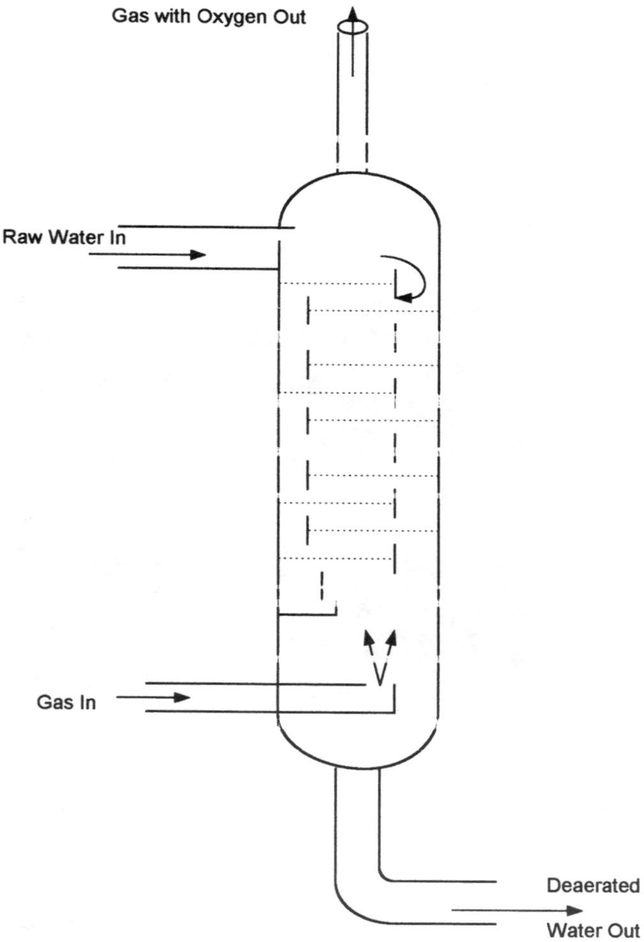

Figure 9.8 Schematic of tray type gas stripping tower.

the tower's trays and eventually put it out of service. At best, only small quantities of free-sulfur will be formed. However, they will be carried with the injection water and very effectively plug injection wells when combined with other possible plugging solids in the water. Removal of free-sulfur from the system and wellbore is difficult and must be done either mechanically or very selectively (and carefully) with a solvent treatment using carbon disulfide.

- The stripping gas should be free of oxygen. Again, this may sound ridiculous to mention, but as stated previously, some residue gas streams do contain oxygen.

- Back pressure on the tower is critical. For example, the difference between operating a specific tower at 18 psig (124 kPa) rather that 50 psig (345 kPa) could mean a difference between 0.1 mg/L and 1.0 mg/L oxygen in the effluent water. It is usually, therefore, more profitable to operate a tower at a low pressure and pump water from it than to operate at a high tower pressure without a transfer pump.

- Fluid level control in the tower is also critical for satisfactory tower operation. Varying levels can result in flooding out the lower tray, entraining gas in the water, or actually "blowing" gas out the water outlet. Some installations may require a surge tank for smooth operation with varying loads. If a surge tank is used, it should be designed and installed so that it does not become a "dead spot," thus serving as an incubation chamber for microorganisms.

- A tower needs to be clean to operate at design efficiency. If the water contains solids that can settle out on the trays, periodic clean out should be scheduled. Towers handling waters containing slime-forming bacteria will require periodic slug treatment with a biocide for microorganism control. **(Figure 9.9)**

- Injection of chemical scavengers into the tower outlet may be needed in some systems to meet the desired oxygen level.

Figure 9.9 Bacterial slime interfered with tray valve action in this deaeration tower. Periodic washing with hypochlorite solution kept the tower operating properly.

All gas stripping towers are not tray towers; sometimes packed column towers are used. However, they're usually harder to properly design and may be harder to operate efficiently than tray towers.

VACUUM STRIPPING TOWERS

When there is not an adequate gas supply for operations of a gas stripping tower or when the gas supply is high in CO_2 or H_2S, vacuum towers are used.

Vacuum towers are not as popular as gas stripping towers because they require packed columns rather than trays. **Figure 9.10** is a drawing of a three stage packed column vacuum stripping tower using gas eductors on each stage. The educators in turn feed a vacuum pump. Packed column towers can be more difficult to design for maximum efficiency than tray towers. Historically, vacuum towers have had high maintenance costs due to the vacuum pump requirements. They also tend to lose efficiency quickly if the packing is fouled. Most vacuum tower installations require the addition of a chemical scavenger after the tower to remove the last traces of oxygen to achieve specification water. Many vacuum towers will also require use of an antifoam, particularly when deaerating seawater.

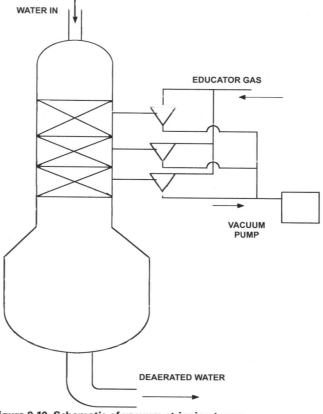

CHEMICAL SCAVENGING

The other method of oxygen removal is the use of catalyzed chemical scavengers. These scavengers are usually one of the sulfite compounds. The ones used the most by many operators are:

- Sodium sulfite in fresh water.

Figure 9.10 Schematic of vacuum stripping tower.

- Sodium bisulfite (or sodium metasulfite) in seawater.

- Sulfur dioxide gas is used in fresh water and brine in areas where a packaged service is provided.

The other sulfite that is sometimes used is ammonium bisulfite.
The sulfites combine with oxygen with the following reactions:

Sodium sulfite $2Na_2SO_3 + O_2 \longrightarrow 2Na_2SO_4$ The weight ratio is: 8:1   (2)

Sodium bisulfite $2NaHSO_3 + O_2 \longrightarrow 2NaHSO_4$ The weight ratio is: 6.5:1   (3)

Sulfur dioxide (gas) $2SO_2 + 2H_2O \longrightarrow 2H_2SO_3$

                     $2H_2SO_3 + O_2 \longrightarrow 2H_2SO_4$ The weight ratio is: 4:1   (4)

Ammonium bisulfite $2NH_4HSO_3 + O_2 \longrightarrow (NH_4)_2SO_4 + H_2SO_4$
                                                         The weight ratio is: 6.2:1   (5)

To calculate the dosage required, the "dosage ratio" will be the above weight ratio divided by the percent purity of the commercial product being used. The final dosage ratio (the actual feed ratio) should include an excess to provide for fluctuations in oxygen content and to provide a residual. For example, sodium sulfite is typically used at a 10:1 ratio (that is, 10lbs of sodium sulfite for each 1lb of oxygen to be removed). When very small amounts of oxygen (100 ppb or less) are to be removed, several times the theoretical amount of scavenger may be required to force the reaction in a reasonable amount of time.

A catalyst is required to "kick off" the scavenger reaction. So it is very important that the chemical purchased is catalyzed. Cobalt and nickel salts are the most common catalysts used.

When using a chemical scavenger, please remember that the scavenger reaction is not instantaneous. There must be sufficient holding time (or reaction time) designed into the system to allow the reaction to take place. The time required for the reaction is a function of the specific chemical, the dosage, the catalyst level, the water composition, and the temperature. Oxygen scavenger reaction rate studies can be performed to select the scavenger if required.[5] Reaction time in a dynamic system may not be as long as it calculates. See the sidebar: Holding Time—Is it really there?

HOLDING TIME—Is It Really There?

By the way, don't be fooled by holding time. There was an instance where a small water flood used a supply water which contained some oxygen. Sulfur dioxide and catalyst were injected into the water source line to the supply tank as the oxygen scavenger. The scavenger was fed only when water was going into the tank. Sulfite residual determinations and some spot checks of dissolved oxygen content indicated that the water was successfully scavenged. However, coupons located at the plant discharge and failures in the manifold indicated otherwise. Investigation revealed that due to channeling in the tank, water was flowing directly from the inlet to the outlet while it was filling. There was insufficient reaction time (essentially zero) for proper scavenging. When the tank was full and the supply line shut, there was sufficient time to complete the scavenging as the tank was emptying. During that time, the plant was handling specification water.

Since this was a cyclic condition, the spot checks of scavenger residual and oxygen content had indicated good scavenging, but the system was being corroded.

The problem was corrected by putting baffles in the tank so that water was held up long enough for the scavenger to do its job. Here's another instance when calculating holding time based on tank capacity and daily throughput did not work.

When scavengers are used, it is quite common to run residual sulfite tests as an indication that oxygen has been removed. Do not depend on these tests alone. Oxygen and sulfite can co-exist in a system if the reaction has not reached completion.

There is another compound that is a very satisfactory oxygen scavenger, hydrazine solution. Unfortunately, it requires temperatures above 125°F (52°C) for the reaction, so its use is normally limited to hot boiler feed waters.

DEHYDRATION OF GAS

Since corrosion in gas systems is dependent upon having moisture present, dehydration is the most practical way to control corrosion in these systems (gas transmission, gas lift, gas injection, and sometimes in gas gathering). Properly operated well site dehydration will often eliminate many field problems, particularly when handling gas with high CO_2 and/or H_2S levels. In fact, if it is dry enough, relatively pure CO_2 or H_2S does not create corrosion problems. The usual "rule of thumb" to assure corrosion control is to: "dehydrate the gas to a water content less than 50% to 60% of saturation based on the lowest pipe or vessel wall temperature expected in the system."

The "50% to 60% of saturation" (or a 50% to 60% relative humidity) value is used because many of the solids found in gas lines can be hygroscopic and will pick up water even from gas that is above its dew point temperature. Corrosion cells can be set up between the metal and these moist solids. Severe pitting attack can result. However, when the gas's water content is less than 50% to 60% of saturation, the gas will dry the solids and corrosion does not occur.

When determining the required water content, be sure to use the lowest wall temperature expected—not the lowest gas temperature. A cold area on the wall can be moist from condensation at that location, even though the bulk gas temperature is not lowered.

Maintaining humidity control has been used in some cases; however, dehydration is a more reliable approach in most systems.

Oftentimes dehydration is designed to only meet hydrate control conditions and, with just a bit more dehydration, corrosion control can be achieved.

If hydrates are to be controlled by methanol or glycol injection, do not expect corrosion control from that approach. CO_2 is soluble in methanol/water and glycol/water mixtures and will lower the pH just as in water alone.

When using glycol dehydration for gases with a high CO_2 and/or H_2S content, do not overlook the needs for corrosion control in the glycol circulation and regeneration systems. The usual methods of corrosion control are to control the pH and stream quality of the circulating glycol. CO_2 and H_2S tend to accelerate glycol degradation and can lead to creation of organic acids and solid particles in the system. The pH is usually maintained at around 6.5: a lower pH cannot control corrosion and a higher pH leads to glycol foaming. "Dirty" glycol (*i.e.*, glycol carrying solids) can cause system plugging and foaming as well as corrosion problems. Solids that fall out and collect in the line can lead to pitting type attack (under deposit corrosion). Filtration is the usual method for solids removal. Many glycol systems use side stream filtration. Full stream is a bit more costly; however, it is a surer way to remove solids. Historically, partial filtration will not satisfactorily keep the system clean, particularly a very dirty stream.

The glycol regeneration package is also susceptible to corrosion, particularly in the reflux tower and the tower overhead system. The overhead, of course, handles the water driven off and all of the CO_2 and H_2S dissolved from the gas, as well as any short chain organic acids from glycol degradation. As the water condenses, this stream can be quite corrosive. Corrosion-resistant materials, such as stainless steels, are often specified for the reflux tower and overhead systems when dehydrating gas with high acid gas content.

DEPOSITS CONTROL (CLEANLINESS)

Corrosion problems in many systems can be avoided or at least minimized by keeping the surface clean. Examples were given in earlier chapters when scale, deposits, and debris can cause accelerated corrosion in many systems by trapping water against the metal surface, creating differential concentration cells, providing growth sites for sulfate reducing bacteria, or by causing "hot spots" on heated surfaces and thus differential temperature cells. Operating and maintenance procedures should be set up to keep the equipment clean (for example, routine pigging of gas lines to remove water and deposits (oftentimes with inhibitor), routine pigging of water injection lines and flushing of vessel bottoms, and periodic cleaning of tanks and vessels).

PIGGING

Pigs come in various sizes and styles—in large diameter lines, the more solid design pigs are often used. Generally, do not depend on spheres to remove solids—they are better for dewatering. Probably the most common pigs for solids removal are some version of the foam pigs. Multiple pigs can be used for cleaning, and foam pigs tend not to get hung up in the line.

Pigging frequency varies with the system and service. Ideally, pigging is done often enough so that the line stays essentially solids-free. In other words, only a small quantity of solids accumulate between each routine pig run.

Actual clean out of vessels (that is, getting in and shoveling out the solids and sludge) is required in many systems. It is not desirable, but it may be necessary.

FLUSHING

Flushing is sometimes used to clean out lines and vessel bottoms and this will work fairly well if the solids are loose (*i.e.*, if they are not compacted or stuck to the walls).

When a line or vessel is flushed, it will need to be surged. That is, the valve should not just be opened for a constant flow rate. Vary the velocity by opening and closing to keep the solids moving.

The solids along the bottom are at equilibrium with the normal flow rate. Each time the rate is increased, some of the solids will be moved. But in many cases, they will just move a bit farther along the bottom. By changing rates (and thus velocities) as rapidly as possible, a surging action is created that will keep the solids moving.

Of course in many cases, flushing may not be sufficient. Manual clean out may be required in vessels. Lines may have to be pigged.

FILTRATION

Filtration is required in some systems to remove solids from the fluids. The use of filters to maintain glycol quality in glycol regenerative systems was mentioned earlier in the chapter. It is very important to remove the products of glycol degradation.

Filtration is also used in amine sweetening systems, and the same comments on full stream filtration apply.

Water injection systems are where filters are usually used. Most surface water supplies (seawater, lakes, rivers) will require filtration. Most subsurface water supplies do not. Filtration and the design of filter systems can be very involved. A thorough discussion is beyond this book. However, many texts have information on filtration. For example, Ostroff's *Introduction to Oilfield Water Technology* devotes an entire chapter to filtration of oilfield waters.[6]

As a generality, try to avoid using filters in produced water systems. They can cause more problems than they solve. Oil carryover tends to plug filters. At best, this requires very frequent backwash. At the worst, the filters will channel (that is, flow will be uneven with most of the water flowing through channels in the filter media and the solids pass right on through).

There are many types, styles, and configurations of filters. The ones most common in oilfield applications are either variations on the so called "rapid sand" filters, both down-flow and up-flow styles, or one of the types of cartridge or "sock" filters. The sand filters, using many materials other than sand as the filter media, are usually installed at a central water plant. The cartridge filters may be at the water plant, but they are often installed at the wellhead of injection wells. Wellhead filters should be used as "emergency filters" (that is, they serve to protect the well in case of upsets at the water plant).

When filtration is needed, sizing of the filter is very important. Generally, it is good practice to install filters rated at greater throughput than is required for the volumes of fluid to be filtered. Many manufacturers rate their filters based on tests using clean water with new media. In those cases, the throughput of dirty water will be much less than the rated capacity.

Although the installation of filters is intended to aid corrosion control by removing materials that can create harmful deposits, if not carefully designed and conscientiously operated, filters can contribute to corrosion. The filter media in "sand" filters present an ideal location for microorganism growth, so extra precaution should be exercised to avoid contamination. It is easy to decide to "clean-up" some waste water through a filter in a water flood. If the waste water is from a surface pit or is transported in a truck that has carried water from a pit, the odds are the water is infected with at least sulfate reducing bacteria (SRBs) and possibly other microorganisms. It can be very costly, difficult, and time consuming to sterilize a large filter system.

Any filter, and particularly cartridge filters, should be equipped with vents. When filter cartridges are changed and the filter shell is closed, it is full of air. If this air is not vented as the filter is filled, a sizable volume of air can be introduced into the injection system.

CONTROL OF MICROBIOLOGICALLY INFLUENCED CORROSION

The next method of controlling the corrosive environment is control of microbiologically influenced corrosion (MIC) (that is, the control of microorganisms, or "bacteria," often referred to in the field simply as "bugs").

As mentioned in Chapter 2, the most common microorganism that creates problems in oilfield operations is the sulfate-reducing bacteria (SRB). The SRBs are anaerobic bacteria (they thrive where there is no air) who use sulfates in their metabolism. The byproduct is H_2S. Although sulfate reducers are anaerobic, they are not necessarily killed by exposure to air. They merely become dormant in a hostile environment and can become active when placed in a friendly environment.

They are quite universal and can be found almost anywhere, a strain could probably be cultured off the floor, that is why the mere presence of SRBs does not necessarily mean control is required. The important considerations are:

- How active are they?

- What problems, if any, are they causing?

Fortunately, they are not in most systems. However, they are native to some field systems and therefore, may require control. The detection and evaluation of SRBs is discussed in Chapter 10. (References for those who want to know more are given with that chapter.)

Problems that may be caused by sulfate reducers would include:

- Souring an otherwise sweet system, thus creating both corrosion problems and possible well plugging solids.

- Plugging of injection wells due to their bodies and byproducts (in some severe cases).

- Souring of the injection reservoir (common when using surface waters).

As far as producing wells are concerned, routine control (use of biocides) is not usually required. However, it is good practice to control SRB in packer fluids, since they can add H_2S to an otherwise sweet fluid. In most cases, the corrosion inhibitor dosages used in clear brine packer fluids will effectively control the SRB.

WATER INJECTION SYSTEMS

As far as water injection systems are concerned, most systems using surface water as a water supply will require some degree of control. Most systems with underground source water do not have SRBs—unless the water has been contaminated on the surface by water handling practices.

Generally, even where sulfate reducers are native to a water source, good design and operating practices can avoid problems, and thus routine biocide treatment is not required. For example:

- Design systems so the water keeps moving. The SRBs like dead areas.

- Avoid dead lines, dead legs, etc.

- Keep systems clean by flushing, pigging, etc., or periodic shutdowns and clean outs.

- Do not pick up waste waters from pits or tank bottoms and add it back into a system (use separate disposal).

Oftentimes, in fact most times, these steps are all that is required. In some cases, occasional use of a biocide is required to sterilize a contaminated system and, in a few cases, routine treatment with biocide is required.

When biocides are required, biocide selection is very important and the method of application is also important and should be matched to a particular system and its problems.

Biocide treatment is expensive. Define the problem. Determine if biocide treatment is required. If so, do it right!!! Initiate the proper physical, mechanical and chemical procedures, and set up and initiate a monitoring program to follow the progress.

Things to remember about biocide treatment:

- Biocide treatment is expensive. Halfway measures are expensive and ineffective.

- Chemical suppliers' data may be optimistic.

- Most test data represents performance of a biocide against a specific organism in a clean system.

- Better biocide performance data is becoming available.

HYDROTEST WATERS

Hydrotest waters are often surface waters from rivers and lakes and can contain many microorganisms. Because of the problems of disposing of treated water after hydrotest, there has been a tendency to not use biocides or other chemicals in the water; that way the water can be dumped on the ground. However, hydrotest water can contaminate a line.

There is no way to tell how many times leaks that occurred within a year or so after hydrotest could have been prevented by killing the bacteria at the time of the test. Drying the line with methanol after the hydrotest water is removed is one approach. Methanol is relatively inexpensive and will control the bacteria as well as drying the line.

OTHER METHODS AND ENVIRONMENTS

pH CONTROL

Controlling the pH (neutralization) is used in some cases for corrosion control. The use of pH control for dehydration glycol was mentioned earlier.

There are other cases where pH control can be used (e.g., gas streams with high CO_2 and/or H_2S). When water is being condensed as the gas passes through coolers, it is very difficult (if not impossible) to get good distribution of conventional film forming inhibitors in each tube. There are some vapor phase amines (ammonia is the cheapest) that are carried in the gas and will dissolve in condensed water to neutralize the acid gases that have dissolved in the water.

The main problem is dosage and monitoring. About the only choice is to monitor the pH at the water draw off and adjust the neutralizer dosage accordingly.

It is because of the dosage adjustment and monitoring problems that it is usually much more cost effective to use corrosion-resistant materials for coolers and to coat the vapor space in vessels.

MOTHBALLING, LAY-UP, AND DECOMMISSIONING

Mothballing of piping, vessels and equipment is important if they are to be out of service for some time. The details will vary depending on the items, the materials of construction, and the fluids it has been handling.

In most cases, mothballing will involve cleaning, drying, and sealing the equipment with an inert atmosphere. There are some inhibitors specifically designed for mothballing and long-term preservation.

Most manufacturers of compressors, pumps, and engines have specific instructions for mothballing their equipment. The Materials Technology Institute of the Chemical Process Industries (MTI) book on mothballing is applicable to production facilities as well as chemical plants."[7]

REFERENCES

1. API Recommended Practice RP-14E, "Design and Installation of Offshore Production Platform Piping Systems" 5th ed., Section 2.3 Sizing Criteria for Liquid Lines (Washington, D.C.: American Petroleum Institute, 1991), p. 15.
2. A. W. Peabody, "Control of Pipeline Corrosion" (Houston, TX : NACE, 1967), p. 157.
3. NACE Recommended Practice RP0286-86, "The Electrical Isolation of Cathodically Protected Pipelines" (Houston, TX: NACE, 1986).
4. H. G. Byars, B. R. Gallop,"Injection Water + Oxygen = Corrosion and/or Well Plugging Solids," MP 13, 12 (1974): p. 33.
5. M. W. Mateer, "Selection of Oxygen Scavengers for Oilfield Waters," Corrosion/86, paper no. 178, (Houston, TX: NACE, 1986).
6. A. G. Ostroff, "Introduction to Oilfield Water Technology" (Houston, TX: NACE 1979), p. 232–261.
7. R. J. Twigg, Guidelines for the Mothballing of Process Plants, MTI Publication No. 34 (St. Louis, MO: MTI, 1989).

BIBLIOGRAPHY

Craig, B. D., "Predicting Critical Erosion-Corrosion Limits of Alloys for Oil and Gas Production," MP 37, 9 (1998): p. 59.

Salama, M. M., "Erosion Velocity Limits for Water Injection Systems," MP 32, 7, (1993): p. 44.

Shirazi, S. A., B. S. McLaury, J. R. Shadley, and E.F. Rybicki, "Generalization of the API RP14E Guideline for Erosive Services," Journal of Petroleum Technology, 47, 8 (1995): p. 693.

APPENDIX 9A

CHECK LIST FOR TROUBLESHOOTING OXYGEN-FREE WATER INJECTION SYSTEMS

The following items should be checked to determine if water injection systems are set up and operating oxygen-free:

GAS BLANKETS ON TANKS AND VESSELS

1. Check source of blanket gas. It must be oxygen-free.

2. Check for individual gas blanket regulators on each tank. One regulator cannot properly serve two tanks. Regulators should be mounted at the top of the tank with a 1 in. or larger gas line.

3. Check gas blanket regulators by opening the thief hatch when the tank level is dropping (not when it is filling). A rush of gas out of the hatch should be heard and the regulator should open to supply more gas to the tank. To confirm this observation, use an oxygen meter, place the oxygen probe in the vapor space of the tank, shut the hatch and take a reading.

WATER SOURCE WELLS

4. Check gas regulator on the annulus of a water supply well. The regulator should maintain a positive pressure when the well first comes on.

5. Check water supply wells without a foot valve (check valve) for fitting leaks. Although it is best to have foot valves, they are not used in cold climates. That way water will drain from wellhead fittings to prevent freezing when the well is shut in. When the well pump has just shut down, check all fittings and valves on the wellhead for vacuum leaks. Fittings and valves can leak under vacuum even when they do not leak under pressure. Check for oxygen at wellhead when the pump first starts.

PUMPS

6. Check all transfer pump check valves for proper operation. When the pump is shut off, it should not run backward. Transfer pumps are usually centrifugal pumps used to move water from a battery location to the main injection plant.

7. Check how much water is bypassed from the high pressure pumps back into the tanks. Pumps should be sized to minimize bypass.

8. Check for leaks on centrifugal pump shafts (air can leak in while water leaks out).

TANKS

9. Check produced and supply water tanks for a downcomer pipe on the inlet line. The pipe should extend to below the lowest operating level. (Water should not free fall in the tank.)

10. Check level controls on all water tanks. Controls should be set to minimize the level fluctuations.

11. Check diverter valves for leaks. These valves are used when two incompatible waters are alternately injected to avoid water mixing. Collect a water sample for analysis; if water is different temperatures, check the temperature downstream of the valve.

INJECTION WELLS

12. Check injection wells that take water on a vacuum. The master valve should be pinched back so that a positive pressure is maintained on all wellhead fittings.

13. Check for air leaks where tubing is packed off around the wellhead (rubber seal); pour water around the seal. If there is a leak, the water will disappear.

14. Check casing (annular space) with a compound gage. A tubing leak could be indicated if a vacuum is observed.

OPERATING PROCEDURES

15. Check procedure used to change filter cartridge (if installed in the system). The procedure to change a filter should include bleeding air from the filter before it is put back into service.

16. Check with the plant operator about the disposal of any water picked up by vacuum trucks after a leak. No oxygenated water (water that has been in contact with air) should be pumped into the injection system.

17. Check to see if any water that is discharged to a pit on occasion is pumped into the system. It should not be pumped back into the injection system.

CHAPTER 10

CORROSION DETECTION AND CONTROL MONITORING

INTRODUCTION

This chapter describes surface and downhole methods of detecting internal corrosion and monitoring corrosion control programs. Corrosion measurements, other than actual physical inspection of equipment, are only indicators of corrosion rates and are not necessarily the actual corrosion rates in the system. Basically the results of a monitoring device will reflect the corrosion rates at the device's location, under the conditions at that location. Thus, selection of monitoring locations and device orientation are very important. Of primary concern are changes in the values that indicate changes in corrosion rates. Experience has verified that when the monitoring device shows increasing corrosion, actual corrosion rates in the system have increased accordingly. Likewise, when a control program is instigated (or modified) and monitoring indicates that corrosion is under control, it actually is under control. This phenomena holds true whether the monitoring is done with corroding specimens (*e.g.*, coupons), probes (electrical resistance or linear polarization), chemical analysis (*e.g.*, analysis of dissolved iron in the fluids), or other monitoring techniques.

All measurements must be interpreted properly with the knowledge of the monitoring location, the system's history and the degree of reliability of the test procedure in the specific environment. An understanding of the monitoring location and the primary corrosion concerns is critical to proper interpretation and utilization of the results. For example, changes in corrosion rates at wellsite surface monitoring locations generally correlate with changes in wellbore corrosion rates; however, in some cases they do not. The person evaluating the results needs to be aware of such situations. The analyst must learn to rule out spurious results when common sense indicates that a system is more corrosive or less corrosive than the measurements indicate. In many cases, where control is critical, or the system is unusually corrosive, and/or risks are high, two or more monitoring techniques are used to evaluate the system and its control program **(Figure 10.1)**. For example, coupons are used to provide a historical corrosion rate and to define the type attack (uniform etching, pitting, etc.), with probes to indicate day-to-day changes or determine inhibitor treatment life, and periodic inspection (ultrasonic and radiographic) to substantiate the results.

Figure 10.1 Monitoring installation on a sour gas gathering line in western Canada. Three monitoring techniques are in use on this line. All three are installed through access fitting that allows servicing the equipment while the line is in operation at normal producing pressure. They are, left to right, an electrical resistance probe, corrosion coupons, and a hydrogen probe.

CORRODING SPECIMENS

Probably the most common method for the detection and monitoring of internal corrosion has been the exposure of test specimens—pieces of a material placed into the environment to corrode and then be analyzed. This approach includes coupons, test nipples, spool pieces, and special devices using "corrosion probes."

COUPONS

It is common in production to "install a coupon" when corrosion in a system is to be evaluated. Many pipelines and process industries also monitor their internal problems with coupons. A coupon is a small piece of metal that is inserted in the system and allowed to corrode. These coupons are carefully cleaned and weighed before and after they are exposed in a system. From the weight loss of the coupon, the corrosion rate can be determined. Pit depths can be measured and pitting rates determined. Coupons also can be used to collect samples of materials that precipitate, deposit, or grow on the surface. As with other tools, coupons are not infallible. There are many variables that can affect the results.

Coupon Types and Mountings. Coupons come in many shapes, sizes, and configurations. The size and configuration will depend upon the system, the type holder being used, the line size, and the orientation. The most common shapes are flat strips of various lengths, widths, and thickness and round rods usually 1/4 in. diameter and various lengths. Both types have advantages and drawbacks. The flat strips are very popular because they have a larger surface to weight ratio, they have flat surfaces for determining pit depths, and the surface area is relatively constant even at high corrosion rates. The round rods are simpler to install and remove since they simply screw into the insulator, and bolts, nuts, and wrenches are not required; further, depending on the holder design, multiple coupons can be mounted on the same fitting. Numerous other shapes and sizes are available for special purposes. For example, ring type coupons are made to be run in drill pipe tool joints. Most coupons run in the field are made of low carbon steel (such as grade 1020 [UNS G10200]). However, coupons of API grade steels or corrosion-resistant alloys (CRAs) are used in special studies.

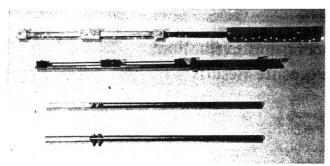

Figure 10.2 Coupons and mounting assemblies designed to be welded to hammer union blanking plugs. Note the top two hold flat coupons in slots in nonmetallic blocks. The flat coupons for the lower two are mounted with bolts and insulators.[1]

There are many types of coupon holders (mounting devices). The holder assembly is basically a means of supporting the coupon in the fluid stream while electrically isolating it from other metal. Many coupon holders are made to be installed and removed when a system is depressurized; others use special devices and access fitting to install and remove coupons under pressure with the system in operation. Most holders are accommodated by standard pipe fittings and valves. **Figures 10.2**[1] through **10.5**[2] show some types of coupons and holders.

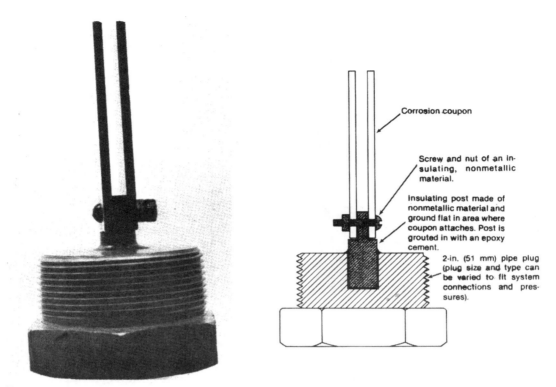

Figure 10.3 Holder for flat coupons using a 2 in. (51 mm) pipe plug. Also shows insulation method and attachment of corrosion coupon.[2]

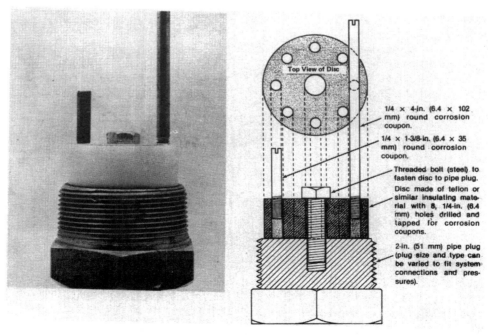

Figure 10.4 Holder for round coupon using a 2 in. (51 mm) pipe plug and an insulating disc that can accommodate eight round rod-type coupons.[2]

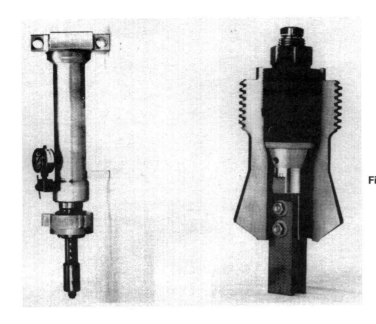

Figure 10.5 Equipment for installing and removing coupons under pressure. The left hand photograph shows the extractor-lubricator tool used to install and remove coupons from the special access fitting shown in cutaway in the right photograph with the holder plug and coupons in place. Note in actual operation the extractor-lubricator tool is connected to the access fitting with a high-pressure full-opening service valve (not shown).[2]

Location and Position. The coupon's location in a system can greatly affect the results because corrosion does not always take place uniformly throughout the system. Multiple coupon locations are required for most surface facilities in order to adequately monitor the various environments, and because corrosive conditions often will be different in the various parts of a system. Basically, a monitoring location should be installed at the beginning and end of flow, gathering or injection lines, and before and after each vessel, tank and piece of equipment. In other words, to have a comprehensive monitoring system, locations are required each place the environment changes (or could change).

Figure 10.6 shows coupon locations in a gas condensate well facility where corrosion problems are expected and inhibitor is being used for control. Coupons exposed at the well are used to monitor downhole inhibition; those ahead of the choke in the heater monitor inhibition of the high-pressure flowline, and those after the heater reflect the increased liquids and the new pressure and temperature. Coupons exposed at the separator inlet reflect the environment in the heater-to-separator flowline; the locations on the condensate, gas, and water lines off the separator monitor each of those streams, and the sales gas location monitors the effectiveness of the dehydration tower in providing

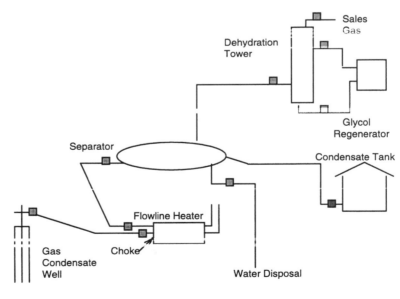

Coupon location = ▨

Figure 10.6 Corrosion coupon locations for comprehensive monitoring of a gas handling system.

dry gas to sales. The two locations in the glycol system monitor the dry and wet glycol. By changing coupons in all these locations on the same schedule, a corrosion profile or history is developed. Profiling the system becomes quite useful for troubleshooting when changes in corrosion rates and problems occur.

Multiple coupon locations are particularly important in water flood systems. A typical water injection system will require coupons in each of the water supplies, after tanks and pumps (possible points of air entry), at intermediate headers, and at key injection wells scattered throughout the system. Locations only at the water plant or at the injection wells will not tell the full story. (See the sidebar, "Location—Location—Location.")

LOCATION—LOCATION—LOCATION

The word "location" is considered an important word in the real estate business. Location is equally important in the corrosion monitoring business. In fact, multiple locations are needed to fully evaluate the corrosion problems and corrosion control efforts in a particular facility.

For example, **Figure 10.7** shows coupons from one exposure period in a water flood system. Those exposed at the main header and at WIW #22 (a well off the main header) look good, whereas, the south header and WIW #1 coupons show accelerated corrosion. If the main header location was the only one in the system, the results would indicate corrosion was under control.

The coupons shown in **Figure 10.8A** present quite a different story. The left hand coupon from the water flood supply well WS #4 was severely attacked, as were the coupons from well #201, which was near the water plant. Coupons exposed at well #145, which was at the end of the north trunk line some 14,000' from the water plant looked good. Yet coupons exposed at well #259 at the end of the south trunk line (also about 14,000' by line from the plant) showed severe pitting.

This is almost a classic case of oxygen acceleration of corrosion: A corrosion inhibitor/biocide was being pumped into the supply well. The pump suction line had an air leak so the chemical pump was injecting air with the chemical. Thus, pitting was accelerated at the supply well (WS #4) and the close well (#201). Since very little water was injected north of the plant, all the oxygen had time to be consumed by corrosion of the line as the water slowly moved out of well #145. On the other hand, the south line took high volumes of water and there was little time lag between the plant and well #259. The next set of coupons, after the leak was repaired, indicated that corrosion was back under control. Fortunately, well #145 was not the only monitoring location.

Figure 10.8B shows coupons from the next exposure at the same four locations. Since there was a few days time lag between pulling the coupon shown in 10.7A and the repair of the oxygen leak, the coupons from WS #4 show some pitting.

The third example **(Figure 10.9)** illustrates the importance of monitoring each incoming stream, as well as the combined injection waters. Only one of the water's sources, the Cambrian, showed significant corrosion. (From the appearance of the pitting, SRB activity seems to be the culprit.) Of course, mixing the three source water and the produced water resulted in a very aggressive injection water. At the time of these coupons the problem had not reached the T1 well. Once again, multiple coupon locations were required to pinpoint the problem areas.

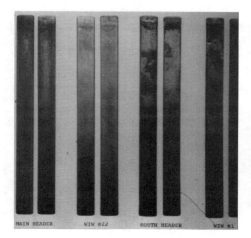

Figure 10.7 Corrosion coupons from four locations in a West Texas water flood injection system. This injection system is divided into two sections. Water from the main header is distributed to injection wells in the north section and to the south header for distribution to the south section injection wells.

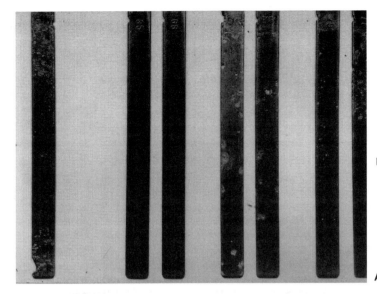

A

Figure 10.8A & B Corrosion coupons from a New Mexico water flood. The coupons were exposed in pairs (one coupon was lost from the leftmost pair in 10.7A) at four locations in the water injection system. The locations, from left to right, were the wellhead of the water supply well (WSW), and injection wells WIW 145, WIW 201, and WIW 259, respectively.

A. Coupons removed on the normal exposure schedule that indicated a problem in the system, with severe pitting at locations WSW, WIW 201 and WIW 259.

B. Coupons removed after the next exposure period, indicating that the repair of the oxygen leak was successful.

B

Figure 10.9 Corrosion coupons from a Wyoming water flood. The coupons were exposed in (left to right) the three source waters (Cambrian, Madison, and Tensleep), the produced water, the mixed water at the injection pump, and at a remote injection well.

Coupons in multiphase systems must be oriented so that they will be exposed to the water present, or they will not reflect corrosion in water wet areas. **Figure 10.10** shows three different coupon positions in a portion of wet gas piping under two different operating conditions. The coupon results at each position will be different. In fact, under the conditions illustrated, coupons exposed in position "A" would indicate corrosion rates of "little-to-none," since they would not normally be wetted with water. Positions "B" and "C" should show corrosion because of water buildup and carryover. However, the numerical values of the corrosion rates may not be the same—it will depend on how much of the time position "B" is exposed to water and water wet conditions have been maintained. Fortunately, experience has shown that changes that affect corrosion rates, such as inhibitor addition, will affect both coupons.

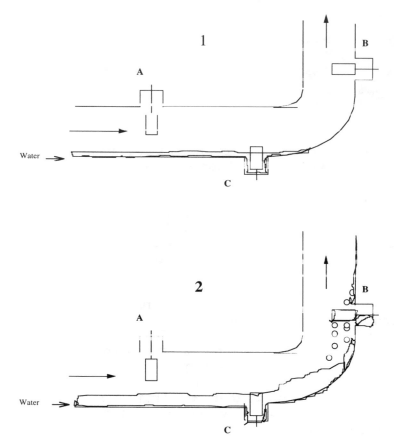

Figure 10.10 Corrosion coupon positions (A, B, C) in wet gas piping under different conditions.

Of course, "C" is the ideal position for wet gas piping **(Figure 10.11)**. Even under condition 1, the submerged portion of the coupon will reflect the corroding conditions (general attack, pitting, attack at the water-gas-interface, etc.), although the overall corrosion rate may have to be recalculated based on the actual water wetted or corroding area. When "C" is not possible due to piping configuration and insufficient clearance, "B" is the preferred alternate position. As a generality, "A" should only be used for water packed piping where submergence is assured. If "A" is the only choice in multiphase piping, it should be located in areas where the turbulence will be the highest (*e.g.*, just after valves or 90° ells as in the installation shown in **Figure 10.1**). Thus, the chance of water wetting the coupon will be increased and if reproducible corrosion rates occur on coupons in position "A," it can be used in that system.

Figure 10.11 Corrosion coupon monitoring location on a wet gas line in a gas treating facility. The coupon is mounted in the bottom of the line through an access fitting just to the right of the flange.

Environment. The fluids to which the coupons are exposed are also important. As can be imagined, a blob of paraffin or an oil film coating part of a coupon can give inconsistent results. Paraffin or oil cannot be expected to coat the same area on every coupon put in the system. Consequently, coupons are most often used in gas wells, water systems, and other situations where such problems are kept at a minimum. However, the use of coupons can be helpful in any environment if factors such as water dropout, velocity, multiphase flow, etc., that may affect the results are taken into consideration. The visual descriptors of the type of attack discussed later in this chapter can be very important in evaluation of coupon exposures from variable environments.

Care and Handling. The handling of the coupon during installation and removal can affect the results. A drop of sweat or sweaty hand prints can increase the rate of corrosion at that point. A greasy thumb print can protect or partially protect an area of the coupon. The coupon must be free from corrosion when it is installed in the system and must be prevented from corroding further while it is being shipped back to the laboratory. One way of protecting coupons is to use inhibited paper envelopes. When installing coupons, they should be carefully handled by their edges and with clean rags or gloves. To avoid further corrosion after removal from the system, coupons should be immediately returned to their protective envelopes or wrappings (most coupon suppliers provide vapor phase inhibited paper envelopes or wrappers).

Exposure Time. Exposure time (that is the time the coupon is in the system) is also important. Short-term exposures give a quick answer, but these can be misleading. For example, if the coupon's surface was prepared by sand blasting, a short (only a few days) exposure may indicate higher than actual corrosion rates due to the removal of the surface roughness. On the other hand, if the coupon has a polished surface, a short exposure may be misleadingly low because it takes time for corroding sites to begin. If pitting is a problem in a system, the pits may take several weeks to develop to the point where they may be detected and measured. Therefore, if an exposure time of a month or less indicates that a system is under control, the exposure time should be increased and the results compared with the shorter term data.

Results, Evaluation, and Reporting. There are other variables such as surface preparation, cleaning, etc., which can affect the results of coupon studies. Thus, in order to be able to compare results from one exposure period to another and one coupon location to another, coupons should all be supplied by the same vendor. Each supplier has a somewhat different procedure for coupon preparation and processing; therefore, the corrosion rates determined from one supplier will not exactly agree with those from a different supplier. Fortunately experience has shown that even though the numbers are not exactly the same, different vendors' coupons will track each other. That is, when corrosion rates vary, the results of the different vendors will likewise vary. As a generality, vendors are consistent with their coupon procedures, and results can be compared from one exposure to the next.

When analyzing the results of a coupon exposure, it is important to get the complete story. Four types of information are determined from coupon exposures:

- Overall (or weight loss) corrosion rate.

- Pitting details (pit depths, pitting frequency, and or pitting rate equivalent).

- Visual appearance of the type of attack.

- Analysis of deposits or microbiological culture.

Overall corrosion rate is based on the coupon's weight loss, its surface area, and the exposure time. The corrosion rate, in mils per year penetration (mpy), is determined using the following formula:

$$mpy = \frac{(Wt\ loss\ in\ grams)\ (22{,}300)}{(Area\ [sq.\ in.])(metal\ density\ [grams/cubic\ centimeter])(time\ [days])} \quad (1)$$

Note: 1 mil = 1/1,000 in. = 0.0254 mm

The overall corrosion rate values, determined from the weight loss, assumes the corrosion was uniform over the coupon's entire surface. Of course, this is not usually true. Therefore, a complete report should include a visual inspection of the coupon to determine the type of attack. With a particular control program, overall corrosion may have decreased (*i.e.*, the mpy dropped to an acceptable level, but what about pitting)? Sharp pits can perforate in short order.

Pitting is often the most important corrosion characteristic determined by coupon exposures. As discussed in earlier chapters, pitting (and similar forms of localized attack) is the usual corrosion mechanism in oil field systems. Long-term (one month or greater) coupon exposure is the one monitoring method that allows an evaluation of pitting:

- Visual examination can describe the shape and form of pits (broad and flat, small and sharp, round, or irregular, etc.). Changes in pitting shape can flag changes in the corrosion environment.

- The number of pits or pitting frequency (per coupon or per unit area) can be determined.

- Pit depths may be measured and the "pitting rate equivalent" in mpy can be determined by the following:

$$Pitting\ Rate\ Equivalent\ (mpy) = \frac{[pit\ depth\ (in\ mils)]\ [365\ (days/year)]}{exposure\ (days)} \quad (2)$$

Figure 10.12[1] illustrates the importance of pitting evaluation to the proper interpretation of corrosion monitoring results and subsequent decisions. The three coupons shown were exposed in three different water flood injection systems. The system of the bottom coupon with a 140 mpy (3.6mm) pitting rate equivalent and a 3.5 mpy (0.09mm) overall corrosion rate obviously needs attention. In fact, visual inspection when the coupon was pulled, flagged the need for action. The results for the middle coupon (the highest overall rate of 10 mpy [0.25mm]) would often signal the need for a change in the corrosion control program. However, when the

Figure 10.12 Pitted coupons illustrating the need to measure the pit depth to be able to fully evaluate the exposure results.[1]

system's piping wall thickness, its remaining life, and the lack of pitting were evaluated, the decision was made to continue to monitor and to maintain the current control program as long as no pitting developed. The top coupon's 0.3 overall mpy (0.008mm) looked very good, but what appeared to be tiny insignificant pits, measured and calculated a pitting rate equivalent of 35 mpy (0.035 in/yr [0.9mm]). Since the water injection system was installed with 0.109 in. (2.8mm) wall thickness pipe, this system required immediate attention.

Type of attack description is a method of evaluating the corrosion on a coupon. The descriptor can include terminology such as:

- "Etched"—which would indicate a more or less uniform roughening of the coupon.
- "Overall attack"—would be obvious corrosion over the entire coupon surface.
- "Areas of attack"—would indicate nonuniform corrosion over irregular areas as opposed to distinct pitting. Some of the surface would show little if any corrosion while other areas could be severely corroded.
- "Isolated pits"—would describe a few pits scattered over the coupon.
- "Pitting"—would imply pitting over most of the coupon's surface.
- "Sharp pit," "broad pit," or "round pit"—would identify the shape and appearance of pits.

These descriptions can aid in the interpretation and evaluation of coupon results. Changes in the type of attack from previous exposures can be an indication of a change in the corrosion environment. The descriptors also can help explain differences in results in systems where paraffin or deposits may cover parts of the coupon's surface. In some cases, such deposits may shield the surface from attack; in others, the opposite may be true.

Analysis of Deposits collected from the coupon when it's removed from the system can be used to distinguish between scale, precipitates, and corrosion products as well as determine the type of corrosion product. Samples of deposits or films on a coupon may be placed in prepared culture media for microbiological analysis.

Special Studies. Although, as stated earlier, most coupons used in routine monitoring are made of low carbon steel, often grade 1020 (UNS G10200). Coupons are fabricated from other materials for special studies. Alloy coupons, including some of the stainless steels and the other CRAs discussed in Chapter 4, are exposed in field systems to evaluate their performance in actual producing situations. While laboratory studies can give very good data, it is virtually impossible to duplicate all system conditions in the laboratory. Thus, just as mentioned in other chapters, field studies and tests are necessary. **Figures 10.13A** and **10.13B** show examples of coupons in the evaluation of the effects of a wet gas stream on carbon steel pipe welded to type 316L stainless steel (UNS S31603) fittings.

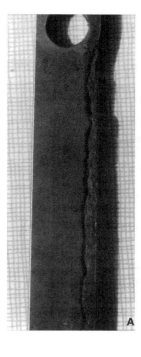

Figure 10.13 A & B Special coupons fabricated from strips of carbon steel welded to strips of type 316L stainless steel. These coupons were exposed in a field system handling wet natural gas containing about 12% CO_2 and traces of H_2S.
A. Side view of a coupon showing severe galvanic attack on the carbon steel.
B. An end view if another coupon shows most of the attack in the heat-affected zone (HAZ) with the remainder of the carbon steel only etched.

A review of multiple exposures can be used to illustrate the change in corrosive conditions with time. Oftentimes, photographs such as those in **Figures 10.14 A** and **10.14B** will tell a better story than the corrosion rate data alone. It's rather obvious a dramatic change took place in the field in the second quarter 1987, and that corrosion was still not under control by the end of the year.

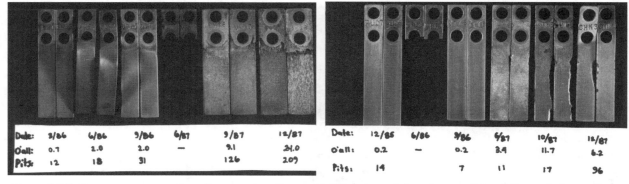

Figure 10.14 Coupon exposures from the same location can tell the story of changing conditions. These photographs are of coupons exposed in two different produced fluids gathering lines in the same field. Each pair of coupons was installed when the previous pair was removed. The overall corrosion (O'all) rates and the pitting rate equivalents (pits) are given in mils per year (mpy).

TEST NIPPLES

Many operators install specially prepared nipples or spools in a line to serve as large coupons. Such test nipples are often used in connection with other monitoring techniques and may be exposed for several months. The results of their exposure reflect the long-term effects of corrosion. They also represent a 360-degree sampling of the interior pipe surface and give an accurate sampling of dynamic effects. Test nipples may be weighed, and corrosion rates determined as with coupons. Furthermore, the ends of the nipple can be capped and sealed as soon as it is pulled and thus preserve any deposits and corrosion products for laboratory examination and analysis. However, their biggest contribution is usually their physical appearance. The test nipples can be cut open, inspected and pit depths measured.

ELECTRICAL AND ELECTROCHEMICAL METHODS

Electrical and electrochemical methods include electrical resistance (ER) probes and linear polarization (LP) probes that measure corrosion rate, galvanic probes that are primarily used as oxygen or inhibitor film detectors, and hydrogen probes that detect corrosion by detecting hydrogen atoms passing through metal. Each technique has its advantages and limitations but all can provide useful information for evaluating corrosion control programs.

ELECTRICAL RESISTANCE PROBES

The electrical resistance (ER) technique determines metal loss by measuring the increase in resistance of a metal specimen as its cross sectional area is reduced by corrosion. The ER probe is basically similar to a coupon, except the amount of metal loss is measured as a function of the change of resistance with time. It has been called an "electric coupon." **Figure 10.15** shows a schematic of the essential components.

Several styles of ER probes are available to fit different situations. The measuring element may be in the form of a wire or in the form of a very thin wall tube. Probes are available with different wire diameters and tube wall thicknesses to provide a range of sensitivities. **Figure 10.16** shows one type of probe element.

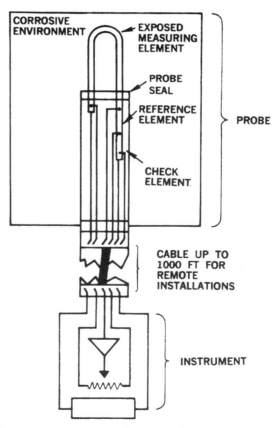

Figure 10.15 Schematic of an ER probe and instrument.

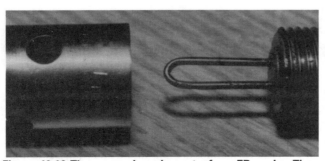

Figure 10.16 The measuring element of an ER probe. The shield on the left screws onto the body to protect the tubular measuring element from damage.

Like coupons, they can be used in almost all situations. The same comments on location and orientation apply to ER probes, as were discussed for coupons. In fact in many cases, coupons and ER probes are used together. The ER probe is used to closely follow changing rates and/or to flag sudden changes (*e.g.*, the lack of inhibition), and the coupon results are used to determine overall rates and pitting effects over longer periods of time. ER probes do not measure pitting. In fact, severely pitting situations may dictate the use of the tubular element probes rather than the wire element probes (the cross section [resistance] of a tubular probe is less affected by pits).

The probe is installed in the system and the change of resistance is measured with a meter. These probes can be read periodically by hand or essentially continuously with automatic recording instruments **(Figure 10.17)**. A base line instrument reading is made after the probe is installed and a suitable time elapses for the probe to come to equilibrium with the environment (temperature, surface conditioning). The equilibrium time will vary with the environment; the least will be a few hours, but more commonly will be a day or two. At suitable times, an instrument reading is obtained (a change in resistance) and converted from meter reading to mils per year

Figure 10.17 This shows an ER probe installed in an access fitting and connected by cable to an automatic readout device.

penetration, using conversion factors and a formula supplied by the manufacturers.

Data may be plotted graphically to obtain corrosion rates. Typical information obtained from an ER probe is shown in **Figure 10.18**. The dashed lines indicate dial readings and the solid lines indicate the slope of the different segments. These slopes are the corrosion rate for each segment. The steeper the slope, the higher the corrosion rate. Corrosion rate is calculated by a simple formula where "K" is the probe factor supplied with each probe:

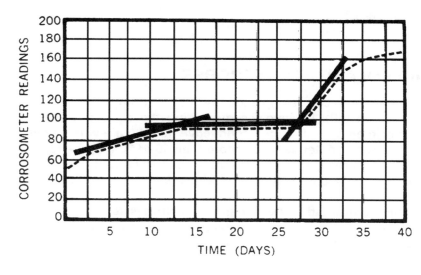

Figure 10.18 Plot illustrating graphical presentation of electrical resistance probe data.

$$mpy = \frac{\text{(change in dial reading)(probe factor)}}{\text{(days between readings)}} = \frac{\Delta d \, (K)}{\Delta t} \qquad (3)$$

Interpretations of the data obtained with an ER probe are subject to the same general limitations as the data from coupons. For example, deposits on the probe surface can shield the element from the corrosive environment. In some cases, iron sulfide scale laid down on the element is electrically conductive, causing an apparent increase in the cross section of the exposed element. This results in a lower corrosion rate measurement, zero apparent corrosion or a negative reading (as an apparent increase in metal rather than decrease through corrosive attack). Probes are more fragile than coupons and, even with a perforated shield around the element, their use may be limited in high velocity situations. Shields can also create an artificial "dead" (no flow) area.

As implied, ER probes are the most useful in systems or situations where corrosion rates may change rapidly and may be varying. Probes have been used to troubleshoot corrosion problems and to evaluate treating schedules and chemical changes in corrosion inhibition programs. **Figure 10.19** is a plot of actual field data used in monitoring a well receiving tubing displacement inhibition treatment.[3] The figure also presents the results of coupon exposures over the same period.

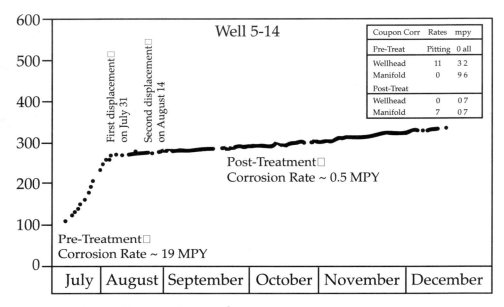

Figure 10.19 A plot of ER probe field data.[3]

LINEAR POLARIZATION PROBES

This technique measures instantaneous corrosion rates by utilizing an electrochemical phenomenon known as linear polarization (LP). LP involves measuring the current required to change the electrical potential of a specimen corroding in a conductive fluid by a few millivolts. It has been shown that as long as the change in potential is no more than 10 to 20 mV, the rate and nature of the corrosion reactions are undisturbed, and the amount of applied current necessary to effect the potential change is proportional to the corrosion current. Thus, the instrument can be calibrated to give a direct readout in mpy.

LP instruments are available, which utilize either two or three electrodes for corrosion rate measurements. Several electrode configurations are also available. Some are made with standard pipe plugs **(Figure 10.20)**. Others are made for insertion and removal through access fittings.

Use of the LP technique for corrosion rate measurements is limited to electrically conductive solutions since current must flow from one electrode to another through the solution. Measurements cannot be made in gas or oil; reliable measurements are difficult to make in intermittent gas, oil, and water flow. However, the corrosiveness of oil-water mixtures can be measured if water is in the continuous phase. Probe elements can become "shorted" by conductive media to produce erroneous results. Once installed in a system, sufficient time must be allowed for the electrodes to reach equilibrium with the environment before a valid measurement is possible. LP probes should be installed in such a manner that they can be easily removed for cleaning, inspection, or replacement.

Figure 10.20 A linear polarization probe for installing in a 2 in. threaded connection.

GALVANIC PROBE

As the name galvanic probe implies, it is a bimetallic couple (usually brass and steel) so constructed that the current output can be measured on a microamp meter (or recorder). **Figure 10.21** is a sketch of a galvanic probe and meter in their simplest form.[4] **Figure 10.22** shows an actual field installation. Other mountings and meters are available. For example, the body of a two electrode LP probe designed for installation in access fittings can be equipped with dissimilar metal elements and converted to a galvanic probe. Such access fittings (as shown for coupons in **Figure 10.5**) allow changing the probe while the system is on stream.

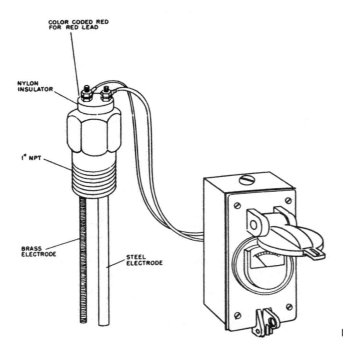

Figure 10.21 Galvanic probe assembly.[4]

When a galvanic probe is placed in a water system, the current output will stabilize at some value which reflects the conditions in the system. Any change in the system that will change the current output will be reflected on the meter. While the probe is affected by many conditions (flow rate, temperature, inhibitor films, etc.), it is extremely sensitive to oxygen. In most oxygen-free systems, the probe will polarize and the output will approach zero. Even small amounts of oxygen will depolarize the probe, and the current output will be increased. Anyone who has not used a galvanic probe will be surprised at its sensitivity and response to minute quantities of oxygen. **Figure 10.23** shows a comparison of charts from galvanic probe and oxygen meter recorders.[4]

Figure 10.22 A galvanic probe and meter installed in the discharge line of a water flood injection pump. By observing the meter the plant operator could determine when centrifugal charge pump seals needed replacing. Experience had shown that as the seals wore, air would leak in before water would start leaking out. Prior to installing the galvanic probes, the injection system had problems due to oxygen corrosion.

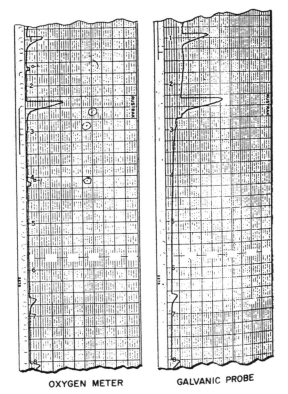

OXYGEN METER   GALVANIC PROBE

Figure 10.23 Galvanic probe and oxygen meter recorder charts.[4] Note oxygen meter calibrated in % oxygen saturation = 0.10% full scale (equivalent to 0-0.84 mg/liter oxygen in the specific water). Galvanic probe calibrated in microamps = 0-400 μamps full scale. Recorder internal resistance, 1,000 ohms.

Because of these properties, the galvanic probe can be an extremely valuable asset for routine monitoring and trouble shooting problems. The galvanic probe is a rugged, inline instrument that requires a minimum of care. It provides a "telltale sign" that the operator can watch. It will "flag" air leaks and malfunctions in water systems so that corrective measures may be taken before severe damage has occurred.

Like most tools, the galvanic probe has its limitations. Unlike the previous probes that have meters connected to their probes only when taking readings, the galvanic probe and meter must be connected all the time so the probe can remain polarized continuously. In a few produced water systems, it fouls quickly and may require frequent cleaning. In many systems, such as seawater, only infrequent cleaning is required. Most systems can get by with only quarterly maintenance.

Although the galvanic probe oxygen detector is not a true oxygen meter (that is, it does not give a readout in ppm oxygen), it does indicate very small changes in low levels of dissolved oxygen. It cannot be used at high levels, because once it is fully depolarized, the reading levels out. Fortunately for our purposes, it's the most sensitive at zero to about 200 ppb (parts per billion).

HYDROGEN PROBE

The simplest form of a hydrogen probe consists of a hollow steel tube sealed on one end and equipped with a pressure gage on the other end (**Figure 3.27** and **Figure 10.1**). Such probes are primarily used in systems containing hydrogen sulfide (H_2S) and take advantage of the fact that, as discussed in Chapter 3, sulfides retard hydrogen atoms combining to form hydrogen gas molecules. Similar to the phenomena of hydrogen blistering, a portion of the atomic hydrogen generated by the corrosion reaction will diffuse through the tube wall. Once inside the void space in the tube, the hydrogen atoms will form hydrogen gas molecules, which are too large to diffuse back through the tube wall. Thus, the pressure in the tube will rise in proportion to the amount of hydrogen in the tube, which is a function of the amount of hydrogen generated by the corrosion reaction. The higher the rate of hydrogen generation, the higher the corrosion rate.

In addition to the simple probe, a number of other configurations have been developed which do not require entry into the corrosive media. These devices collect and measure by various means the hydrogen that diffuses through the pipe or vessel wall. Sometimes referred to as "strap-on" probes, the trapped hydrogen is measured electrochemically in some devices and by reducing a vacuum in others. All seem to work well as long as the device is sealed at the wall of the pipe.

The hydrogen probe is a qualitative or semi-quantitative tool that can be used with other corrosion rate measurement techniques. It has been most commonly used in sour systems but has found application in some "sweet" systems. However, in the absence of sulfide, the sensitivity is much lower. If oxygen is present, the hydrogen probe will not work since the oxygen will combine with the hydrogen atoms to form water and there will be very few, if any, atoms to penetrate the probe.

CHEMICAL METHODS

Chemical analyses come into play at various times in monitoring programs. Sometimes samples are taken when troubleshooting problems, or evaluating procedures (*e.g.*, those collected during injection line pigging) other times the need is for routine monitoring of liquid streams (*e.g.*, dissolved iron in gas well water samples, dissolved oxygen in injection waters, or even glycol samples to determine pH, inhibition levels and glycol quality).

Analysis of the H_2S and CO_2 content of gases will indicate changes in the systems and can give an indication of corrosiveness in the system. There are now oxygen meters available that will detect oxygen in gases in the ppb range. These meters have proved particularly valuable in troubleshooting oxygen entry into gas lift systems.

The analysis of liquid samples can cover both composition of the liquid stream and composition of contaminants. Sampling techniques become extremely important if the analysis is to be representative of the conditions in the system.

SAMPLE CONNECTIONS

Many of the troubleshooting and monitoring procedures involve analysis of the gases, liquids, and solids from a system. As a "rule of thumb," sampling valves should be installed at each point in a facility where a change can occur (*i.e.*, at producing, supply, and injection wells, at manifolds, and before and after each vessel or piece of equipment). It is a good practice to "double valve" sampling connections, particularly in high pressure applications. Typically sample valves are needle valves. A large pressure drop across valves can "cut" the valve out in short order and needle valves can be quite easily plugged by any debris present in the system. In either case, the sample location is unusable until the system can be shut in for valve repair, replacement, or clean-out. **Figure 10.24** illustrates the close-coupled double valve sample connection that simplifies valve maintenance. As noted, the nipple connecting the valves to the system should be as short as practical to assure that representative samples can be collected with a minimum of flushing to waste. The "inner" valve is preferably a ball or other more or less "full opening" valve, and is always opened fully for sampling. The "outer" valve is a needle valve and is used to control the flow while sampling. By having double valves, the outer valve can be changed whenever it cuts out. This valve arrangement may be used for all types of sampling (oil, gas, water, or mixtures).

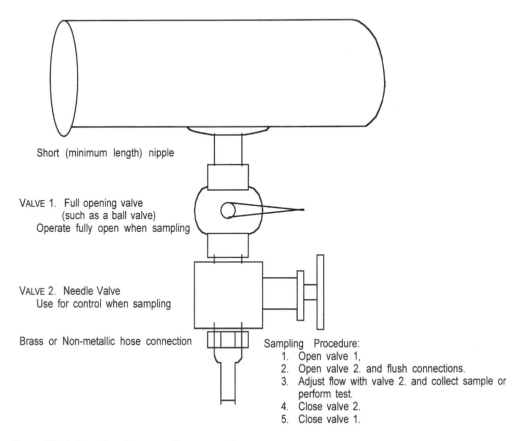

Short (minimum length) nipple

VALVE 1. Full opening valve
(such as a ball valve)
Operate fully open when sampling

VALVE 2. Needle Valve
Use for control when sampling

Brass or Non-metallic hose connection

Sampling Procedure:
1. Open valve 1,
2. Open valve 2. and flush connections.
3. Adjust flow with valve 2. and collect sample or perform test.
4. Close valve 2.
5. Close valve 1.

Figure 10.24 Double valve sampling connection.

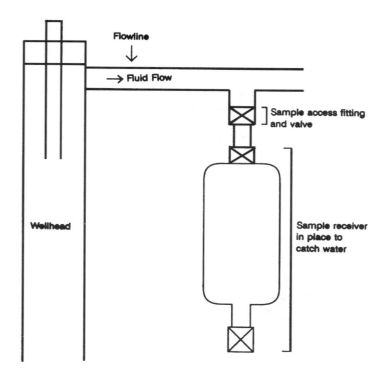

Figure 10.25 Typical double-ended sample receiver, and connection on the bottom of a flowline.[5]

Gas condensate wells often make small amounts of water or produce water in heads (or slugs). Therefore, a sample accumulator (sample pot or sample receiver) at the well is needed. **Figure 10.25** presents a sketch of a sample receiver for a gas well.[5]

DISSOLVED IRON

One method of attempting to detect corrosion and to evaluate control effectiveness is to measure the iron content of the fluid. In the field, the iron content analysis is, more often than not, referred to as the "iron count." An iron content study can be broken down into three basic steps: sampling, analysis, and evaluation or interpretation. The following discussion will review these steps. Monitoring of dissolved iron is covered in more detail in NACE RP0192-92, "Monitoring Corrosion in Oil and Gas Production with Iron Counts."[5]

Sampling. Since the usefulness of the study depends entirely on the validity of the data, the most important step of the three is the collection of representative, uncontaminated samples. In some studies, only the produced water is collected and analyzed. However, many companies determine iron in the oil or iron in the total fluid. The technique used when collecting the sample is of utmost importance. The following should always be considered when collecting samples for iron content:

- Cleanliness of equipment is very important. The sample jar must be clean and free from iron. Glass bottles or jars are the preferred sample container because they are impermeable to air (oxygen). Plastics such as polyethylene and polypropylene are permeable to oxygen. Oxygen in the water will precipitate the dissolved iron. Many times, unless special steps are taken to avoid precipitation (such as acid in the sample jar), the precipitated iron will be difficult to remove or to put back into solution and a lower than actual iron content will be reported. Standard glass "medicine bottles" or glass "fruit jars" are satisfactory sample containers. Normally glass bottle lids will be heavy plastic. However, jar lids are usually metal and a nonmetallic insert should be used to prevent contact between the well fluids and the metal lid. This insert can act as the sealing gasket.

- The sample valve must be free of rust and scale. Any nipples or fittings downstream of the sample valve which are open to the air should be removed if possible. One technique found, as an effective aid to sampling, is to use brass or polyvinyl chloride (PVC) plastic sample fittings screwed into the sample valve **(Figure 10.26)**. These fittings serve to minimize splash and replace steel fittings which may have rusted in the air. It is sometimes advisable to wash out the sampling valve. Diluted hydrochloric acid in a plastic wash bottle can be used to rinse iron oxide particles from a valve before it is flushed for sampling.

Figure 10.26 Brass fittings used to make a sampling "faucet" from a wellhead bleed valve. Brass or plastic fittings will not corrode in the air and contamination of iron content samples is avoided.

- The sample valve and upstream nipples should be flushed out completely. Since it is usually desired that the sample represent the flowing fluid, the fittings must be flushed to assure that fresh fluid is being sampled, not the fluids that have been standing in the dead space in a nipple or bull plug.

- Splash and overflow should be avoided when collecting samples for iron analysis. Iron in solution may oxidize while it is being collected or particles of corrosion product may be carried in the fluid. Splash and overflow of the jar can tend to concentrate these solids and can result in misleading results.

- Above all, the sample must represent the fluid being sampled, and must not be contaminated by rust, scale, etc., from around the sample valve.

Cleanliness and flush out have been emphasized because it is very easy to contaminate an iron count sample. Even in the worst conditions, only a few hundred parts of iron are found in a million parts of water, and very often in the range of around 20 ppm. A piece of iron oxide (rust) about the size of a large pinhead dissolved in a pint (0.48L) of fluid is equivalent to about 10 ppm of iron. It is very easy, therefore, to contaminate a sample by carelessly letting rust or scale particles get into it.

Quite often, the water in a sample turns red or rust color as it is collected, or just after collection. This usually means that iron that was dissolved in the sample has reacted with air to form iron oxide. If it turns black, iron sulfide is probably being formed (although some oxides of iron also are black). To keep the iron oxide or sulfide from forming, the sample may be collected with a few milliliters of acid in the jar.

Analysis. There are several methods of actually analyzing the amount of iron in a fluid. NACE RP0192-92 [5] references four sources of procedures for analysis of iron in fluids (these are given as references 6 through 9 at the end of this chapter). Some methods can be used in the field, while other techniques are used only in the laboratory. When starting iron content surveys in a new area, it is necessary to run some checks on the analytical method with the new fluid, since other materials dissolved in the fluids can affect the iron analysis and give erroneous results.

Evaluation and Reporting. Last but not least, of course, is the evaluation of the data. In some gas wells, where production is essentially the same from day to day and where only small quantities of water are produced, it may be satisfactory to use the iron content as is—that is, to compare the iron contents themselves from sample-to-sample or well-to-well. However, high iron counts in wells with low water production do not necessarily indicate severe corrosion; similarly, low iron counts in wells with high water production are not necessarily indicative of low corrosion. Much more important is the amount of iron produced in the system on a daily basis. Therefore, in most wells and systems, for the best comparison, the iron count should be converted to "pounds of iron per day." Pounds-iron-per-day calculations take into consideration the volumes of the produced fluids and, in effect, gives a value to "iron production." A nomograph to simplify this conversion is presented as **Figure 10.27.**

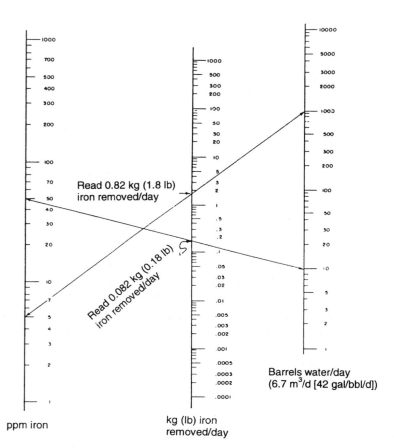

Figure 10.27 Nomograph useful in calculating pounds of iron lost per day. Diagonal lines represent two calculations with different ppm and bbl water per day.

Although the nomograph is handy, actually, the calculation is quite simple:

Pounds of iron/day = 0.00035 (milligrams iron/liter) (bbl/day)   (4)

or expressed on metric terms:

Kilograms of iron/day = (milligrams iron/liter)(cubic meters/day)/1000   (5)

Fluid volumes on a daily basis usually increase over a period of time due to increases in water production or changes of lift conditions. Also, daily volumes usually vary from well to well in the same lease. When evaluating iron content results, other factors should be considered, such as:

- How long has the well been producing prior to sampling? If it is sampled once just after it has started producing and again after it has produced for several days, the iron content may be very different.

- Has the well recently been worked on? If a well has had equipment changes within a few days before sampling, the iron count may be higher than normal even on successfully inhibited wells due to the dislodging of scale or corrosion products, etc., when running the equipment in and out of the hole.

- Does the water have the same composition of minerals each time it is sampled? This can be particularly important in gas well work. Most water in the early life of a gas well is so-called "condensed water." This water was a vapor in the reservoir and at the bottom of the hole. As the vapor comes to the surface, temperature and pressure changes allow the vapor to condense. When the vapors condense, acid gases dissolve in the liquid and corrosion can take place. This is the water that is sampled and the iron found is from corrosion. In many gas wells, however, formation water may be produced along with the condensed water. Formation water is usually salty and contains many minerals. It may even contain dissolved iron from the formation. Unfortunately, the amount of formation water in the total water produced is usually not constant. One sample from a well may analyze as a very pure condensed water, and the next day, a sample might be mostly formation water. As can be seen, if the formation water contains dissolved iron from the formation, this iron will be analyzed along with the iron from corrosion, and the iron count may be higher than usual. Spent acid water which is produced after an acid job on a well may also contain large amounts of iron which the acid dissolved from the formation. One simple way to document the type water is to collect two samples at the same time—one with acid for iron count analysis, the other without acid for analysis of the chloride content. The chloride results can be compared to a previous analysis of the formation water to determine if the current sample is condensed water, formation water, or a mixture.

- Where in the system were the samples collected? Were all samples from the same point? As might be imagined, this can be important when the water is very corrosive, because the iron content may vary depending upon the amount of steel that it contacts. When studying corrosion of wells, it is always best to obtain iron content samples as close to the wellhead as possible.

There are various types of sample arrangements used at the wellhead. On oil wells, it is usually sufficient to have a bleed valve. On most gas wells, as mentioned earlier in the chapter, a sampling pot of some type is required.

In spite of the many variables, iron content is one of the most useful monitoring tools. This is particularly true when evaluating the effectiveness of a corrosion inhibitor program where the reduction of iron content from the pretreatment level indicates the success of the control. **Figure 10.28** presents such a story.

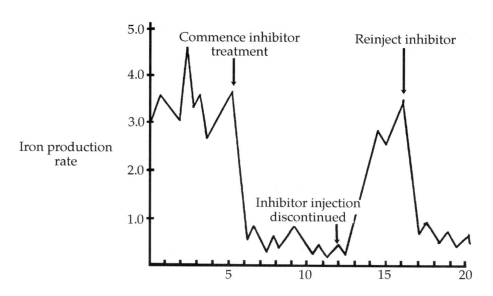

Figure 10.28 Graphical presentation of iron production rate vs time with pertinent operating information.

CORROSION PRODUCTS ANALYSIS

The chemical analysis of samples of corrosion product and deposits from a system can be another important part of a monitoring program. Samples may be taken directly from the equipment or from coupons or test nipples. Knowing the composition of such deposits helps to evaluate the type of problem and to detect changes in the system. For accuracy, analyses should be performed in the laboratory.

Again, sample collection and handling are important for proper interpretation of the results. It is most helpful if the person submitting the sample provides full details on the conditions and location of the samples.

Samples of corrosion product can change chemically once they are removed from a system. For example, when iron sulfide comes in contact with air, it will start to oxidize and convert to iron oxide. A sample that was black from iron sulfide when collected may be red-brown from iron (ferric) oxide when received in the laboratory. Thus, the color of the sample at the time of collection becomes important information.

DISSOLVED GAS ANALYSIS

The gases most important to corrosion include carbon dioxide (CO_2), hydrogen sulfide (H_2S), and oxygen. The degree of importance, and thus the monitoring required, will vary with systems. In water systems, the dissolved gases become very important and monitoring of dissolved H_2S and oxygen is a critical part of troubleshooting and control.

Acid Gases. The most important dissolved acid gases (that is, the gases that ionize in solution to form acids) are H_2S and CO_2. The H_2S may be native to the formation or may be generated by sulfate reducing bacteria (SRB). The CO_2 is native to the formation except in some enhanced oil recovery (EOR) projects. CO_2 injection, flue gas injection, and in-situ combustion (fire flood) all add CO_2 to the formation fluids.

While laboratory test procedures usually are the most accurate, the problems of collecting and transporting representative samples from the field to the laboratory make field tests very attractive. Field tests are readily available to check dissolved H_2S and CO_2 contents. The results of such tests are usually quite acceptable. In many cases, the presence or absence of the acid gas is what is the most important. Sometimes when troubleshooting a problem, the increase or decrease of the acid gas content through the system is the item of primary interest.

Dissolved Oxygen. As mentioned in almost every chapter—oxygen is the greatest accelerator of corrosion in any and all oilfield systems. Therefore, the monitoring of dissolved oxygen is a very important part of any corrosion control program. Since oxygen is the principle corrodent in most oilfield water systems, dissolved oxygen monitoring is particularly important in those systems.

Oxygen meter development was expedited by the needs of the environmental movement. The use of such meters opened the door to a previously unexplored area. Oxygen can be measured with fair accuracy on location in most systems—down into the parts per billion (ppb) range. As with other specialized tools, experience is very important in obtaining data and interpreting the results.

Chemical tests that are relatively easy, rapid, inexpensive, and accurate are also available for field use. Like acid gases, oxygen does not lend itself to sampling and transportation to a laboratory so field tests are ideal. Most of these tests are colorimetric determinations and the eye and the experience of the tester are very important. When considering their use in a specific water system, the test procedure and reagents should be checked for interference from ions native to the water. As a generality, seawater is less likely to interfere than produced brines.

INHIBITOR PRESENCE OR CONCENTRATION TESTS

The determination of the presence and/or concentration of a corrosion inhibitor in the fluid can provide useful information when evaluating an inhibition program. Analytical procedures are available to determine the amount of inhibitor in a system. For some materials, laboratory analysis is required; for others, a simple field test can be used to determine presence and concentration of inhibitor in the liquid stream. The so-called "copper ion" test[10] is used by some companies to determine the presence of the inhibitor in well fluids. In this case, a coupon dipped in or exposed to the liquids is immersed in a copper solution. If or where an inhibitor film is present, no copper will deposit. On the other hand, copper will deposit on any bare steel on the coupon. Thus, an empirical correlation can be made as to an inhibitor's presence or effectiveness.

pH

Since pH measures the acidity or alkalinity of fluids, pH determination is a part of any corrosion study. There are two pH measurements that can be important. The pH in the system at system temperatures and pressures can be quite different than the pH determined on a sample collected from the system. When the pH is primarily acidic due to dissolved acid gases, these gases will escape when the sample is collected and the pH of the sample will be higher (less acid) than the pH in the system. Pressure pH probes are available, but the usual approach is for the analyst to calculate the system pH based on the pH of the sample and the acid gas solubilities at system temperatures and pressures.

Of course, when the pH is the result of components in the water, such as spent acid from well acidization or materials native to the water, the pH of a sample is meaningful.

Note: A pH meter should be used (rather than pH paper) whenever accurate readings are required. As with any analytical instrument, the calibration and maintenance of the pH probes is critical for accurate, reproducible data.

The pH of fluids besides water also can be determined. For example, the pH of dehydration glycol, heating/cooling solutions, and sweetening solutions indicates the "healthiness" of those systems. Some solutions require special procedures in order to determine the pH. The pH of a glycol is usually determined as an "apparent pH." The glycol is usually diluted with distilled water (often 50/50), and the pH is measured on that mixture and reported as an "apparent pH."

GAS ANALYSIS

In gas well or gas handling applications, determination of CO_2 and H_2S is fairly routine when they are present in large quantities. The same is true, along with oxygen, in plant applications. Trace quantities of H_2S and oxygen are harder to detect but can be of extreme importance. For example, under the right conditions, traces of H_2S can cause cracking of high-strength steels. In oil wells, the measurements may be more difficult, and the important factor is usually the presence or absence of the gas. H_2S in gas should be measured at the well. Laboratory analysis of H_2S will invariably be lower than actual. A report of "nil" H_2S basically says "there was none present in the sample as analyzed." There are several methods for measuring H_2S on location, including several brands of "gas tubes."

The determination of oxygen in the lift gas is often quite meaningful in evaluating corrosion possibilities in gas lift system—particularly in rotative systems and those using return gas from plant with vacuum gathering systems.

MICROBIOLOGICAL DETECTION AND MONITORING

As mentioned in Chapter 2, bacteria, particularly the sulfate reducing bacteria (SRB), can cause a number of problems, particularly in water handling systems. Much has been written and said concerning microorganisms and the importance of their role in corrosion reactions. Many consider this a controversial subject and have strong feelings on the matter. Progress in understanding the exact or complete role played by various microorganisms in corrosion reactions is continuing. Microorganisms are quite numerous and exist in many systems. However, the mere presence of bacteria is not necessarily bad. The important thing is how active are they, and do they create or contribute to a particular problem?

Coverage of this subject is quite involved. The important point is that there are monitoring techniques to determine the activity of microorganisms and these should be included in the monitoring program where applicable. NACE Standard Test Method TM0194-94, "Field Monitoring of Bacterial Growth in Oilfield Systems," covers sampling procedures and culture techniques for various types of tests.[11] Techniques for both planktonic (those in the water stream) and sessile (those attached to surfaces) bacteria are covered.

Since the collection of water samples to determine planktonic bacteria is fairly easy as long as sterile containers and techniques are used, they are the most common tests run. However, the results can be quite variable from moment to moment depending on the number of bacteria caught in any sample. In many cases the main value of planktonic tests is to indicate that there are active viable bacteria upstream of the sample location. Sessile bacteria are those colonies that are actively growing, are involved in the corrosion process, and are contributing bacteria to the planktonic count. Cultures of sessile bacteria may be made from scraping equipment surfaces during inspections, from special "bacteria devices" exposed in the system, and from corrosion coupons when they are removed from a system.

More information on oilfield problems associated with microorganisms is available in NACE Publication TPC 3, "Microbiologically Influenced Corrosion and Biofouling in Oilfield Equipment."[12]

Additional sources of information on microbiologically influenced corrosion are listed in the Bibliography at the end of this chapter.

INSPECTION

Inspection is a vital part of any corrosion monitoring program and as such becomes a vital part of any corrosion control program. Various inspection techniques are available, from simple "look in it," to inspection scopes, to electromagnetic, to ultrasonic and radiographic methods. Tools and methods for inspection of downhole, as well as surface facilities are available. Like the other parts of the monitoring program, the types and extent of monitoring will vary with the project, its location, stakes, and risks.

DOWNHOLE INSPECTION

Several tools are available for downhole inspection of tubing and casing. Some detect internal corrosion or metal loss and some measure wall thickness without discriminating between internal and external corrosion, while others permit discrimination between internal and external attack.

Profile Type Corrosion Caliper. Downhole caliper survey tools have been in use for many years. The caliper measures the internal diameter of tubing or casing, and indicates general corrosion or pitting attack. The tool was originally developed to detect downhole corrosion in gas wells and gas-lift wells, but its use has been extended to such applications as the simultaneous measurement of tubing wear (rod wear) and corrosion in rod pumping wells.

Several different designs of profile calipers are available from different oilfield service companies. Some record electrically, while others record mechanically. All utilize feelers that ride the inside wall of the pipe as the tool is pulled out of the well. These feelers draw a profile of the wall as they extend into pits or collars or pick up other variations in diameter. The number of feelers vary with the size of the pipe being calipered and with the service companies proprietary design of the tool. The idea is for the feelers to cover as much of the inside wall of the pipe as is practical. Some tools record the feeler that moves the furthest and, thus, report the deepest penetration at a specific location in the tubing. Other tools record the deepest penetration and also report an average penetration for that location. At least one service company's tools record all the feelers. By doing so, they can draw a cross-section view of the pipe. Each company's tool has its own features. The selection of a specific tool depends on the type of information required as well as the cost of the inspection.

Caliper surveys are of great value when used on a comparative basis to determine the effectiveness of a corrosion inhibition program or a change in well conditions **(Figure 10.29)**. A background profile should be run before starting the program, and this should be followed by subsequent caliper surveys after a suitable time has elapsed. Within the limitations of the tool, such surveys are a direct measurement of the progress of corrosion in subsurface equipment.

Figure 10.29 This photo shows two casing caliper surveys run on the same well about 1 year apart. The tool used for these surveys recorded the one feeler that moved the furthest. Note the progression of the corrosion up the casing.

Like other tools, profile calipers are not the perfect monitoring tools. They have limitations. For example:

- Scale and corrosion products can mask the pits. When possible, the well should be acidized before running a caliper survey if a known scale problem exists in the well.

- Some pits may be missed because of spacing of the feelers; however, the general condition of the tubing will be evaluated.

- Plastic lined tubing could be damaged by a caliper survey. An operator should always check with the lining applicator and the caliper company before running a survey in lined tubing to determine if the tool can be run safely.

- Caliper feelers can remove protective scale or an inhibitor film from the tubing during a survey. If the well is put back on production without immediate retreatment with a corrosion inhibitor, a phenomenon known as caliper track corrosion can occur. **(Figure 10.30)** Wire lines can cause damage similar to that shown in the left hand chart in **Figure 10.31**.[14] Note that the wireline "cut" is not a smooth wear surface but is pitted due to wear-corrosion (discussed in Chapter 3). The wireline removed corrosion product and the bare area became anodic. Since the bare area was much smaller than the rest of the surface (the cathodic area) corrosion was greatly accelerated. This should not be a frequent or serious problem today because operators have learned the need to inhibit any well after wireline or survey work.

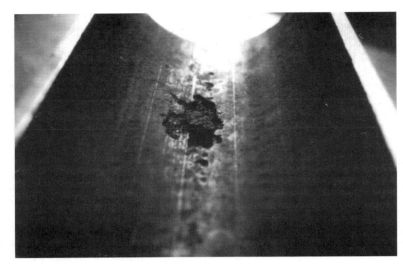

Figure 10.30 The parallel lines in this section of a tubing joint are caliper "tracks." That is, they show where the caliper feelers contacted the tubing wall and removed oil, scale, and corrosion product. A caliper survey was performed on the well just before the tubing was pulled.

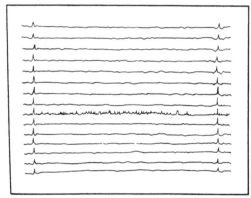 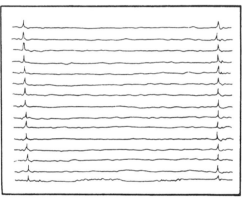

Figure 10.31 Reproductions of caliper survey reports from a survey tool that records a trace for each feeler. Note the left chart shows a wireline cut bare joint of tubing subjected to 50 wireline trips and 100,000 ft. (30,480 m.) wireline drag. The chart on the right is from a wireline cut plastic coated tubing joint subjected to 126 wireline trips and 1.2 million ft. (365760 m.) wireline drag.[13]

Electromagnetic Casing Inspection Tools. Downhole electromagnetic surveys fall into two categories: the casing thickness logs and the flux leakage (electromagnetic) tools, which attempt to determine internal and external damage.

Electromagnetic wall thickness surveys measure casing wall thickness and provide a log of corroded areas, leaks and holes. Current imposed upon a coil generates a magnetic flux in the casing that is evaluated by the tool. The tool is precalibrated for the casing in the well. Changes in wall thickness (due to internal or external loss of metal) of the casing within the sensitivity range of the instrument are detected. The tool can be run in the absence or presence of fluids and is not affected by scale deposits or cement. **Figure 10.32** shows the instrument's response to a variety of defects in a prepared section of casing.

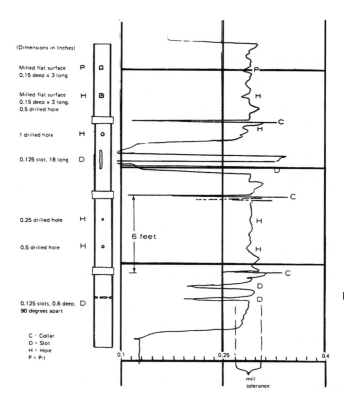

Figure 10.32 Magnetic corrosion detector log. The log of a 17 lb., 5.5 ft. casing test piece is shown on the right. Intentional defects are intended to be representative of corrosion.

Limitations of this type of tool are as follows:

- Differentiation cannot be made between corrosion (metal loss) on the inside or outside of the casing.

- Holes smaller than about an inch in diameter cannot be readily detected with this tool.

- Variations in wall thickness of casing because of mill tolerances, variations in the magnetic permeability, and other factors can produce a log that is difficult to interpret. It is advisable to run a log on a newly completed well for reference if casing corrosion is expected based on history in an area.

Electronic casing caliper tools differs from the profile caliper in that it uses an electromagnetic tool to measure the inside diameter of casing without using feelers to contact the metal surface. The inside diameter is measured over a length of 1 to 2 in., and the average diameter is determined. The caliper is particularly sensitive to vertical cracks or pits but also will detect holes or pits of about 1 in. in diameter.

Limitations of this tool are as follows:

- Holes or pits less than 1 in. in diameter may not be detected with the tool.

- A background log should be run on a well for reference purposes before corrosion takes place.

Combination tools are available that will differentiate between internal and external corrosion even when corrosion has not penetrated the casing wall.

Regardless of the approach, various base data concerning the well, such as size, weight and grade of casing, size and lengths of strings, and other information are required to interpret the logs. An interpretation may show classification of damage to each joint, percentage of penetration, and other effects. Comparisons of successive logs can establish the rates of attack on each joint.

Downhole camera is a term that has been applied to a variety of inspection tools. The new fiber optics video cameras provide excellent views of corroded tubing when the well conditions permit viewing. Others have used ultrasonics to scan the inside of the pipe; computer processing of the signals present a "picture" of the inside of the pipe

Surface inspection of downhole equipment includes electromagnetic as well as visual inspection. The use of electromagnetic type inspection of pipe out of the hole is a viable method for sorting tubing. They also can be used to evaluate the extent and location of corrosion in the string if the joints are numbered as they are pulled. The joint number can then be correlated with depth to determine at what depth corrosion occurs.

Similar inspection techniques are available for sucker rods. Both new and used rod strings can be inspected to make certain imperfect or damaged rods are not run in a well. Such inspections represent the first step in avoiding many rod failures.

INSPECTION OF SURFACE EQUIPMENT

With the possible exception of buried piping, inspection of surface equipment is much simpler than inspection of downhole tubulars and equipment. The basic inspection is visual, simply looking at the equipment or looking in the equipment when it's opened. Instrumented techniques (often referred to as "nondestructive testing" or [NDT] and now usually referred to as "nondestructive evaluation" or [NDE]), such as ultrasonic thickness measurement and radiography present quantified views of the inside of piping and vessels.

Visual Inspection. Of all the methods available for detecting corrosion, visual inspection is the most reliable. It may be difficult to arrange in many cases and impossible in others. However, every opportunity for visual inspection should be utilized. In fact, careful visual inspection should be a part of maintenance procedures any time a line is open, a pump is down, or a tank is being cleaned. At a minimum, the procedure should include taking notes, making sketches, and measuring details which might be relevant. Use a camera where and when possible. Also, probe a sample area for pitting, particularly if significant corrosion product is present. Pits can be obvious, but often they'll be hidden beneath scale or deposits. Pit depth gages are available. Visual inspection may include the use of equipment such as borescopes (including those using fiber optics), and video equipment to record the observations. However, meaningful visual inspections can be accomplished with as little equipment as a tape measure, mirror, safety flashlight, and pocket knife. A pocket magnifier is handy but not a necessity. The key words are: look, see, and document.

Another area of visual inspection that is usually not even thought of as inspection is the external inspection that can be made whenever a person is around wells and facilities. Keeping on the lookout for changes or other signs that affect corrosion control can "flag" problems before they occur. (See the sidebar, "The Eyes Have It—An Inspection Tool.")

THE EYES HAVE IT—An Inspection Tool

Just as visual inspection is the basic inspection, the human eye is the basic inspection tool. But, like any tool, it needs to be properly used. We look—we see—but do we observe? A great thinker once said, "We see with our eyes.—We observe with our minds." It's very important when we're around any well or other facility that we use our eye/mind tools to visually inspect for signs that indicate corrosion may be occurring, or that control programs have gone awry. Watch for any thing that might indicate a problem developing. For example, an open thief hatch on a water tank that would allow air into an otherwise air-free system, or seals on a centrifugal charge pump leaking, or damage to the covering over thermal insulation that could allow water entry, or a shorted isolation (insulating) flange (as was noted in **Figure 9.3** in the previous chapter), or a disconnected vessel anode.

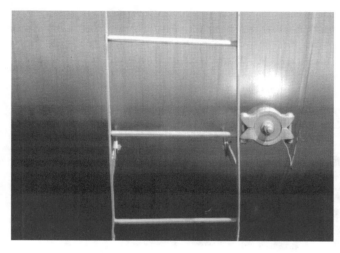

Figure 10.33 A through wall galvanic anode into the water section of a vessel. Note the disconnected wire.

Figure 10.33 is an example of such an observation. The wires on the anodes in the water sections of this vessel had been disconnected and the wires taped with masking tape while the vessel was being recoated. Unfortunately they were not reconnected when the coating job was completed. The loose wires went unnoticed for over three months. The "rest of the story," was that this vessel sat beside the walkway between the parking lot and the field office. Many folks walked by several times a day, yet, like most of us, no one observed the disconnected anodes.

Ultrasonic Inspection. Ultrasonic inspection techniques utilize ultrasonic energy to measure the thickness of a metal object and to locate defects or flaws in the metal.

In ultrasonic inspection, an ultrasound wave, generated by a transducer, is transmitted through a liquid coupling to the metal surface. Ultrasonic waves will travel through the metal until they encounter a change in density (an interface, discontinuity, or the opposite surface of the wall). At that point the waves are reflected back. This reflected sound wave is received and transformed into an electric impulse by the transducer. The time between the initial pulse and the first reflection is relative to the distance traveled by the sound wave. This distance is equal to twice the thickness of the metal or twice the distance to a discontinuity.

The technique just described is known as the "pulse-echo" technique and is very commonly used for both thickness measurements and flaw detection. Lightweight portable units are available for use in the field.

Ultrasonic test (UT) thickness measurements are referred to as "scans." In today's terminology there are three types of scans designated as "A-scans," "B-scans," and "C-scans." The terms have to do with the patterns used to take the readings:

- An "A-scan" is a single point thickness reading.

- A "B-scan" is a number of thickness readings in a line. The line may be along the bottom of a pipe or vessel, along the back of an elbow, circumferentially around a pipe or vessel, vertically across the fluid level in a vessel or tank, etc. B-scan results are often presented as numerical thickness readings and graphically as a thickness profile (cross section).

- A "C-scan" is a large group of thickness readings in a grid pattern. C-scans represent an area of the pipe or vessel wall. C-scan results are most often processed by computer and presented as thickness maps, or as computer generated 3-dimensional graphics with numerical notations for areas of critical metal loss. **(Figure 10.34)** Automated C-scans use probes that are mechanically held in place and moved across the metal surface with computer guidance. The readings are recorded, processed, and displayed by a computer. The automated C-scan can take and process thousands of readings per square foot and thus present very detailed thickness maps or other output. Where appropriate, the computer can construct B-scan type cross sections from the stored data and report specific points of interest as if they were "A-scans."

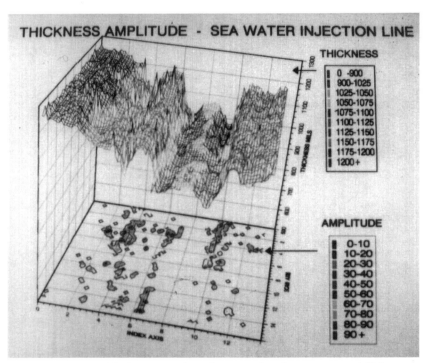

Figure 10.34 A graphical presentation of the results of an automated "C" scan ultrasonic wall thickness inspection along the bottom of a seawater injection line in a water flood. Note the original graphic is in color, with the thickness and amplitude keys color coded.

Sometimes, when less detailed information is required (such as verifying that a wall has sufficient thickness for welding or hot-tapping), a technique known as "scrubbing" may be used. As the name implies, the probe is moved back and forth over an area looking for the lowest wall thickness. That thickness will often be the only one recorded.

Radiographic Inspection. In petroleum production, radiography is used primarily to inspect welds at construction and to inspect piping and production equipment for corrosion and erosion.

Similar to medical x-rays, the process involves passing x-rays or gamma rays from a source through the item being inspected onto a piece of photographic film. Most field inspection radiography uses gamma rays from an iridium source. Thick metal sections, such as large valves, require a more powerful radioactive cobalt source when radiographed.

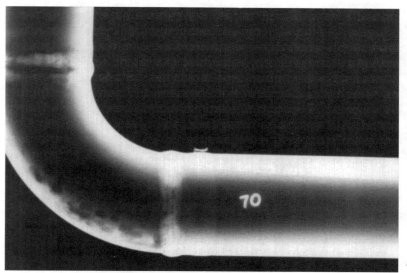

A

Figure 10.35 A & B An ell in an overhead line off a tower in a gas plant.
   A. The radiograph of the fitting showing the pitting and thinning on the outer radius. Note that there is weld attack at both welds.
   B. One half of the actual ell; notice the excellent correlation between the radiograph and the actual corrosion.

B

Radiography can be used to determine the wall thickness of pipe as well as to detect pitting or other localized corrosion damage. Metal defects such as porosity or laminations can be detected, and weld quality can be determined. **Figure 10.35** has photographs of a piping ell and its inspection radiograph. In this case, thinning of the back of the ell was detected with ultrasonics during an annual inspection of the plant; the ell was radiographed to verify the condition of the pipe and then removed and replaced. Photographs A through D in **Figure 10.36** also present comparisons between radiographs and actual piping samples. In these instances, corrosion along the bottom of field gathering lines was detected.

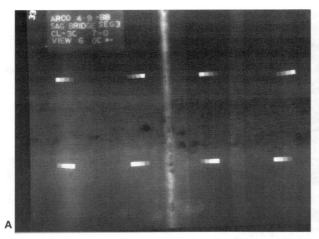

Figure 10.36 A, B, C & D   Results of the inspection of the bottom quadrant of large diameter field gathering lines handling full well streams (that is, oil, gas, and water). Photographs A and C are the radiographs of the pipe sections shown in B and D, respectively. The step-blocks for determining density, and thus thickness, show up as eight dashes on the radiographs. The darker the image, the thinner the pipe wall. Note how well the dark spots on the radiographs correlate with the pits in the actual pipe. Weld line corrosion can also be seen in A and B.

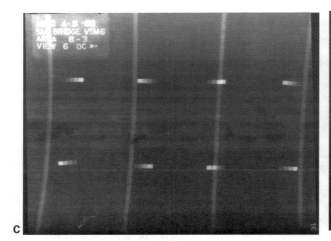

Inspection of large amounts of piping may require a more cost efficient approach—real time radiographic testing (RTRT). A crawler moves along the pipe carrying an x-ray or iridium source and a detector with a video camera. A computer analyzes the taped radiographs. This technique can be used to inspect piping through insulation.[14] The use of RTRT continues to expand as techniques and equipment are improved.

It should be noted that developments continue in the area of inspection through insulation with techniques other than radiography.

Electronic Pipeline Inspection. Inspection tools are available, which can be pumped through a pipeline and will give a continuous record of pipe wall condition. Sometimes referred to as a "smart pig," "intelligent pig," or "electronic pig," they are self-contained units. Most smart pigs utilize the electromagnetic flux leakage technique to detect both internal and external defects. Some of the newer ones use ultrasonic technology.

Smart pigs are available in most size ranges. The smaller diameters have become available as the electronics, power, and recording packages have been further miniaturized. The use of smart pigs continues to increase, and their use has become routine for some companies.

Even lines built without pigging facilities are being modified to accept temporary pig launchers and receivers.

Not only do the pigs show linear location and depth of corrosion, but the orientation is also recorded. Thus the circumferential location is identified. Smart pig technology continues to be an evolving technology with continuing improvements in accuracy, reliability and interpretation. More and more interpretation and reporting is being done by computers.

Tank Bottom Inspection. Tank bottom inspection is paralleling the development of new and better pipeline inspection equipment. Spurred by leak prevention regulations for inspection of aboveground storage tanks (ASTs), a number of "floor scanning" devices have been developed. Both magnetic flux and ultrasonic technology are being used to determine the condition of tank floors. Visual inspection can evaluate the interior side, but the soil side is often the most severely corroded. The new scanners allow a more accurate determination of damage. The computer processed data from the scanners can draw "contour maps" of the corroded areas. Since most of the scanners are manually guided over the tank floor, the tank must be clean, purged and cleared for safe entry. For proper operation, most of the machines require a relatively clean floor for the scan.

RECORDS AND FAILURE REPORTS

Many people do not think of records as monitoring, but the importance of keeping complete records on corrosion control programs and equipment failures cannot be overemphasized. The maintenance of good records is vital in troubleshooting problems, evaluating the results of other types of monitoring, and in optimizing corrosion control programs. A record of performance is the ultimate proof of the effectiveness of any program and provides a factual basis for future decisions.

The broad category of records not only includes corrosion control program records but also failure and/or inspection records and very importantly production and process records. If good records are not available, it's only a guess as to what may have changed, or why the system performed as it did.

Most companies utilize electronic data processing for accumulation of corrosion failure frequency and cost information on wells and other major equipment.

SUMMARY

In order to summarize monitoring:

- Keep in mind there are a number of techniques available.
- Plan the monitoring along with the rest of your planning.
- Install necessary equipment on initial installation.
- Use the appropriate monitoring techniques throughout the project's life.

REFERENCES

1. H. G. Byars, B. R. Gallop, "An Approach to the Reporting and Evaluation of Corrosion Coupon Exposure Results" MP, 14, 1 (1975): p. 14.

2. NACE Standard RP0775-91, "Preparation and Installation of Corrosion Coupons and Interpretation of Test Data in Oilfield Operations" (Houston, TX: NACE, 1991).

3. J. M. Galbraith, J. A. Disbrow, K. A. Van Buskirk, "Installation and Use of Automated Electrical Resistance Probe Systems to Monitor Corrosion in The Eastern Operating Area of the Prudhoe Bay Oil Field" CORROSION/84, paper no. 239 (Houston, TX: NACE, 1984).

4. H. G. Byars, B. R. Gallop, "Injection Water + Oxygen = Corrosion and/or Well Plugging Solids" MP, 13, 12, (1974): p. 34.

5. NACE Standard RP0192-92, "Monitoring Corrosion in Oil and Gas Production with Iron Counts" (Houston, TX: NACE, 1992).

6. R. G. Rydell, W H. Rodewald, "Iron in Oil Technique as a Corrosion Control Criterion" Corrosion 12, 6 (1956): p.271.

7. API RP 45-68, "Recommended Practice for Analysis of Oilfield Waters" (Washington, D.C.; American Petroleum Institute, 1968).

8. ASTM D 1068. "Standard Test Methods for Iron in Water" Annual Book of ASTM Standards, (West Conshohocken, PA; ASTM, 1987).

9. Standard Methods for the Examination of Water and Waste Water, 17th ed. (Washington, D.C.; American Public Health Association, 1989).

10. W. B. Hughes. J. Pet. Tech. 10, 54 (1958); also V. L. Stromberg, MP, 4, 4, (1965): p. 60.

11. NACE Standard TM0194-94, "Field Monitoring of Bacterial Growth in Oilfield Systems" (Houston, TX, NACE, 1994).

12. NACE Publication TPC 3, "Microbiologically Influenced Corrosion and Biofouling in Oilfield Equipment" (Houston, TX, NACE, 1990).

13. G. R. Robertson, "Comparison of Corrosion Rates: Wireline-Cut Plastic Coated Oil Well Tubing vs Wireline-Cut Bare Tubing" MP, 13, 12 (1974).

14. D. E. Hill, J. M. Galbraith, "Development of a Real-Time Radiographic System for Inspection of Corroded Crude Oil Flow Lines in the Eastern Operating Area at Prudhoe Bay," Alaska, CORROSION/84, paper no. 238 (Houston, TX: NACE, 1984).

BIBLIOGRAPHY

Moore, W. P., and H. G. Byars. "Oil Field Corrosion," Part 1—"Measurement Records Vital for Effective Program." *Oil and Gas Journal* 88, 28 (1990): p. 97–101.

Ibid., Part 2—"Field Measurements Involve Various Techniques." *Oil and Gas Journal* 88, 31 (1990): p. 90–93.

Ibid., Part 3—"Economics Important in Selecting Monitoring Techniques." *Oil and Gas Journal* 88, 32 (1990): p.68–73.

Kobrin, G., ed. A Practical Manual on Microbiologically Influenced Corrosion. Houston, TX: NACE, 1993.

Little, B. J., P. A. Wagner, and F. Mansfeld. ed. B. C. Syreh. Corrosion Testing Made Easy—Microbiologically Influenced Corrosion. Houston, TX: NACE, 1997.

APPENDIX 10A

CORROSION DETECTION AND MONITORING TECHNIQUES

METHOD	MOST COMMON USAGE AND REMARKS
CORRODING SPECIMENS	
Corrosion Coupons	Widely used for routine monitoring to determine overall corrosion rates, pitting rates and type of attack in water injection systems, gas well and gas handling systems. May be used in any environment. (A comparative technique to evaluate corrosion and corrosion control in various parts of a system and changes with time.)
Test Nipples (Spools)	Used in water and gas lines for long-term exposures. (May be used for periodic inspection or may be processed as coupons.)
Corrosion Probes (Electrical Readout)	(Requires experienced personnel to read and interpret results.)
Electrical Resistance Type (ER)	May be used in any environment—usually used in plant type applications.
Linear Polarization Type (LP) Also called Instantaneous Rate Type	Requires sufficient water to provide current path between electrodes.
CHEMICAL TESTS	
Routine Water Analysis	Used to identify type of water and water sources.
Dissolved Iron	Determined on samples collected specifically for iron analysis. Used to monitor inhibition programs in gas wells and oil wells. Iron in water used for gas wells. Iron in total fluid used for oil wells.
Sulfite Residual	Used to determine treatment dosages where sulfite or sulfur dioxide is used as an oxygen scavenger.
Chlorine Residual	Is used to determine chlorine dosages in fresh water where chlorine is used for microorganism control.
Inhibitor Presence	May be used in some water systems with certain inhibitors to determine the amount of inhibitor carry through.
pH Determination	Used to monitor and adjust pH where control is used as corrosion control. Such as glycol systems, drilling fluids, and plant applications. (A pH meter should be used [rather then pH paper] whenever accurate readings are required.)
OXYGEN MEASUREMENT AND DETECTION	
Oxygen Meters	Used to spot check for content of dissolved oxygen in water and oxygen in gas. (Continuous measurement possible but not usually practical.)
Galvanic Probe	Most practical approach to "flag" oxygen entry in water systems. Permanently mounted in system, read on meter or recorder. May be used with recorder to spot "cyclic" air entry.
GAS ANALYSIS	Carbon dioxide and hydrogen sulfide contents are determined to establish the environment. (For accuracy, measurements should be made on location.)

METHOD	MOST COMMON USAGE AND REMARKS
SCALE AND DEPOSITS	Samples of scales and corrosion products are analyzed to identify material and determine type of problems.
MICROORGANISMS	
Bacterial Activity Index	Used to determine activity of sulfate reducing bacteria, usually in water injection systems. Preferred method of detection.
Bacteria Count	Occasionally used in study of microorganisms. Not normally recommended. (Many consider the activity is more important than the number.)
Microscopic	Laboratory tests often used to characterize or identify organisms.
Specific Property Tests	Tests are continually being developed to detect the presence of specific strains or specific properties of bacteria.
CATHODIC PROTECTION	
Potential Surveys	Used to determine need for and/or monitor cathodic protection systems (pipelines, well casing, offshore structures).
Current Flow	Used to measure and regulate anode output.
Electrical Isolation (Insulation) Tests	Used to determine condition of insulated flanges, unions, and nipples.
INSPECTION	
Visual Inspection	Scheduled and occasional, a most improtant detection and monitoring technique applicable to all situations. Records of equipment condition should be kept.
Downhole Corrosion Calipers	Used to determine conditions of downhole pipe. Tubing calipers usually run in gas wells and flowing oil wells. Casing calipers used in all types of wells. Pipe should be free of deposits. Usually run to verify results of surface monitoring.
Casing Wall Thickness	Several different types of tools, most are electromagnetic. Used to determine casing condition.
Radiographic (x-ray)	Used for inspection of wellheads, valves, manifolds, and lines in critical applications. May be run while equipment is on stream.
Ultrasonic Thickness	Used to measure wall thickness of vessels and pipe. May be run while equipment is on stream.
Smart Pigs (also called Intelligent Pigs or Electronic Pigs or Pipeline Calipers)	Used to determine remaining wall in pipelines. Instrumented pig pumped through the line.
Tubular Goods Inspection	Magnetically inspect and grade tubing and line pipe.
Magnetic Particle Inspection	Used to locate cracks in steel materials, particularly thread areas and equipment parts.
Optical (Borescope)	Used to inspect inside tubular goods and exchanger tubes.

CHAPTER 11

CORROSION CONTROL PROGRAMS AND ECONOMICS

INTRODUCTION

Previous chapters have presented many different methods for controlling corrosion in oil and gas production operations. They have generally been handled on an individual basis. The various approaches are summarized in **Appendix 11A,** which also indicates the most common use of each approach. Many times more than one approach is valid for a specific use. The challenge in developing a corrosion control program is to select the best approach(es).

Several times in earlier chapters, the mention was made that the selection of corrosion control methods is a "technical/economic" decision. The question always is: "What's the easiest and cheapest way to handle this corrosion problem?" Basically, the concern is: "What's the most cost effective of the technically feasible control methods?" Sometimes the choice is obvious—other times a detailed economic analysis is required. One way to achieve cost effective programs is to have an "Integrated Corrosion Control Program" or an "Overall Corrosion Control Program" for a project—that is, a program that uses several methods of corrosion control in the same project. This chapter will review some of the approaches to evaluate the economics of corrosion control programs and present examples of integrated programs.

CORROSION CONTROL PROGRAMS

Corrosion control should be a vital part of all petroleum production operations—from conception to abandonment. **Table 11.1** lists the six keys to an economically successful corrosion control program. These steps are important whether the project is a single well program or an entire field facility for a unitized enhanced recovery project. The emphasis on a particular key will depend on the project.

TABLE 11.1 Keys to Corrosion Control

KEY STEPS TO AN ECONOMICALLY SUCCESSFUL CORROSION CONTROL PROGRAM
$—PLANNING
$—INSTALLATION
$—OPERATION
$—MONITORING
$—REVIEW
$—UPDATE

PLANNING

The first key step to economically successful corrosion control is planning. Unfortunately, for many field operations, there is little if any planning for corrosion. Corrosion becomes a concern only after the first failure. At that time the pressure is to get back on production and the most cost effective control method may not be selected. Justification for the selection is quite often "Justification by Panic" rather than a good engineering/operations/management decision.

The exceptions, that is when corrosion is considered at the early stages, are offshore structures and buried and subsea lines. Even in these situations, internal corrosion is often ignored until problems develop.

Since most corrosive gas condensate wells will be corrosive from the time of completion, corrosion control is more likely to be considered for them than for an oil well. As mentioned in the first chapter, most oil wells do not have corrosion problems until appreciable water is produced, therefore corrosion issues are often ignored until a failure occurs.

At the planning stage, the minimum corrosion considerations should provide for corrosion detection and monitoring facilities and should address the design issues to avoid or minimize building in corrosion problems. Contingency plans to handle future problems can be developed for many facilities. For example, if inhibitor injection will be required for later water production, fittings and valves dedicated as "future chemical injection points" can be installed during initial construction at a fraction of the cost of later shutdown and retrofit.

When corrosion control issues are reviewed and control methods are selected, it is very important to consider changing environments or extraneous conditions that can affect the control program. (See the sidebar, "Consider The Unexpected—Look at the Big Picture.")

CONSIDER THE UNEXPECTED—Look at the Big Picture

Sometimes corrosion control programs do not give the expected results because a key issue in the corrosive environment was overlooked. Consider the following examples:

A refinery was being built at a seacoast location. A large tanker berth was included. Corrosion control and environmental concerns were addressed from the planning stage through commissioning. For example, the lines from the onshore tank farm to and from the tanker loading arms were coated with a coating system designed to last for many years in the marine atmosphere. However, within months the coating started to fail. Poor surface preparation? No! Poor application? No! What was missed? Sea gulls like to roost on overwater lines. Roosting sea gulls unload their waste. Yes, the coating system that would withstand the rugged marine environment was not resistant to the chemicals in sea gull droppings **(Figure 11.1)**.

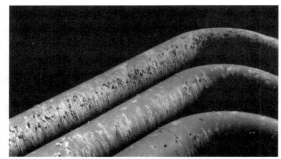

Figure 11.1 Transfer lines between storage tanks and a tanker berth. These overwater lines were coated to withstand the marine atmospheric environment.

An onshore production facility and tank farm to handle offshore production was constructed on an island in the Middle East. The production platforms were many miles from the island. A subsea pipeline brought the crude to the island. A coastal atmospheric coating system was selected for the overhead piping and receiving tanks at the facility. The coating did not hold up well. With high humidity coastal air, atmospheric temperatures in the 120+°F (50°C) range, and crude that was cooled as it was pipelined along the sea bottom to less than 80°F (27°C), there was continuous condensation on the lines and tanks. In fact, the report was that walking under a pipe rack was like walking in the rain. Under the actual circumstances, rather than the atmospheric coating system chosen, an immersion coating would have been a better choice.

A West Texas water flood was started using deaerated Ogallala fresh water for supply water. The designers installed type 410 stainless steel (UNS S41000) valves at the well (at that time the cheapest corrosion-resistant alloy valve). Type 410 stainless steel had worked well with the Ogallala water in other installations. Overlooked was the fact that as produced water increased, Ogallala injection wells were switched to the San Andres produced water—a sour brine. Type 410 stainless steel failed due to chloride pitting.

In all three cases, the primary environment (or what was thought to be the primary environment) was considered—but the look to the future or the look for other influences was omitted.

INSTALLATION

Installation of corrosion control includes not only the obvious construction items like coatings and resistant materials, but it also includes the initiation of other methods such as chemical treatment, cathodic protection and air-free operation. When chemical treatment is to be used on new installations, it is important that the treating program begins on startup. Whether it's corrosion inhibitor in a well flowline or biocide in a seawater water flood, the treatment should start while the metal is still clean (no corrosion product or microbiological slime). The initiation of treating programs are often delayed at facility startup because the programs do not directly affect startup operations. More than one seawater injection system has regretted operating on raw untreated water for several weeks before starting their biocide program. Those systems were so badly infected that it took many months, innumerable cleaning pig runs and truck loads of biocide to get the system under reasonable control.

OPERATION

The procedures set up to operate and maintain the corrosion control efforts are another key step in the effective control of corrosion. This is important to all phases of a program, especially those that are "people dependent." Thus training of operating and maintenance personnel is critical. Training should include the "why something is important," not just "how and what to do." No matter how good a program has been devised, if the operations and maintenance folks have not "bought in" on it, the program will not be a success.

Another part of this key is to set up the appropriate operating procedures in such a fashion that the corrosion control program is not neglected. When corrosion has been under control for several years and there are few if any failures, it is very easy to forget the program. This has happened often, when personnel have changed since the program was started or since a failure; vessels with internal coating have attachments welded to the outside destroying the coating. Isolation flanges are shorted, inhibitor treatments dropped, gas blankets not maintained, and similar occurrences. Of course, when the next two steps are followed, the odds are much better that proper operation will continue.

MONITORING

Since the monitoring program is an integral part of any corrosion control program, monitoring should be in use from a project's startup until its abandonment The type and level of monitoring may vary during the life of the project as corrosion control changes. Today's computerization of data has made it much simpler to integrate corrosion monitoring and inspection results with equipment performance and production data and information. Records set up to "flag" changes and excursions will alert personnel of anomalies.

REVIEW

Periodic reviews are another step in a successful program. Since production changes with time, it is important to determine if the corrosion control program is still adequate or in some cases if it is excessive. Both external and internal programs should be reviewed. Pipeline coatings can deteriorate—is the cathodic protection adequate? Offshore platform coatings weather and are damaged—is it time for inspection and maintenance painting? Rod pumping well water percentages and volumes increase—does the inhibitor dosage or treatment frequency need to be changed? A gas well flowing pressure has decreased and a compressor has been installed—are the acid gas partial pressures low enough to stop the wells inhibition? These and similar changes should be on the review schedule. Ideally, engineering and operating personnel, as well as those directly responsible for corrosion control, should get together for the review. The objective of the reviews should be to maintain two way communication and to determine what, if any, program changes are to be made.

UPDATE

Making the necessary changes and maintaining an updated program will assure a cost effective profitable program.

INTEGRATED CORROSION CONTROL PROGRAMS

An integrated corrosion control program involves the use of several of the methods listed in **Appendix 11A** in the same system, project or equipment. It utilizes the best combination of technical and economic choices throughout the system—not just piecemeal. Of course this approach is easiest to instigate on a new project—one in the planning/design stage. At that point it's fairly easy to look at the whole project—the proposed flow diagram—the process variables—and the various corrosion environments. Developing an integrated program as part of the design allows the selection of the most cost effective combination of corrosion control methods. Large installations and offshore facilities present excellent opportunities to apply the integrated approach. **Table 11.2** summarizes the internal corrosion control methods that were used in an integrated program at Prudhoe Bay, Alaska.[1] As noted, monitoring is a part of the corrosion control program.

TABLE 11.2 Internal Corrosion Control Methods Used in the Eastern Operating Area, Prudhoe Bay Unit

Oxygen-Free Operation	– A *must* throughout all systems. – Includes gas blanketing of water handling vessels, glycol vessels.	Inhibition	– Common flowlines, glycol heating/cooling systems, well annulus fluids, selected gas piping, well flowlines, producing oil well, water disposal system.
Resistant Metals (Corrosion-Resistant and Cracking-Resistant)	– Corrosion-resistant metal used in selected environments for valve trim, downhole tools, piping, pumps, compressors, vessels internals, and exchangers. – Sulfide stress corrosion cracking-resistant metals used in well equipment and all process streams.	Dehydration (Water Removal or Dewpoint Control) pH Control Stream Quality Control	– The primary control method for oil to pipeline, gas gathering, gas injection, fuel gas. – Dehydration glycol. – Dehydration glycol, heating medium for water well annuli, produced water injection system.
Coatings	– Wellheads, vessels, wet gas piping, water piping, tubing strings.	Temperature Control	– To hold temperature above dewpoint on selected gas lines.
Cathodic Protection	– Supplements coatings in water sections on vessels.	Corrosion/Erosion Control	– Piping in corrosive service designed for velocities below erosional velocities.
Electrical Isolation	– Separate carbon steel form stainless steel and other dissimilar metal unions.	Monitoring	– All systems.

The integrated approach is not limited to large installations. It can be developed for individual well projects as well. For example, the corrosion control program for a corrosive gas well could include: internally plastic coated tubing, supplemented with a tubing displacement corrosion inhibitor program; corrosion-resistant alloy downhole equipment, wellhead and christmas tree; monitoring facilities at the well (coupon and water sample (iron content)); continuous corrosion inhibitor injection into the flowline; and the buried flowline's external coating supplemented with cathodic protection.

Another example of utilizing several techniques to handle corrosion is illustrated in **Figure 11.2**. Corrosion control in this vessel uses five different methods:

- Oxygen is excluded.

- The carbon steel shell is internally coated with an immersion coating system.

- Sacrificial anodes (partially spent in the plastic shield/box) provide cathodic protection for holidays and damaged places in the coating.

- Uncoatable items such as baffles and the water draw line along the bottom are type 316L stainless steel.

- All stainless steel internals are electrically isolated from the carbon steel with insulating gaskets and washers.

Figure 11.2 Five methods of corrosion control in a single vessel.
1. Air-free operation.
2. Internally coated carbon steel shell.
3. Sacrificial anode cathodic protection.
4. Stainless steel for uncoatable internal parts.
5. Electrical isolation to separate the stainless steel from the carbon steel.

COSTS OF CORROSION

Because of the complexity of determining the cost of corrosion to a specific industry, most estimates are done on a national or international basis. For example, it has been reported that more than two decades of research has repeatedly shown that between 4% and 5% of the world's gross national product (GNP) is lost to corrosion.[2] In the United States the cost of corrosion has been reported as approximately 4.2% of the GNP (around $250 billion).[2] Estimates indicate that up to 70% of this cost could be avoided by using the best corrosion control technology and improved maintenance.[2] In spite of the fact that the petroleum production industry has been "corrosion conscious" for many decades, the 70% figure for reducing the cost of corrosion is probably reasonable.

MAKING MONEY WITH CORROSION CONTROL

An investment is usually required to make a profit. Oil people are in the habit of thinking in terms of investments—investments in property, in drilling wells, and in facilities. One type of investment that is seldom thought of as an investment is a corrosion control program. A properly planned, operated, and maintained corrosion control program will generate profit, thus it should be thought of as an investment.[3]

PROFIT IMPROVEMENT

One problem with management's understanding of corrosion's economic issues is the way many companies evaluate a project. Economic appraisal methods (and the computer programs to evaluate the options) are designed to evaluate increases in revenue and/or increases in reserves or asset bases. Corrosion control does not generate revenue, nor reserves, nor assets. The typical appraisal method is geared to look at corrosion control as an added cost. What many folks fail to realize is that corrosion control is a method of "profit improvement"—achieving maximum profit from existing income and assets. The profit improvement is the result of decreasing failure costs and risks. Failure costs include costs of repair or replacement and the costs of downtime (lost or deferred production). The lost production is often greater than the repair/replacement costs.

One explanation of the difficulty to evaluate or understand corrosion control costs is that management is trained to evaluate costs that can be easily quantified and audited. Costs due to corrosion are only estimates until after the fact—and then it's too late. Thus, corrosion cost studies are based on experience—historic costs.

COMPARATIVE ECONOMIC EVALUATIONS

The evaluation of which corrosion control method to use in a given situation is based on both technical and economic considerations. Sometimes there is only one technical solution; however, often there are several solutions to choose from—and like all of engineering and operating decisions—that's where economics comes into play. Sometimes the economics are obvious; in other instances, a comparison between methods (including the do nothing but repair and replace option) come into play.

When considering the costs, all associated costs should be considered, including:

- Capital costs.

- Repair and replacement costs.

- Operating and maintenance costs (including personnel requirements).

- Risk factors (of safety, damage, pollution, etc., should a failure occur).

- Revenue loss from downtime and lost production.

Not only are the economics of various control methods compared, but they should be compared with the cost of doing nothing. That is, letting the equipment corrode, then replacing it just before failure. When the severity of corrosion on specific equipment has not been established and the control is very expensive, the best decision may be to let the equipment corrode to determine its life. At that time the decision can be made to continue as is or to take corrosion control measures. For example, a design calls for a low pressure water transfer pump. A corrosion-resistant pump will cost 4 times the cost of a standard carbon steel pump. The pump is to be needed for 10 years. The decision could be to initially install the carbon steel pump, if it needs replacement in three years or more the expense of an alloy pump has been deferred. At the time of failure, the economics should be reevaluated to determine which pump is more cost effective at that time.

The details of the economic decisions will depend upon the way a particular company looks at money—its tax position, its rate of return, its policies on what costs are expensed and what costs are capitalized, and whether it considers salvage value of equipment. As far as salvage value is concerned, many producing companies do not include equipment salvage value in their economics. When a property reaches its economic limit for the owner company, it is sold. Traditionally the sale price is based on the value of the remaining reserves—not on the value of any equipment.

In simple cases, the only comparison may be between the cost of one technical solution and the cost of doing nothing but repair and replace. For example, when a sucker rod pumping well starts having rod and tubing failures, the most cost effective approach to corrosion control usually is inhibition. The question becomes which is more cost effective—an inhibition program or continuing to pull and replace rods. In most cases the cost of repair will easily exceed the cost of an inhibition program. In other cases, the cost of inhibition could be comparatively high and the answer might not be as clear cut. In those wells more detailed estimates may be required. Oftentimes, the reduction of costs other than repair/replace may be the controlling factors. In many cases, the elimination of a failure will increase the profit from a well by eliminating downtime and lost or deferred production. This can be especially true in marginal wells that "water out" whenever they are shut-in. Such wells may take several days after the repair to return to normal production rates—the lost production is not just for the day or two it took to get a pulling unit and replace the rod, but could amount to the equivalent of 4 to 7 days income.

Not only are the costs due to downtime and lost production often overlooked, but the risk costs are also ignored. The impact of corrosion failures on health, safety, and environmental issues continue to increase in importance. Some feel that these factors are of equal importance to the costs of poor corrosion control.[4]

APPRAISAL METHODS

The costs of different methods of control are relatively easy to calculate. The sum of the installation costs (materials and labor) and operating and maintenance costs (materials, power, and labor) for the life of the project is determined for each option.

The estimate of the "do nothing" option is a bit harder to come by. Failure histories and costs for similar properties can present a basis for estimates. Costs should be estimated for the life of the project.

Standard calculation methods used may include: payout (PO), present worth (PW), present worth after taxes (PWAT), or variations on these methods.

Payout is the cost of an item divided by the savings (or income) it produces per year. Many companies want the expense to payout within a specified time period. Payout is the simplest and the least definitive way of describing a project in terms of maximizing profits. It is a quick method for estimating the payout of an investment but has limited use in evaluating corrosion control options.

PW and PWAT, on the other hand, consider the time value of money and thus are more realistic ways to evaluate complicated investments. Most company appraisal methods utilize the time value of money. It is very important that economic appraisals include all the pertinent information, both costs and benefits.

Since each company has its own appraisal methods and most appraisal mechanics are handled by computer programs, NACE no longer maintains its standard on economic calculation.[5] However, most economics texts cover the calculations for PW, PWAT, and similar time value procedures. Many books on corrosion also show examples of corrosion and materials related economics.[6, 7]

Sometimes when evaluating corrosion control, particularly on new projects, there is no detailed failure history. In such cases, a slightly different approach to economics is required to justify the initial costs of corrosion control. When the complete picture is not available because all the facts are not known, it may be necessary to show a payout based on the number of failures that will have to be avoided. An example of that approach is the case history cited in the sidebar, "ANOTHER WAY—The Break Even Figure."

ANOTHER WAY—The Break Even Figure

· Offshore Gulf of Mexico gas condensate fields often have multiple pay zones. Some of the zones have caused serious corrosion problems—others are much less aggressive. Typically, a given well may be equipped to produce from several zones—sequentially or concurrently. A thirty well project was being developed. Several wells had been completed and were producing. It was established that at least one zone's gas was sufficiently corrosive to justify corrosion control. The obvious choices at that time were monitoring each well to establish which wells were problem wells and then start an inhibition program, hoping that too much damage had not occurred before the problems were identified; inhibit all wells; or run plastic coated (PC) tubing when the wells were completed, replacing the existing bare tubing when it failed with PC tubing.

Because the producing formations were extremely sensitive to back pressure, all forms of inhibition had been ruled out. That left PC tubing as the choice. Management wanted to know which wells would be problems so that the PC tubing would be run only in "corrosive" wells. In this case it would be virtually impossible to determine which wells would be corrosion problems until failure history was established. Thus, a stalemate developed.

The stalemate was broken when management was shown that the expense of coating ALL wells in the project would be less than the expense of repairing and restoring ONLY ONE well whose tubing had failed due to corrosion. Based on the experience to date, there was no doubt (and no disagreement), that if left uncontrolled, there would be several corrosion failures. The cost basis for running PC tubing in all wells included the cost of properly handling and running the PC pipe, as well as the cost of the coating. The repair estimates for a failure included not only the cost of replacing the tubing (rig up, pull tubing, run new PC tubing, and rig down), but also the costs of restoring these wells to production (clean-out or stimulation to overcome the formation damage from the inhole work).

SUMMARY

Corrosion control is an important and major part of failure cost control. Corrosion control programs are methods of profit improvement. Integrated corrosion control programs utilize several methods to provide the most cost effective control for a property. Current computerized records allow the correlation between various types of data and information to be used to maintain control programs.

REFERENCES

1. H. G. Byars, J. M. Galbraith, "An Integrated Corrosion and Monitoring Program For Prudhoe Bay," CORROSION/83, paper no. 50 (Houston, TX: NACE, 1983).

2. "Real-time Monitoring System Launched to Reduce Corrosion Costs," Corrosion Prevention & Control 44, 1 (1997): p. 1.

3. H. G. Byars, "Corrosion Control Programs Improve Profits, Part 1—How to approach the problem," Petroleum Engineer International, October 1985, p. 62.

4. M. B. Kermani, D. Harrop, "The Impact of Corrosion on the Oil and Gas Industry," SPE Production and Facilities, 11, 3 (1996): p. 186.

5. NACE Standard RP0272 (withdrawn), "Direct Calculation of Corrosion Cost Control Methods" (Houston, TX: NACE, 1972).

6. R. J. Landrum, Fundamentals of Designing for Corrosion—A Corrosion Aid for the Designer (Houston, TX: NACE , 1989), p. 4–11.

7. H. Van Droffelaar, J.T.N. Atkinson, Corrosion and its Control—An Introduction to the Subject, 2nd ed. (Houston, TX: NACE, 1995), Chapter 10, p. 149–164.

APPENDIX 11A

CORROSION CONTROL TECHNIQUES USED IN OIL AND GAS PRODUCTION

METHOD	MOST COMMON USAGE
ENVIRONMENTAL (OR PROCESS) CONTROL	
Design	All Systems: • Consideration of dead areas. • Velocity (erosion). • Coatability. • Bi-metallic couples, etc. As well as inclusion of the following as appropriate.
Oxygen Exclusion	All Systems—Prime method of control in many systems.
Dehydration and/or Humidity Control	Gas gathering, pipeline, injection; gas-lift systems; oil pipelines may involve water removal or maintenance of elevated temperature of gas.
Neutralization	Concerning Acids and/or Acid Gas—Special applications such as wet gas streams (w/ H_2S and/or CO_2) in plants or pH control of glycol.
Sweetening	Removal of acid gases (such as H_2S and CO_2) from gas streams and injection waters.
Line Pigging	Flowlines, Gathering Systems, Injection Lines—Routine: • Gas—To remove water and solids—often in connection with an inhibition program. • Oil—To remove water from low places, particularly when water percentage is low. • Water—To remove settled solids to avoid microorganism and/or pitting sites.
Cleanouts (Equipment)	Surface Vessels—Oil and water handling: for periodic removal of accumulated solids that can accelerate corrosion.
Operating Procedures	Sometimes operating procedures can be modified to minimize effects of corrosion or erosion/corrosion. For example, flushing dead areas; controlling pressure and velocity.
Microbiological Control	Cooling Water Systems—Water injection systems; sometimes producing wells. Design and cleanouts may be all that is required; biocides and combination corrosion/inhibitor/biocides sometimes justified.
CHEMICAL INHIBITION	
Film Forming Corrosion Inhibitors	Downhole in oil and gas wells. Flowlines and gathering lines. Water injection systems (if required, when oxygen-free operation does not completely control).
Neutralizing Inhibitors	Special wet gas applications (see also "Neutralization").
Other Corrosion Inhibitors	Cooling waters, heat/cooling mediums.
Scale Inhibitors	May sometimes be used when scale deposits cause concentration cells and thus pitting.

METHOD	MOST COMMON USAGE
PROTECTIVE COATINGS AND LININGS	
Internal Tubing (Plastic Coatings)	Gas wells, gas-lift wells, "critical" oil wells. Water supply and injection wells may be supplemented with inhibitor in critical wells.
External Pipe	"Pipeline" Coatings—For buried and submerged lines. May be supplemented with cathodic protection in "critical" service.
Cement linings	Water gathering and injection lines. May be used when line is welded.
Vessel Internal Coatings	Water sections and vapor space of production and water injection vessels and tanks. May be supplemented with cathodic protection in submerged service. Vessels must be "designed" to be coated.
Fiberglass Epoxy (or Polyester) Linings	Repair or salvage of vessels handling water.
Atmospheric Coatings	Exterior of vessels, pipes, structures. • Onshore—Standard paints. • Offshore, Marine, or Severe Environments—Plastic coatings.
Metallic Coatings or Linings	Internals of valves and wellheads in severely corrosive service.
CATHODIC PROTECTION	
External	Buried and submerged pipelines, flowlines, gathering systems often w/ pipeline coatings. Well casing tank bottoms offshore structures (submerged zone).
Internal	In water handling portions of separation equipment and tankage. Water handling vessels.
NON-METALLICS	
Plastic Pipe (Thermoplastic and Fiberglass Reinforced)	Flowlines, gathering systems for produced fluids and water (usually low pressure).
Fiberglass Reinforced Tanks	Special services such as chemical tanks (must match to service).
METALS	
Crack-Resistant Steels	All equipment and tubulars where H_2S is handled.
Alloy Steels	Valves and wellheads in severely corrosive service (may use for trim or for complete assembly). Tubulars in highly corrosive service downhole equipment. Special service piping, exchanger tubes, pumps, and chemical tanks.
High Alloys	Tubulars, valves, wellheads and special equipment in extremely corrosive service.
Copper Alloys	Exchanger tubes, pumps, etc., in water service.
OTHER CONTROL APPROACHES	
Corrosion Allowance	The use of extra wall thickness to extend the "useful" life or "time-to-failure" of piping and vessels. Useful if corrosion is uniform. Not too dependable for pitting and high localized attack, but will "buy" time to correct a problem.

INDEX

C

Calcium salts, 194
Caliper feelers, 275
Carbide distribution, 74
Carbon and alloy steels, 48, 64, 76
Carbon dioxide (CO_2), 3, 9, 13, 22, 26–27, 41, 52, 63, 156, 240, 265, 273, 285
   dissolved, 29–30
   and pitting, 48
Carbon steels, 23, 72
Case hardening, 73
Casing corrosion, 9
   external, 9
   internal casing/tubing annulus, 9–10
Casing potential profile tool, 188, 191
Casing-tubing annulus, treatments down, 203
Cast irons, 79
Cathode, 1, 24–25
Cathodic inorganic inhibitors, 194
Cathodic protection, 165–92
   application of, to oil and gas production
      equipment, 175–83
      flowlines, 177
      gathering lines, 177
      injection lines, 177
      offshore drilling and structures, 181–83
      oil storage tanks, 180–81
      pipelines, 177, 186–87, 191
      surface equipment and vessels, 177–80
      well casings, 175–77, 191–92
   criteria for, 166–68
   current requirement surveys, 190–92
   definition of, 165
   E log I surveys, 191–92
   principles, 165–66
   role of coating, 183–84
   survey and test methods
   in, 174–75, 186–92
      current flow, 189–90
      current requirement surveys, 190–92
      potential measurements, 186–88
      soil (or water) resistivity
      measurements, 190
   systems, 169
      impressed current, 171–74
      sacrificial anode, 169–71
Cathodic protection interference, 174
Cavitation, 56
Cement, 85–86
Cement-asbestos, 86
Ceramic tile, 87

Chemical injector valve, 222–24
Chemical methods, 265–71
Chemical resistance, 91
Chemical scavenging, 239–40
Chemical tests, 272
Chemical treatment, 193–226
   application, 200
      inhibition of producing wells, 200–204
      inhibition of surface facilities, 204–7
      volatile corrosion inhibitors, 208
      water injection systems, 207
      well acidizing inhibitors, 207–8
   and corrosion control, 228
   downhole corrosion inhibitor
      application techniques for oil and gas wells, 211–26
      batch and flush/circulate treatment down annulus, 225–26
      chemical injector valve, 222–24
      dump bailer, 219–20
      formation squeeze, 211–12
      gas lift gas, 224–25
      inhibitor sticks, 221–22
      nitrogen formation squeeze or tubing displacement, 214
      partial tubing displacement and yo-yo treatment, 215–16
      treating string, 216–17
      tubing displacement, 212–14
      wash bailer, 220–21
      weighted liquids, 217–18
   fundamentals of corrosion inhibitors, 193
   inorganic corrosion inhibitors, 194
   organic corrosion inhibitors, 194–99
   selection of inhibitor, 200
Chemisorption, 193
Chlorine-resistant high-silicon cast iron anodes, 178
Christmas trees, 10
Chromium, 77
Circulate and park, 203
Coal seam gas, 13
Coatings, 97. *See also* Protective coatings
   air dried, 98
   atmospheric, 98, 103–4
   baked, 101
   and corrosion control, 228
   fusion-bonded, 101
   immersion, 98
   inorganic, 100
   organic, 100
   pipeline, 99, 120, 183

Stainless steels, 72, 76–79
    austenitic, 78
    duplex, 49, 72, 78–79
    ferritic, 77–78
    martensitic, 77
    precipitation hardening, 78
Steels, 1
    austenitic, 72
    austenitic stainless, 78
    carbon, 72
    carbon and alloy, 76
    carbon and low-alloy, 48, 64
    corrosion of, 23
    duplex stainless, 72, 78–79
    ferritic, 72
    ferritic stainless, 77–78
    heat treatment of, 73–75
    high-strength, 64–65
    low-alloy, 72
    martensitic, 72
    martensitic stainless, 77
    names for, 72–73
    precipitation hardening (PH) stainless, 78
    stainless, 72, 76–79
    structure of, 72
    Steel Structures Painting Council (SSPC)
        standards, 108
Storage tanks, 11–12
Strength, 60
Stress alloying, 66
Stress corrosion cracking (SCC), 49, 64–65, 80
    aluminum alloys, 65
    carbon and low-alloy steels, 64
    copper-based alloys, 65
    high-strength steels, 64–65
    nickel and nickel-based alloys, 65
    titanium and titanium alloys, 65
Stress level, 60
Structure-to-electrolyte reading, 166
Submerged zone, 14
Subsea structures, 183
Sucker rod, 4–5, 7–8, 18, 53–54, 61–63, 94,
        201, 203, 204
Sucker rod pumping wells, 7–8, 203–204, 225
Sufficient dehydration, 227
Sulfate-reducing bacteria (SRB), 47, 177,
        253–254, 273
Sulfide stress cracking (SSC)-resistant
        materials, 227
Sulfide stress cracking (SSC), 31, 59–60
Sulfur dioxide gas in chemical
        scavenging, 4, 239
Superaustenitic stainless, 76

Supply wells, 236
Surface equipment, 10–12
    Christmas trees, 10
    flow lines, 10
    inspection of, 278–83
    processing equipment, 10–11
    storage tanks, 11–12
    and vessels, 177–80
    water systems, 12
    wellheads, 10
Surface facilities, inhibition of, 204–7
Surface potential, 189–90
Surface preparation, 107–11

T

Tank bottom inspection, 283
Tank liners, 95
Tanks, 246–47
    brine storage, 179
    fabrication requirements for internally
        coated production, 129–32
    fiberglass, 93
    gas blankets on, 246–47
    inhibition treatment for, 205
    oil storage, 180–81
    storage, 11–12
Temperature, 33, 60
Tempering, 73–74
Tensile strength, 73
Test nipples, 260
Thermal stability, 198–99
Thermoplastics, 87–88
Thermosetting, 89–90
Thick film coatings, 99
Thin film coatings, 99
    application of, 133–62
Threaded connections, 91
Titanium, 65
Titanium alloys, 65
Topcoats, 105
Transformation ranges, 73
Treating strings, 202, 216–17
Tubercles, oxygen, 46
Tubing displacement, 201–2, 212–14
Tubular goods, 6–9, 117–20
Two-electrode survey, 189–90

U

Ultrasonic inspection, 279–80
Underground coatings, 99